Only a few days after I had finished the manuscript for this book, a business acquaintance asked me, "Can aluminum be welded?" He would not have asked me, "Can aluminum be machined?" Everyone, it seems, understands machining, or pretends to, but welding seems incapable of developing the public image it deserves. A welding rod is not a status symbol.

No doubt many persons will agree that welding is a process more easily learned than understood. Although this book has much to say in the matter of how to weld, it hopes to convey an understanding of what happens when weld metal is deposited. And since metals have intriguing methods of misbehaving when welded, the beginning of wisdom in welding lies through welding metallurgy. But this is not enough. As welding methods become rapidly more diversified, welding personnel are becoming less and less familiar with the selection and operation of welding equipment; everyone, it appears, does *not* know the difference between TIG and MIG welding. This book is intended to provide enlightenment in these matters. Those types of welding which have as yet a somewhat restricted use, but which will surely become more commonplace in the future, are included. The differences between welding methods are not stressed, but the similarities are, for it is easier to learn generalizations than disconnected facts.

The section of the book dealing with the Inspection and Testing of Welds devotes considerable attention to nondestructive testing theory and practice. The author has been a little sobered by the demand for informa-

A WORD

FROM

THE AUTHOR

tion on these techniques, and decided that an element of thoroughness was desirable in presenting these topics.

I have been privileged to have trained and supervised welders in industry, and I hope that this book will be useful to them and perhaps even to their supervisors. The book attempts to tackle forthrightly the basic scientific topics required for an understanding of welding processes. The mathematics has been kept simple. A slightly higher level of mathematics will be required to follow through the theory of radiography, though this is not carried beyond the mathematics of logarithms and exponential functions.

A word to educators is necessary, perhaps of reassurance. This book sets out substantially the subject matter for a variety of long and short courses in welding technology, metals science, and nondestructive testing that are taught, with perhaps some degree of success, at the Manitoba Institute of Technology. Regardless of educational background, student motivation has been uniformly good.

And now for that important matter of acknowledgments. The author of a book is only the operator of the typewriter, and I suppose a thousand people have written this book. My greatest thanks must go to that important group of educators, the manufacturers and welding supply companies and their marketing staffs, who only dimly realize what a substantial fraction of their selling time is devoted to training and education. A hundred working men, with no pretensions to expertise, and with far less formal education than I, have shown me techniques that I should never have discovered for myself. My colleagues in the American Society for Metals and the Canadian Welding Society have also contributed to this book. The credit for its virtues belongs to these people, even as its deficiencies will as surely be of my doing. Special thanks must go to Mr. Norcross of Arcos Corporation and his staff, Mr. Ed Pierre of Miller Electric Manufacturing, the marketing staff of Linde Gases, Mr. C. Finn of the Manitoba Institute of Technology, and the staff of Bristol Aero-Space Industries. It is usual to thank one's wife for her forbearance during the writing of a book: instead, I thank her for her medical references on the toxicity of metals. Two articulate engineering critics, my sons Matthew and Andrew, have indexed the book.

W. J. P.

THE SCIENCE
AND
PRACTICE
OF
WELDING

Submerged arc welding. Linde gases unionmelt process.

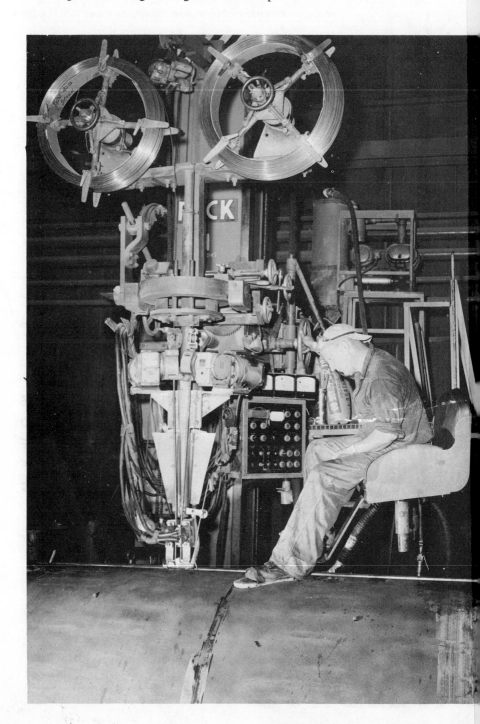

Prentice-Hall, Inc.   Englewood Cliffs, New Jersey

W. J. PATTON

Chairman
Department of Mechanical Technology
Manitoba Institute of Technology
Winnipeg, Manitoba, Canada

THE SCIENCE
AND
PRACTICE

OF
WELDING

Library of Congress Catalog Card Number: 67—12974
Printed in the United States of America
Current printing (last digit):
10 9 8 7 6 5 4 3 2

© 1967 by Prentice-Hall, Inc., Englewood Cliffs, New Jersey

PRENTICE-HALL INTERNATIONAL, INC., London
PRENTICE-HALL OF AUSTRALIA, PTY. LTD., Sydney
PRENTICE-HALL OF CANADA, LTD., Toronto
PRENTICE-HALL OF INDIA (PRIVATE) LTD., New Delhi
PRENTICE-HALL OF JAPAN, INC., Tokyo

BASIC PRINCIPLES *Part* **1**

CONTENTS

Part III WELDING METHODS

221 WELDING GASES AND GAS WELDING **13**

237 ARC WELDING PRACTICES **14**

15   RESISTANCE WELDING   264

16   BRAZING, SOLDERING, AND ADHESIVE BONDING   288

FABRICATION METHODS *Part* **V**

The following list of metals includes only those of interest in the technology of welding. The table includes also a number of non-metallic elements, such as carbon and the welding gases.

Light metals

Beryllium	Be	Light weight, great stiffness, toxic.
Boron	B	In welding fluxes, such as borax.
Magnesium	Mg	Aircraft metal.
Aluminum	Al	Light-weight structural metal.
Titanium	Ti	Aircraft metal and alloy in other metals.

Standard Metals

Vanadium	V	Alloy metal in steels.
Chromium	Cr	Chief alloy in stainless steels.
Manganese	Mn	Alloy metal in steel and brasses. Present in all steels.
Iron	Fe	Basic constituent in steels.
Cobalt	Co	Alloy in tool steels.
Nickel	Ni	Corrosion-resistant metal.
Copper	Cu	Basic constituent in brasses and bronzes.
Zirconium	Zr	Nuclear metal and alloy in other metals.
Silver	Ag	Alloy element in brazing metals.
Cadmium	Cd	Alloy element in brazing metals.

THE STRUCTURAL METALS
AND
THEIR ABBREVIATIONS

Tin	Sn	Alloy element in bronzes.
Antimony	Sb	Alloy element in lead.
Lead	Pb	Used for X-ray shielding and corrosion resistance.

Refractory Metals

Columbium	Cb	The refractory metals are distinguished by their
Molybdenum	Mo	high melting points.
Hafnium	Hf	
Tantalum	Ta	
Tungsten	W	
Rhenium	Rh	

Radioactive Metals

Uranium	U	Nuclear fuel. Weldable.
Thorium	Th	Alloy element in magnesium and nuclear fuel.
Cobalt-60	Co-60	For gamma-ray testing of thick welds.
Iridium-192	Ir-192	For gamma-ray testing of thin welds.

Welding Gases and Other Materials

Hydrogen	H	Oxyhydrogen welding.
Helium	He	Inert shielding gas.
Carbon	C	Welding electrode.
Nitrogen	N	Shielding gas.
Oxygen	O	Oxygas welding.
Silicon	Si	Alloy element in structural metals. Present in all steels.
Phosphorus	P	Deoxidizer for brasses.
Sulphur	S	Undesirable element in metals. (But used in free-machining steels)
Argon	A	Commonly used shielding gas.
Selenium	Se	Selenium rectifiers for DC welders.

THE SCIENCE
AND
PRACTICE
OF
WELDING

BASIC
PRINCIPLES

Part I

1.1 manufacturing processes

Almost all of the very great number of manufacturing processes that convert raw materials into finished products and that we generally refer to as "production technology," may be grouped into three broad classes: shaping, joining, and finishing. Each of these three classes also can be subdivided into two subgroups:

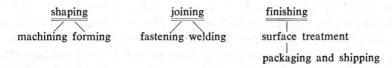

Machining is shaping by removal of chips of material and includes such operations as machining, sawing, grinding, and spark machining. Machining is in general competitive with forming, which includes bending, drawing, rolling, pressing, extruding, and forging.

Shaping is necessarily preliminary to joining, which may be the final operation before painting and packaging. Again, the two types of joining operations are in general competitive with each other. Fastening is the assembling of products by devices such as bolts, studs, pins, lock washers, keys, dowels, rivets, hooks, and sheet metal screws. If the product is expected to be disassembled for maintenance or other reasons, it is more usual to fasten than to weld.

Welding, however, is more than a production process. It is a highly important maintenance process too. Some of the most difficult welding

WELDING—A PRODUCTION
AND MAINTENANCE PROCESS

1

problems occur in maintenance, and therefore a good maintenance welder has a wide knowledge of the welding business.

1.2 what is welding?

Welding techniques have become so versatile that it is difficult nowadays to define "welding." Formerly welding was "the joining of metals by fusion," that is, by melting, but this definition will no longer do. Even though fusion methods are still the most common, they are not always used. Welding was next defined as the "joining of metals by heat," but this is no longer a proper definition either. Not only metals can be welded, so can many of the plastics. Furthermore, several welding methods do not require heat. Every machinist is familiar with heatless welding. When the chip slides over the cutting tool on a lathe, it often leaves a built-up edge of chip material welded to the top of the cutter bit. This is cold pressure welding, which under other circumstances is a proper production welding method. Besides pressure welding, we can weld with sound and even with light from the famous laser. Faced with a diversity of welding methods that increase year by year, we must in this book adopt the following definition of welding: "Welding is the joining of metals and plastics by methods that do not employ fastening devices."

The joining of metals by methods that do not employ fastening devices is an art as old as blacksmithing. The village blacksmith welded metals by an almost-forgotten method called forge welding. Nevertheless welding as a manufacturing process must be considered a development of the twentieth century. In the 1880's carbon arc lamps were used for street lighting. At that time it was noted that the carbon arc lamp, like all lamps, produced more heat than light, and the first attempts were made to use this heat for welding metals. Thus the first welding method of those still in use was carbon arc welding, perfected about the turn of the century. Stick electrodes and oxyacetylene welding also appeared about 1900. Welding was generally used only for repair and maintenance until World War I. X-ray examination of welds came soon afterward and did much to develop confidence in welded joints. World War II did as much for the development of welding as it did for any other technical development and among other things gave us inert gas welding. Since then welding has progressed at such a furious rate that we can say that probably no other technology progresses at a faster rate than welding does, not even the glamorous field of electronics (which owes its present position to welding development).

Welding activities may not make the newspaper headlines, yet the technology of welding embraces a wide area. Even though electronics

Fig. 1 Final adjustments on a Black Brant III Rocket at NASA'S Wallops Station. Present aerospace programs would not be possible without the technical support of a highly developed welding industry. (Courtesy Bristol Aerospace Industries, Ltd, and U.S.A.F. Office of Aerospace Research)

may owe much of its progress to joining techniques developed by welders, at the same time many electronic circuits too complex for discussion in this book are required to control the more intricate welding machines. Even radio frequencies have their applications in welding, in induction brazing and the ultrasonic testing of welds. Photography is also drawn into the scope of welding, for more photographic film is used in the X-raying and gammagraphing of welds than is used for ordinary photography. It is quite possible to use a mile of X-ray film in checking a welding job. Finally, welding has made important contributions to two outstanding technical creations of our time, the nuclear reactor and the aerospace rocket. Indeed, neither reactors nor rockets could be built without welding, for both are weldments. On the other side of the coin, those products of the nuclear age, radioisotopes, are familiar around welding shops in their function of weld testing. All these and other developments are established and familiar practices in welding technology and will be discussed in this book in their proper turn. Welding is no longer what it was in time past, the simple matter of running a bead with a gas flame or a stick electrode.

The frontispiece shows a man sitting in a comfortable chair, doing nothing at all. He may be "doing" nothing, and he wears no welding helmet or goggles, but he is welding the heavy-walled pressure vessel beneath him. By doing nothing by means of automatic welding, he is depositing weld metal about fifteen times faster than he could by

welding—a production and maintenance process

busier methods. His welding rods are the two large coils of wire at the top of the welding machine, and these are automatically fed into the weld. The arc is not visible in this method of welding, and so no helmet is required. The welding controls are grouped on the control panel to the immediate right of the operator. This is Unionmelt submerged arc welding, a commonly used welding method that can in an hour deposit weld metal equal in weight to that of the operator himself. At the opposite extreme is microwelding, in which the operator may need a microscope to see what he has welded. Between these two extremes in size and welding capacity are perhaps five dozen other welding methods, too many to be discussed in a single book.

So far there have been about five dozen years to the twentieth century. If there are five dozen different welding methods, the average is one welding development per year for the century. This simple statistic is perhaps the best measure of welding progress and the best measure of its potential in the future.

1.3   *what is a weld?*

In most of the common methods of welding, the welded joint between the two pieces of metal joined is made by fusion of the metal, the joint being made when the metal freezes. When a quantity of metal is melted and then allowed to freeze, the frozen metal is called a *casting*. The beginning of wisdom in welding science is to understand that *a weld is first of all a metal casting* like those made in metal foundries but usually on a smaller scale. In general, cast metals tend to be brittle, like gray cast iron. Much welding technique therefore is directed to the problem of preventing casting brittleness, and in almost all cases such brittleness can be prevented by some means; indeed, welders are tested on their ability to produce nonbrittle welds.

A weld then is first of all a casting, but there is more to any weld than just the casting of the deposited metal. The metal adjacent to the fusion weld was not melted but was heated to a high temperature. This heated but unmelted metal is called the *heat-affected zone* because it has received a heat treatment. Heat treating, which necessarily has a whole chapter devoted to it, is the process of altering the characteristics of a metal by the use of a temperature less than the melting point of the metal. If the heat-affected zone has been heat-treated, we must assume that its characteristics have been changed in some way. Such changes are almost always harmful and in order to prevent damage to the metal call for examination of these heating effects. Summing it up, *a fusion weld is a casting surrounded by a heat treatment.*

When metals are heated to a red heat, in the range of about 1500 F, two damaging effects are produced. First, any metal when heated has a strong tendency to combine with oxygen in the air and thus convert itself to an oxide. Second, heated metals will dissolve gases, chiefly oxygen, nitrogen, and hydrogen, from air and water vapor. If any of these three gases are dissolved in the metal, the metal becomes embrittled. Only extremely minute amounts of these gases may be involved, but even such small amounts may ruin the metal.

Both of these effects of heat lead to the same result: embrittlement and loss of ductility. Much welding technique is concerned with keeping hydrogen, oxygen, and nitrogen away from the metal being welded. Since these detriments are the result of heating the metal, interest now centers on methods that either do not heat the metal, such as ultrasonic welding or adhesive bonding; which heat the metal so rapidly that there is no time for the damaging effects to take place, such as induction welding or laser welding; or which weld the metal in the absence of atmospheric gases.

Besides casting and heat-treating, one other process takes place in fusion welding—*dilution*. Welding rods and filler metals rarely have the same composition as the material to be welded. Suppose a steel containing 1% carbon and no chromium is being welded with a steel welding rod containing 20% chromium and no carbon. The molten pool of weld metal contains some of the 1% carbon steel and some of the 20% chromium steel, so that a new steel, containing less than 1% carbon and less than 20% chromium, is created in the welded joint. Each of the two metals has diluted the other of its alloys. Now, what about this new diluted metal? Is it strong enough to maintain the joint? Is it brittle? Will it corrode? How will it perform? How much dilution has occurred, and what kind of metal do you have? The art of running the bead does not help solve these mysteries. If the operator is to feel confidence in his welding, he needs to know a little metallurgy.

1.4 welding metallurgy

The preceding discussion simply argues that all welding activities are metallurgical processes. Indeed, experience indicates that the solution to most of the difficulties in welding lies in a knowledge of welding metallurgy. Therefore, following the old rule that one should know what he is doing before he does it, we shall discuss metals before we discuss welding methods.

The science of metals is termed *metallurgy*. Besides being useful, it is one of the most interesting technical subjects. Metallurgy is divided into two branches: *extractive metallurgy* and *physical metallurgy*. Extractive metallurgy is the study of the extraction of metals from their ores. This branch of metallurgy has some bearing on welding technology, for the characteristics of a metal are influenced by the method of extraction from the ore. Physical metallurgy is the study of the properties of metals and is the subject matter for Part II of this book.

Most of the hundred or so elements out of which our universe is built are metals, and most of these merit attention in any book on the broad subject of welding technology. In addition to the pure metals, industry uses tens of thousands of *alloys*—mixtures of metals—usually a base metal with a few per cent of other metals or carbon added. Actually the welder rarely welds the pure metals; he usually works with such alloys as structural steel, stainless steel, gray cast iron, and brass.

For convenience, the industrially significant metals are separated into two major groups:

ferrous metals
nonferrous metals

The ferrous metals include all those which originate from iron ores and use for their base metal iron. The ferrous metals therefore include the cast irons, wrought iron, the thousands of steel alloys, and several dozen stainless steels. The nonferrous group comprises all metals and alloys that do not include in the alloying more than a few per cent of iron. The most important nonferrous metals are nickel, copper, aluminum, lead, zinc, chromium, tungsten, and manganese, as well as the brass and bronze alloys. Such metals are particularly valued for their corrosion resistance.

This grouping into two broad classes is convenient on at least two counts. First, ours is a steel civilization. We use about ten times as much steel and other iron alloys as all other metals together, so that the lumping of all noniron metals and alloys into a single group, leaving the predominant iron group in a separate class, is justified. Second, for the ferrous group of metals the heat-treating methods are different from those for the nonferrous group.

This classification, however, leaves every pure metal except iron in the nonferrous group. Uranium, titanium, and nickel, for example, do not have very much in common. The nonferrous group requires further breaking down. The platinum and precious metals—platinum, palladium, gold, silver, etc.—make a convenient subgroup with specialized welding practices. The radioactive metals radium, thorium, uranium, and others, are an obvious group, also with specialized welding. Another natural group comprises the fourteen metals called the "rare earths," which are neither rare nor earths—cerium, samarium, gadolinium, dysprosium, and others. The rare earths are only now beginning to find their place in industry. The last of these natural groups comprises the refractory metals, those with melting points above 3600 F, such as tungsten, columbium, and molybdenum. Grouping by melting points is particularly convenient from the welder's point of view, since we can call the low-melting-point metals easy to weld and the refractory metals difficult to weld. The melting point also indicates cost. By and large, the low-melting-point metals cost less than a dollar a pound, whereas the refractory metals cost from a few dollars to several hundred dollars per pound.

The most practical and useful classification of metals is that which divides them according to crystal structure, but this is more complicated and must be dealt with in a later section of this book.

1.5 metals and ceramic materials

A *metal* is an elemental substance that conducts both heat and electricity well at ordinary temperatures. Most metals are solid, hard, and crystalline, have a silvery luster, and melt at a definite temperature. Most are also ductile and can be stretched or formed under pressure without fracturing. Compared with other solid substances, metals are weldable by one or another of the many welding processes.

A *ceramic* material is a hard, brittle, rocklike, heat-resisting material, usually an oxide or a carbide of some metal. Familiar examples of the ceramics are Carborundum (silicon carbide), Carboloy (usually tungsten carbide), glass (silicon oxide), brick and clay (both metal silicates), metal ores, slags, fluxes, and welding rod coatings.

The interrelationships between the metals and the ceramics are so intimate that it is impossible to study the one group of materials without studying the other. Thus metals are extracted from ceramic ores, but when heated, the metals oxidize, which means in effect that they are reverting back to the original ores from which they were extracted. Many of the ceramic materials are of great importance to welding, such as melting slags, brazing fluxes, and the flux coatings on stick electrodes. A great many types of welding rods are used for arc-welding mild steel: the difference between one rod and another lies almost entirely in the flux coating, for all these rods are made of the same steel. For these and a variety of other reasons some attention must be given to the ceramic materials, otherwise all the metallurgical processes that take place in the weld cannot be understood.

Earlier civilizations were ceramic civilizations based on clay, brick, stone, and similar materials. But almost a century ago, Europe and America converted to a steel civilization, which has been maintained to this day and may well continue indefinitely. In a ceramic civilization, there could be no welding trade.

Fig. 2 A "stank." This is the combination ventilating stack and overhead welded tank shown under erection at the Whiteshell Nuclear Research Establishment, Pinawa, Manitoba. (Courtesy Atomic Energy of Canada, Ltd.)

The welder's job is to bond together the steel and metal sinews of our steel civilization in the making of bridges, boilers, buildings, storage tanks, ships, conveyors, and electronic components. His counterpart in the earlier cultures based on ceramic materials was the stonemason and the bricklayer. Their trades are ten thousand years old. The welding trade is young in comparison with these, perhaps sixty years old, for welding is one of the technical gifts of the mightiest of all centuries, the twentieth century.

2.1 a classification of welding methods

In Chapter 1 we noted that there are in use about sixty methods of welding. No useful purpose would be served by listing all these welding methods. Instead, we shall begin a general description of the available methods of welding by grouping all welding methods into four general types:

1. gas welding
2. electric resistance welding
3. electric arc welding
4. special methods

The second and third types are electrical methods, although a great many of the methods that are "special" also use electricity for the source of welding power.

2.2 energy

A good definition of energy is difficult. Energy is usually explained as mechanical work or the capacity to do mechanical work, much like defining an expert as a person whom other experts consider to be an expert. At any rate this definition of energy means: energy need not

WELDING

METHODS

2

necessarily be used for performing mechanical work, but all forms of energy can be expressed as an equivalent of mechanical work. Mechanical work includes such physical tasks as moving a freight train, turning a shaft, raising an elevator cage, pumping water, hanging up an overcoat, and so on.

Energy exists in a great many forms, including heat, mechanical work, acoustic energy of sound, electric energy, the chemical energy in a cylinder of acetylene, kinetic and potential energy, nuclear energy, and many others. It is no particular handicap to the human race if the energy available happens to be in the wrong form, because we have developed thousands of devices to convert energy from one form to another. An electric motor converts electric energy into the mechanical work of turning a shaft. A welding arc converts electric energy into heat. An oxyacetylene torch converts chemical energy into heat. A microphone converts acoustic energy into electric energy, and a loudspeaker converts electric energy back into acoustic energy. Most welding methods use as their basic principle the conversion of electric energy as raw material into heat energy as the useful output of the welding process.

Energy, then, exists in a number of forms. Unfortunately, in north America at present, we use different units to measure energy in its different forms. Consider conversion of energy by an electric motor. The energy input to the motor is electric energy, measured in kilowatts. The useful energy output is mechanical work, measured in horsepower. The wasted energy is heat energy, measured in British thermal units or Btu per hr. A simple thing like energy is complicated by having too many ways of measuring it.

2.3 units of energy

By definition, energy = work. Work (mechanical work) is measured in foot-pounds. If your car is out of gas, it takes a force of about 100 lb to push it along a road to the nearest gas pump. If you push the car 7.78 ft, your energy expenditure has been 100×7.78 ft, or 778 ft-lb. However, the foot-pound is of limited interest in welding, the Btu being a more useful unit of energy.

The Btu is the amount of heat needed to raise the temperature of 1 lb of water at 60 F by 1 degree Fahrenheit, or from 60 to 61 degrees. In terms of work, 1 Btu = 778 ft-lb.

In welding calculations it is more convenient to measure power than energy. Power measures the rate at which energy is expended. The car may be pushed along the read slowly or rapidly. The following is a table of power units and their conversions:

watts (w)	= amperes × volts (v)
1 kilowatt (kW)	= 1000 watts
1 watt	= 1 joule per second
1 kilowatt-hour (kWH)	= 3412 Btu
1 horsepower (hP)	= 746 watts (= ¾ kw approx.)
1 kilowatt	= 1⅓ horsepower approx.
1 horsepower	= 33,000 foot-pounds per minute
1 horsepower	= 550 foot-pounds per second
1 horsepower-hour (hp-hr)	= 2544 Btu
1 electron-volt (ev)	= 1 electron times the voltage across which it travels

As an example of these energy conversions, consider a case of manual arc welding with a current setting of 100 amp and 18 v across the arc.

$$\text{the watts} = 100 \times 18 = 1800 \text{ w, or } 1.8 \text{ kw}$$
$$\text{the arc horsepower} = \tfrac{4}{3} \times 1.8 = 2.4 \text{ hp}$$

An electron traveling across the arc acquires an energy or 18 ev. How much heat is developed by this arc? For convenience, take the arc time as 1 hr, and 1 kwhr = 3412 Btu.

Then 1.8 kw for 1 hr = 6140 Btu, or just over 100 Btu every minute.

PROBLEMS

1 How much heat in Btu is produced by 1 hr of arc time when welding with 130 amp and 22 v across the arc?

2 A cubic foot of acetylene can produce 1475 Btu. How many watts must be supplied by a welding arc to produce the same heat as the burning of 6 cu ft of acetylene per hr?

2.4 gas welding

Gas welding utilizes the energy released during combustion of a fuel gas with air or oxygen.

The most commonly used fuel gases are acetylene (C_2H_2), hydrogen, natural gas, which is largely methane or CH_4, propane (C_3H_8), or butane (C_4H_{10}). These gases must usually be burned with oxygen rather than air. Air is about 78% nitrogen and 21% oxygen. The large amount of nitrogen in air contributes nothing to the gas welding process

and absorbs much of the heat of combustion, thus greatly lowering the temperature of the flame. Few metals could be welded by the low temperature of a gas-air mixture.

The most commonly used flame is of course the oxyacetylene flame. This combination of oxygen and acetylene gives a flame temperature of about 6000 F, which is above the melting point of all metals except tungsten. No other available fuel gas can provide as high a temperature. This source of intense heat fuses the edges of the joint to be welded and also melts a filler rod, which is then deposited at the joint. The Btu content of acetylene is 1475 Btu per cu ft, but the amount of heat released per cubic foot depends on the proportions of oxygen and acetylene supplied to the torch.

All the fuel gases mentioned above contain both carbon and hydrogen, and all are burned with oxygen. Gas welding therefore cannot be performed upon metals harmed by the presence of carbon, hydrogen, or oxygen, for example, titanium. There are many such metals.

Gas welding has other disadvantages. It is slow and inefficient, and it does not concentrate the heat within the narrow area of the weld. It produces more heat distortion of the metal than other welding methods do. As a result, gas welding is rarely used as a factory production method.

All these are serious disadvantages of gas welding, but they are not the full story. Oxyacetylene welding offers an outstanding advantage in the fact that it requires very little equipment. Basically all that is needed is a torch, hose, regulators, and cylinders of acetylene and oxygen, all these components being small, portable items.

The flame temperatures of gas welding are lower than the temperatures of an electric arc. This consideration may make gas welding preferable to arc welding when joints must be welded on metals of low melting points, such as lead. Gas welding serves excellently for such work as brazing, soldering, refrigeration, general repairs and maintenance, auto body work, plumbing and small piping, and the welding of thin sheet metal and lead.

Certain types of welding, such as TIG (tungsten inert gas), MIG (metal inert gas), and plasma torch welding, are a combination of gas and electric welding, since they use an electric arc carried through a stream of gas of special composition.

2.5 special methods of welding

The "special" welding methods must obviously include all those welding methods that do not use for energy either the combustion of a fuel gas or the electric energy of an arc or a resistance. Welding can be performed with virtually any kind of energy, whether it be the combustion of a fuel gas, electric energy, light energy, acoustic energy, the energy of fast-moving electrons, or any other kind of energy.

At the top of the list of special welding methods is electron beam welding, simply because it is the ideal method of welding. The principle of the electron beam welder can be understood from Fig. 4. An electron gun, basically a heated filament such as is used in radio tubes and incandescent lamps, produces a supply of free electrons. A high-voltage source, actually a transformer, is connected between the electron gun and the workpiece. The workpiece is the positive terminal and the electron gun is negative, or in the language of welding, the hookup is a straight-polarity hookup. Under the influence of the high voltage, 20,000 v or more, the negative electrons produced by the electron gun are rapidly accelerated toward the positive workpiece and may have velocities of the order of half the speed of light when they strike the workpiece. These high-impact velocities produce the heat for welding. No filler rod is used. The purpose of the focusing magnetic coil is to concentrate the stream of electrons into a narrow beam. In Fig. 4 the electron beam welder is shown welding two channel sections together, producing both a top weld and a bottom weld at the same time. Although the two channels are shown separated, with the stream of electrons between, no weld can be produced unless the two channels are butted tight together.

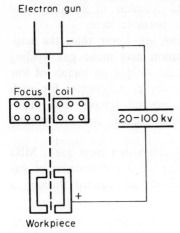

Fig. 4(a) Electron beam welding.

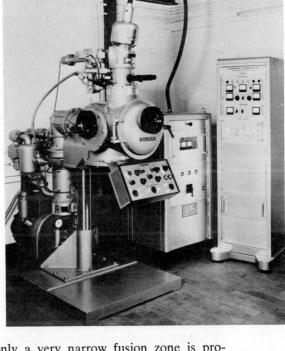

Fig. 4(b) Small electron beam welder. (Courtesy Philips Electronics, Inc.)

In electron beam welding, only a very narrow fusion zone is produced, and only the welded joint is heated, the surrounding metal being unaffected by heat. Thus the problems common to the heat-affected zone, such as cracking or hardening, are avoided simply because there is no heat-affected zone. This ideal method, however, has two disadvantages: the welding must be done in a vacuum, and X rays are produced by the process. As we shall see later, an X-ray tube and an electron beam welder do not differ much basically. Finally it must be noted that these welding machines are expensive, usually costing more than $100,000.

Two special welding methods more difficult to understand are induction welding and brazing, and the more famous laser welding. Induction methods obtain their energy from a powerful magnetic field. To anyone who watches induction heating for the first time, it seems an incredibly fast method of heating. Induction welding is discussed in Chapter 16. The laser uses some kind of radiant energy, such as light or infrared, for its heat.

Thin materials are sometimes welded by means of acoustic energy in the ultrasonic range above 20,000 cycles per second (cps). This is ultrasonic welding. A pulse of acoustic energy is fired into the material, producing a weld at the joint. The various uses of ultrasonic energy in welding are discussed in Chapter 18.

welding methods
17

Two pieces of metal can also be welded together by means of severe pressure by *cold welding*. This is somewhat the same action that occurs when an engine "seizes" or when a built-up edge develops on a cutting tool in a machine shop. Closely related to cold welding is friction welding, in which the two pieces of metal are rubbed against each other and then pressed together to make a welded joint.

A special welding method of historical interest is forge welding, the method traditionally used by blacksmiths. Two pieces of metal were welded together in a lap joint by a special forging technique performed by heating in a forge and hammering on an anvil. Like most of the work of the village blacksmith, this technique called for a high degree of skill.

It should be obvious that there are a great many ways of concentrating energy at a joint to be welded. The few methods described above do not exhaust all the possibilities, and it is reasonable to suppose that welding methods will proliferate as rapidly in the future as they have in the immediate past.

2.6   resistance welding

In resistance welding two or more metal pieces are welded by means of both pressure and heat, usually in a lap weld. Figure 5 shows the circuitry for a resistance welder of the alternating current (a-c) type.

Line voltage is brought to the primary winding of the welding transformer. The low voltage required for resistance welding is picked off by a single turn on the secondary winding of the transformer. Voltage and current are varied by means of taps on the primary winding as shown; these cut in or cut out windings. If extra primary turns are cut in, then the secondary voltage is increased and the secondary current is decreased. The resistance welder is frequently operated by means of a foot switch and a timer to control the duration of the current. The current pulse will be about 6 cycles long, more or less, which is of course about one-tenth of a second on 60-cycle mains frequency. Before the current is applied, the upper electrode is forced down onto the work to be welded with considerable pressure; the current then flows, passing from the upper electrode through the workpieces to the lower electrode and fusing a nugget of weld metal joining the workpieces. The upper electrode lifts and the workpiece can be removed.

To apply the principles of electricity to resistance welding, recall that an electric current is a movement of electrically negative particles called electrons through a circuit. This movement of electrons is called an electric current, and the unit of measurement of electric current is the

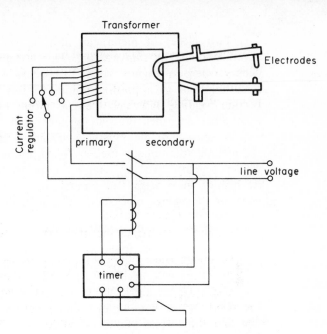

Transformer

Electrodes

Current regulator

primary   secondary

line voltage

timer

**Fig. 5   Principle of the re-
sistance or spot welder.**

ampere (amp), measured with an ammeter. One amp, which is approximately the current through a 100-w light bulb, means that the number of
electrons passing any point in the circuit in 1 sec is 628 billion billion
(6.28×10^{18} electrons). With numbers such as these, it is easier to
measure amperes than to count electrons.

However, electrons, like anything else, do not move unless some
force compels them to move. Most forces are measured in pounds, but
forces on electrically charged objects such as electrons are measured in
volts. Thus a table may be moved across a floor by a certain number of
pounds of force, but it conceivably could be moved by a voltage force
if it were electrically charged.

Any electric circuit has another characteristic—resistance to the flow
of electrons. This electrical resistance is measured in ohms. The basic
relationship between volts, amperes, and ohms is the famous *Ohm's law*:

$$\text{volts} = \text{amperes} \times \text{ohms}$$
$$E = I \times R$$

This relationship indicates that with a given voltage across a circuit, say
110 v, if the resistance is low, a large current will flow, or if the resistance
is high, only a small current will flow. If the resistance is many millions
of ohms, the current may be so small that it is almost zero: such a circuit
is called an *open circuit*. If the resistance is almost zero, then we have
a *short circuit*, and the result is an unmanageably high current. The currents across welding arcs and through resistance welders are very nearly
short circuits.

welding methods
19

Electric energy is measured in watts or electron-volts. These two units are similar. A watt is the product of 1 volt times 1 amp, and an electron-volt is the product of 1 electron (the unit of amperes) times 1 volt. We shall not discuss the electron-volt at this time.

$$\text{watts} = \text{amperes} \times \text{volts}$$
$$P = I \times E$$

or, substituting IR for E,

$$P = I \times (I \times R)$$
$$= I^2R \text{ watts} = \text{current squared} \times \text{ohms resistance}$$

To obtain some notion of the electrical quantities involved in spot welding (resistance welding), consider the following example: Two steel sheets $\frac{1}{32}$ in. thick are to be spot-welded together in a lap joint. The resistance across the two sheets between the electrodes is 0.0005 ohm and the current applied is 8000 amp. What is the voltage across the two steel sheets, and what is the energy used in watts?

$$E = IR$$
$$= 8000 \times 0.0005$$
$$= 4 \text{ v}$$
$$P = I^2R$$
$$= (8000)^2 \times 0.0005$$
$$= 32,000 \text{ w}$$

In terms of horsepower, this is more than 40 hp, but this energy is applied for only 7 cycles, or about one-eighth of a second. The actual energy used is $32,000 \times \frac{7}{60}$ watt-sec.

The heating effect, or the number of Btu produced, is proportional to the product of the watts and the time of application. As the data in the example suggest, metals offer very little resistance to the flow of electricity, therefore to obtain sufficient power, a very high current must be used, otherwise the metals will not fuse. Actually, almost all the electrical resistance is represented by the contact resistance between the two steel sheets, and therefore this contact area is the source of the heating effect.

2.7 electric arc welding

There are a great many uses for electric arcs in industry. Arc welding is one. Another useful type of arc is used across the spark plug of an automobile cylinder to ignite the gas mixture in the cylinder. It will be instructive to compare the electrical characteristics of these two arcs.

Welding arc, say, 100 amp, 20 v

$$E = IR$$
$$20 = 100\ R$$
$$R = \tfrac{1}{5}\ \text{ohm across the arc}$$

This is such a small resistance that we might almost call such an arc a short circuit between the welding rod and the workpiece.

Spark plug, say, 20,000, 0.001 amp

$$E = IR$$
$$20,000 = 0.001\ R$$
$$R = 20,000,000\ \text{ohms}$$

This arc is virtually an open circuit.

The welding arc is virtually a short circuit, the other an open circuit, yet both are arcs.

The explanation is simply that an arc represents an unusual kind of electrical resistance, in that the resistance to be overcome in initiating the arc is not the same resistance found in an established arc. At the start, the arc voltage must overcome a very high air-gap resistance, but once started, the gases in the air gap break down, becoming ionized and electrically conductive, so that the arc resistance reverses and becomes a virtual short. The spark plug arc and the welding arc are both characteristic arcs. In the spark plug, as soon as the arc is established it is quenched, otherwise it would turn into a welding arc and melt the engine. On the other hand, the welding arc cannot be established by making it jump across from the welding rod to the workpiece (although high frequency welding arcs can be started in this manner); the spark plug's 20,000 are needed to do that. Since only 20 or more are available in welding, the arc is started by touching or shorting the rod to the work and then drawing out the arc by pulling the rod away from the workpiece.

A spark plug has two electrodes. So has a welding arc, one being the welding rod, the other being the workpiece to be welded. The arc voltage is the voltage drop across the arc between the two. Each of the two electrodes is given a special name. The *anode* is the positive electrode. Since electrons are electrically negative, they are attracted to the positive anode. The *cathode* is the negative electrode, and any positively charged particles or ions will be attracted to it. The terms anode and cathode apply to the electrodes of many types of industrial equipment, including electronic tubes, X-ray tubes, and others.

If direct current is used for arc welding, there are two possibilities, or polarities, as they are called. If the workpiece is *positive* (anode), this condition is termed *straight polarity,* abbreviated DCSP. If the workpiece is *negative* (cathode), this is *reverse polarity,* abbreviated DCRP. Both polarities are used in welding.

About two-thirds of the useful arc heat appears at the anode, and about one-third at the cathode. This means that there is a greater heating effect at the workpiece with DCRP, and penetration of the weld metal into the joint is much deeper with DCRP. In a-c welding, the welding heat will be equally distributed between the welding rod and the workpiece, since alternating current is an alternation between straight and reverse polarity.

Metal is transferred across the arc whether the supply voltage is DCSP, DCRP, or a.c. The rod metal is transferred even against the force of gravity, as when welding overhead. The explanation for the transference of metal across the arc is not really known yet, although there are some excellent theories. These, however, cannot be discussed here. The theories do not explain the occasional irregular behavior of the arc, such as the blowing of pieces of rod metal out at right angles to the arc or even in the opposite direction to the work, that results in spatter in certain types of semiautomatic welding. The method of transfer of metal to the workpiece depends on the magnitude of the current. At very high currents the rod can be *boiled* away (iron boils at the comparatively low temperature of 5500 F), although this is never done in practice. At lower currents the metal transfer is in a fine spray. At still lower currents the metal transfers in small globules, and at still lower currents in larger globules.

PROBLEMS

1 As a general rule, copper and silver cannot be resistance-welded. Why?

2 Why are the welding tips of resistance welders made of copper?

3 Find from a reference book the horsepower of an average horse as determined by James Watt. The answer is *not* 1 hp.

4 How many electron-volts are in 1 w?

5 What gases are produced by burning acetylene with oxygen?

6 Will it take more or less current to resistance-weld thicker sheets of a material?

7 Which will require more current to spot-weld, other things being equal, steel or aluminum?

ow many Btu are produced by a 1500-w heater which is turned on for min?

9 A DCRP welding arc has a voltage drop of 25 v and draws 150 amp. The arc time is 1 hr. If all this energy is converted into heat, approximately how many Btu are released at the rod and at the workpiece?

10 A DCSP welding arc drawing 140 amp has a voltage drop of 22 v. The arc time is 10 min.
(a) If all this energy is converted into heat, approximately how many Btu are released at the rod and at the workpiece?
(b) What is the arc resistance?

11 Operating conditions for an electron beam welder are 40 kv and 30 ma for 1 min. What is the total energy produced in Btu?

12 A small X-ray tube operates at 100 kv d.c. and 4 ma for 30 min.
(a) If 1% of this total energy is converted into X rays, determine the X-ray energy expressed as watts and as Btu.
(b) What is the resistance across the X-ray tube?

3.1 kinds of welds

The classification of Fig. 6 includes perhaps the most common of the various types of welds.

The *butt weld* may be an open or a closed butt weld, depending on the thickness of the metal and the welding method. In a closed butt joint, which would be used for steel plates up to $\frac{1}{8}$-in. thick, or 10 gauge, the two workpieces to be joined would be butted tight together. For manual arc welding of steels thicker than $\frac{3}{16}$ in., a gap between the two plates would be required in order to obtain penetration of the weld metal deep into the joint, and the joint would be an open butt. Certain types of welding, including submerged arc and electron beam welding, can use a closed-butt joint for greater thicknesses than are possible with manual welding. But generally, for very thick plates to be butt-welded, some type of edge preparation is necessary to ensure full penetration for the weld.

A *fillet weld* is made on an inside corner joint. A good fillet weld is more difficult to produce than a butt weld, at least for manual arc welding. The fillet must have equal legs (usually), no undercutting, and preferably should be a flat miter between the plates, without concavity or convexity (see Fig. 7). In manual arc welding with direct current, the arc may wander when fillet-welding because of variations in the magnetic field around the arc caused by the presence of metal on two sides of the fillet triangle. A short arc is used, and the welding rod should bisect the angle between the plates.

TYPES OF
WELDS

3

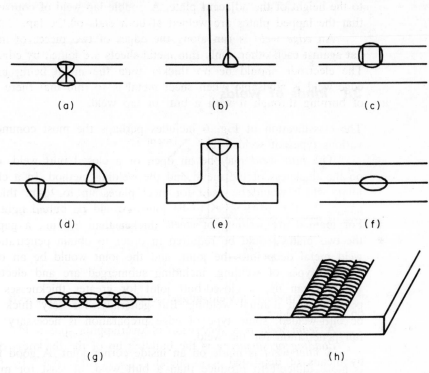

Fig. 6 Types of welds. (a) Butt weld, (b) fillet weld, (c) plug weld, (d) lap weld, (e) edge weld, (f) spot weld, (g) seam weld, (h) surfacing or padding.

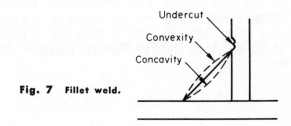

Fig. 7 Fillet weld.

The *leg* of a fillet weld is the length of the side of the fillet along one of the plates, and the *throat* is the length of the line bisecting the included angle of the fillet (see Fig. 8). However, if the fillet is convex, the additional throat length due to convexity is not considered. If the fillet weld is concave, then the actual throat length is used.

A *plug weld* is a method of joining two overlapping plates by drilling a hole in one plate and filling the hole with weld metal.

The *lap weld* is a variant of the fillet weld. The weld bead is filled to the height of the adjacent plate. A double lap weld of course indicates that the lapped plates are welded at both ends of the lap.

An *edge weld* is run along the edges of two pieces of metal lying flat against each other. Only thin metal sheets are joined by edge welding. The electrode should be no thicker than the metal being joined. An edge weld is advisable when sheet metal is so thin that there is danger of burning through it with a butt or lap weld.

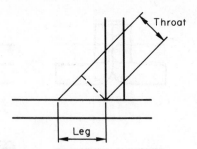

Fig. 8   Leg and throat of fillet weld.

A *spot weld* is a weld nugget joining two or more sheets, produced on a spot welder.

A *seam weld* is a succession of overlapping spot welds.

Padding or surfacing is the building up of the thickness of a metal by means of deposited weld metal. This is often done by running a series of overlapping beads over the surface to be built up. Surfacing may be executed to repair a worn part, or to provide a wear-resistant, corrosion-resistant, or hard surface to a part. A large rock crusher may require 40 lb of hard-surfacing welding rods daily to replace worn surfaces.

Surfacing can be done by metallizing or plating. A metal is sprayed on the part to be surfaced by atomizing molten metal in a suitable spray gun.

3.2   edge preparation

For the butt welding of heavy plates, edge preparation is necessary to ensure full penetration of the weld through the cross section. Figure 9 illustrates various methods of edge preparation. Such contours are shaped by either machining or oxygas flame cutting. In selecting a suitable method of edge preparation, the objective is to obtain full penetration and at the same time lay down the minimum amount of weld metal in making the joint. This is a problem in economics. Thus for very thick plates, a single V forms too wide a groove at the top to fill up with

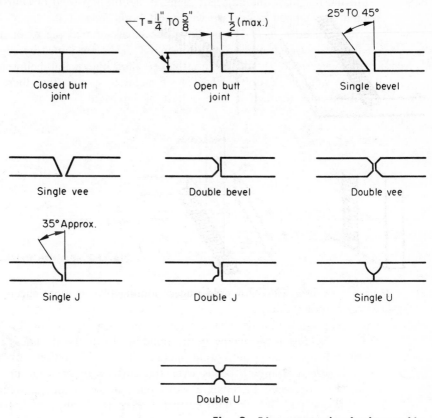

Fig. 9 **Edge preparation for butt welds.**

weld metal. The J weld may then be preferred, although it is a more expensive type of edge preparation to produce.

3.3 *position welding*

Welding may be done in the four positions shown in Fig. 10: flat, horizontal, vertical, and overhead. Flat welding is the easiest and cheapest and is therefore the preferred position, the other positions being used when conditions make them unavoidable, as in pipe welding. Although many welding methods are restricted to the horizontal position, such as submerged arc welding, manual arc and gas welding may be done in any of the four positions. Again, certain manual welding rods are all-position rods. Welding rods for use in vertical or overhead welding must necessarily be fast-freeze rods if the molten metal is to remain in the bead.

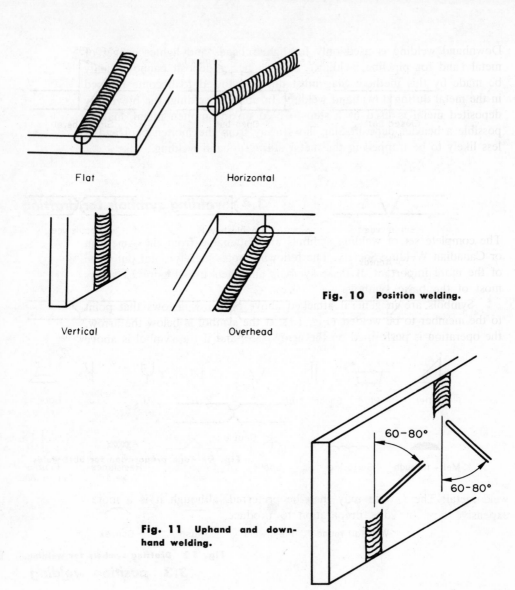

Flat

Horizontal

Vertical

Overhead

Fig. 10 Position welding.

60—80°

60—80°

Fig. 11 Uphand and down-hand welding.

Once the weld metal has been deposited in any weld position other than flat, gravity tends to make the molten metal run out of the bead. The effect of gravity can be only counteracted by the surface tension and viscosity of the molten metal and only if the weld metal freezes quickly. Arc current must not be excessive, and the metal must not be superheated too far above its melting point. Short arcs are used to help prevent sagging of the metal by confining the heat to as small an area as possible.

Vertical welding may be done uphand or downhand (see Fig. 11).

Downhand welding is used only for lighter beads and lighter gauges of metal (and for pipeline welding), since a heavy deposit cannot usually be made by this method. Slag must not be allowed to become trapped in the metal during downhand welding. In uphand welding, the previously deposited metal is used as a step to hold up the molten metal, making possible a heavier deposit. Slag flows away from the molten pool and is less likely to be trapped in the metal during uphand welding.

3.4 welding symbols for drafting

The complete set of welding symbols are obtainable from the American or Canadian Welding Society. The following notes merely point out some of the more important of these symbols and their use. Figure 12 shows most of the basic symbols.

Symbols are in general attached above or below arrows that point to the member to be welded (Fig. 13). If the symbol is below the arrow, the operation is performed on the arrow side, and if the symbol is above

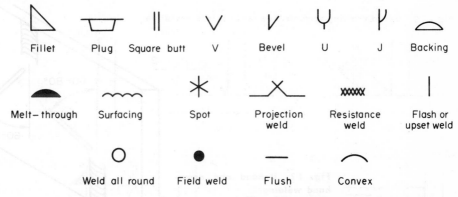

Fig. 12 Drafting symbols for welding.

Fig. 13 Arrow designations.

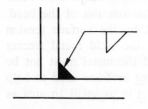

Fillet weld on arrow side

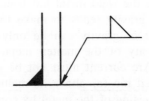

Fillet weld on other side

the arrow, the operation is performed on the other side or side opposite that to which the arrow points.

In symbols for fillets, bevels, or J's, the perpendicular leg of the symbol must be to the left. The length of a weld is placed to the right of the symbol. The backing weld symbol means a single weld pass on the back side of the joint. The field welding symbol indicates that the weld is not to be made in the shop, but at the jobsite. The melt-through symbol is required if 100% penetration is expected on welds made from one side only.

Built-up surfaces have no arrow side significance. The symbol is always placed on the arrow side, usually with a dimension to indicate the thickness of the deposit. Projection welds too have no arrow side significance, but like built-up surface symbols are placed on the near or arrow side always.

Figure 14 illustrates the use of the drafting symbols. Nine examples are shown, the explanation of each being as follows:

(a) Fillet-weld both sides of the joint.
(b) Fillet-weld 6 in. on both sides of the joint and space 12 in. (on

Fig. 14 Use of drafting symbols. See text for interpretation.

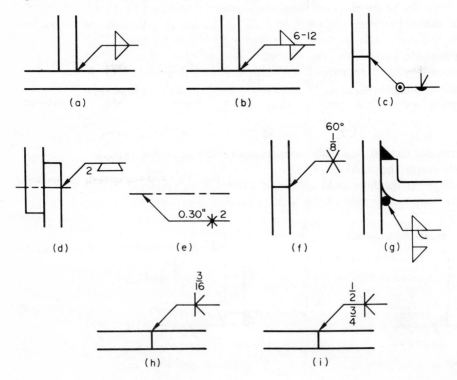

centers); stagger the welds on one side of the joint with respect to the welds on the other side.

(c) Bevel-groove the far side of the weld; weld all round at jobsite; melt through to the other side of the joint.

(d) Make a 2-in.-diameter plug weld on the near member.

(e) Make spot welds 0.30 in. in diameter and space 2 in. o.c.

(f) Separate the members ⅛ in.; vee-groove both sides of the joint 60°.

(g) Make two fillet welds as indicated.

(h) Separate the two members ³⁄₁₆ in.; double-bevel one plate.

(i) Bevel ½ in. deep on lower side; bevel ¾ in. deep on top side.

Nondestructive testing symbols The subject of weld testing must be deferred until later in this book. However, drafting symbols are recognized for four types of nondestructive testing. These tests, and their drafting symbols, are

radiographic (X-ray or gamma ray) test	RT
magnetic particle test	MT
penetrant test	PT
ultrasonic test	UT

If these tests are to be executed from the arrow side of the joint or the far side, the abbreviations should so indicate by being placed below or above the arrow line as with other drafting symbols. If there is no near- or far-side significance, the symbol should be centered in the line. The symbol for "weld all around" can also indicate "test all around the full length of the joint."

Typical use of the nondestructive testing symbols is shown in Fig. 15:

(a) Ultrasonic-test on near side; magnetic-particle-test on far side.

(b) Radiograph the weld.

(c) Radiograph the fillet weld all round (100% radiography).

(d) Take four radiographs of the weld at random locations.

Fig. 15 Nondestructive testing symbols.

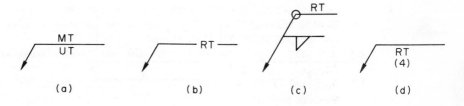

(a)   (b)   (c)   (d)

PROBLEMS

1 Explain in words the drafting symbols sketched in the accompanying diagrams (a) to (o).

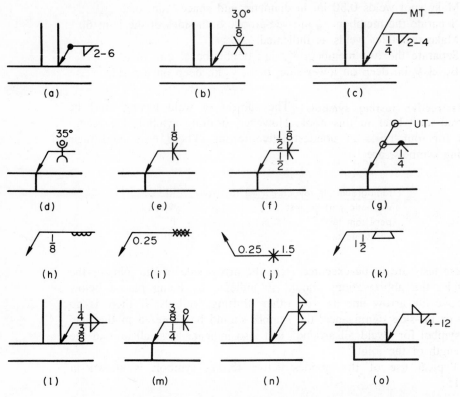

(a) (b) (c)

(d) (e) (f) (g)

(h) (i) (j) (k)

(l) (m) (n) (o)

2 Draw the welding symbols to convey the following directions:
  (a) Butt-weld. Bevel top and bottom ¼ in. deep, separate plates ⅛ in.
  (b) Spot-weld. Spots to be 0.25 in. diameter, 0.5 in. o.c.
  (c) Fillet-weld. Bevel far side, weld both sides with ⅜ in. leg.
  (d) Resistance-weld. Weld all round with seam weld 0.30 in. wide.
  (e) Surface-weld ³⁄₁₆ in thick.
  (f) Butt-weld. Double J-weld ½ in. deep both sides, 35° angle, do not separate plates, weld in field and ultrasonic-test all around.
  (g) Butt-weld. V-out the far side ½ in. deep and weld with backing weld on near side. Take three radiographs at random.
  (h) Double fillet-weld. Bevel both sides ¼ in., weld both sides in field and magnetic-particle-test all around.
  (i) Butt-weld. V-joint on near side with 60° angle. Weld and melt through. Test with dye penetrant on far side.
  (j) Butt-weld. U-groove both sides with included angle 40°. Do not separate plates.

WELDING
METALLURGY

Part **II**

4.1 metals and oxides

The first step in processing any metal is extracting a ceramic material, called a mineral, from the earth for processing into a primary metal casting in an industrial furnace. The processing of steel begins in an open-pit iron mine, where iron oxide (usually hematite or magnetite) is mined for blast furnace feed. In the blast furnace the iron oxide is reduced to crude iron, which is later refined into steel. Similarly, aluminum begins as aluminum oxide (usually bauxite), which is reduced in an electrolytic cell to aluminum metal. For iron and aluminum, the ore mineral is almost always an oxide.

The metallic condition is essentially unstable, for metals will revert back to oxides if conditions permit. This oxidation is so familiar that it scarcely needs mention. When iron rusts, it converts to the more stable iron oxide Fe_2O_3, or at higher temperatures to Fe_3O_4, (mill scale). Magnesium readily burns to magnesium oxide with a brilliant white flare, and uranium, zirconium, and others of the metals are also pyrophoric. In general, the surface of any metal is oxidized to a greater or less extent, whether the surface is a heavy iron rust or a microscopically thin coat of aluminum oxide on aluminum. This oxide surface may have to be removed if the metal is to be welded, brazed, or soldered, since few welding methods will weld or braze ceramic oxides.

Most metals are designated by the suffix "ium," most oxides by the suffix "a"; thus

CERAMIC
MATERIALS
IN WELDING

4

aluminum (aluminium in Great Britain)	alumina
zirconium	zirconia
thorium	thoria
magnesium	magnesia
beryllium	beryllia
lithium	lithia
titanium	rutile
calcium	lime

4.2 ceramic materials

The mineral oxides are typical of the large group of ceramic materials. The ceramic materials are hard, abrasive, and brittle and generally have high melting points, usually much higher than the melting point of the corresponding metal. The following table compares the melting points of some of the common metals and ceramics. It should be observed that these melting points belong to pure materials, which are rare in industry, especially pure ceramic materials.

TABLE OF MELTING POINTS

(Fahrenheit)

Pure Metals		Pure Oxide or Carbide	
Al	1220	Al_2O_3	3720
Cr	3410	Cr_2O_3	4130
Fe	2800	Fe_2O_3	2840
		Fe_3O_4	2800
		Fe_3C	3340
Mg	1200	MgO	5070
Ni	2650	NiO	3560
Si	2570	SiO_2	3110
		SiC	4900
Ti	3035	TiO_2	3360
U	2070	UO_2	3950
Zr	3370	ZrO_2	4930

Unlike the metals, ceramic materials, with a few exceptions such as silicon carbide, are electrical insulators. However, ceramic materials become more conductive with higher temperatures, whereas metals become less conductive as the temperature increases.

Most of the industrially significant ceramic materials occur naturally and are extracted by open-pit mining. They may be oxides, such as bauxite (Al_2O_3) or hematite (Fe_2O_3), or silicates, such as clay (chiefly aluminum silicate), or aluminates, phosphates, etc. In addition to the naturally occurring ceramics are a growing number of synthetic materials, including silicon carbide (often described by one of its trade names, Carborundum); tungsten carbide (trade name Carboloy); aluminum oxide (Alundum or Aloxite); and many other carbides, nitrides, borides, and other synthetics.

Many of the ceramic materials have little significance for welding technology at present. The behavior and characteristics of the oxides and carbides, however, have a strong influence on welding techniques. Generally, oxides coat the surface of metals and metal carbides appear as inclusions within the microstructure of steels, but a few exceptions to this generalization exist. The tool steels in particular obtain their hardness from carbides distributed throughout the metal. For example, a high-speed steel of 80% steel and 20% tungsten carbide owes its excellence as a cutting tool largely to the 20% fraction of hard ceramic tungsten carbide. Steels high in carbides, however, present difficulties for welding.

4.3 influence of oxides on welding and cutting of metals

The tendency of a metal to convert chemically to an oxide in the presence of air or oxygen increases rapidly with temperature. Most welding methods are fusion methods under high temperatures, and of course such conditions mean rapid oxidation if oxygen is present. For reactive metals, such as zirconium and titanium, conditions of rapid oxidation commence at temperatures below a red heat, or less than 1000 F. Welding techniques for these or any metals must either prevent or control oxidation.

On many welding techniques, then, surface oxides exert a major influence. In resistance welding, variations in the thickness of the surface oxide skin will result in variations in electrical resistance, which in turn will result in variations of heat output and quality of the spot welds. In the TIG welding (gas tungsten arc welding) of aluminum and magnesium, direct current reverse polarity (DCRP) is used in order to break through the surface oxides. The reason why DCRP is effective appears to be this: the workpiece being negative, positive ions in the arc are attracted to it, and these heavy positive ions sandblast and thus remove the oxide film.

The fact that iron oxidizes rapidly is the basis for oxygen cutting of carbon steels. The heat of the flame first raises the temperature of the steel to ignition (not melting) temperature. Then a stream of oxygen is directed under pressure at the hot metal, which is thus oxidized to black iron oxide, Fe_3O_4. This technique is basically a combustion process using iron as the fuel. The melting point of iron oxide is virtually the same as that of the steel, so that the oxide melts in the flame and can be blown out of the kerf by the gas stream. This being a combustion reaction, heat is released through the chemical reaction of iron and oxygen, at the rate of 2870 Btu per lb of iron, as well as through the oxygas flame.

Iron oxide is unusual, however, in that its melting point is not higher than that of its metal. Oxygas cutting depends on this peculiarity. If the metal oxide has a much higher melting point, as the oxides of magnesium, aluminum, and chromium do, then it cannot be blown out of the cut but will remain in place unmelted. Oxygas cutting is therefore confined largely to low-alloy steels that do not contain constituents producing refractory oxides in the flame.

4.4 slags and fluxes

A slag is a prepared mixture of oxides that floats on the surface of a molten metal. Slags serve at least two purposes: they absorb impurities from the molten metal, and they prevent the molten metal from absorbing harmful gases from the atmosphere. The liquid slag will be either acid or basic (alkaline). Silica is the usual acid slag, limestone or lime being used to make a basic slag. Except in the melting of cast iron in foundry cupola furnaces, acid slags are not usual in melting metal. A furnace using an acid slag must be lined with an acid firebrick, such as silica brick, and that using a basic slag must be lined with a basic brick such as magnesia, otherwise the slag will rapidly corrode the furnace lining.

In the furnace melting of metals, the slagging material, for example, lime, must be dumped into the furnace. As the fusion welding of a metal is no different in principle from the furnace melting of the same metal, a slag is usually required for this method. The most convenient method of supplying the slag is to coat the welding rod with it, but in submerged arc welding a slag blanket is first supplied and the arc struck underneath it. Recently a third method of supplying a welding slag was introduced: the use of flux-core wire, in which the slag is the core.

Most, but not all, of the coatings for manual arc welding rods are either lime base or rutile base, and these materials are the only ones supplied for stainless steel rods. Lime slags in general are used to remove phosphorus from molten steels, the phosphorus being taken up by the slag as calcium phosphide. Rutile (titanium oxide) will remove nitrogen from molten steels, the nitrogen being taken into the slag as titanium nitride. Nitrogen in steel forms iron nitride needles, which have an embrittling effect on the steel, but titanium nitride is harmless. However, these slagging effects during welding are less important than the protection from atmosphere provided by the slag blanket.

Alloying metals, in addition to the metal impurities such as phosphorus and sulfur, can sometimes be lost to the slag. Chromium is one such metal. When welding high-chromium steels, such as stainless steels, the welding rod must be richer in chromium than the weld deposit is expected to be, since some chromium will be lost to the slag as chromium oxide.

The words "flux" and "slag" are often used synonymously. They should be distinguished, however. A slag is used for melting; a flux is used to dissolve surface oxides while the metal is in the solid phase. Soldering and brazing require fluxes to remove surface oxides, since in general these oxides are not brazeable. A great many fluxes are in use, most of them being proprietary, such as the familiar Handy Flux. For electronic wiring and soldering, a mild rosin flux is sufficient to control surface oxides. But a mild flux is generally not active enough to remove the oxides on thermocouple or other wire with high chromium or nickel content. For brazing, borax is often used, sodium, potassium, and lithium borated being good dissolvers of oxides. But for very refractory oxides, such as magnesia, alumina, and chromium oxide, more active fluxes such as fluoborates, fluorides, and chlorides must be used. These are highly corrosive.

4.5   refractories

The term *refractories* refers to those materials, usually brick or concrete, which are used to line industrial furnaces, refractory brick being called firebrick and refractory concrete being called refractory castable. Refractories replace ordinary brick and concrete in high-temperature applications, not because they stand up better to high temperature, but because ordinary brick and concrete readily crack and spall with changes in temperature, and refractories resist spalling much better. All refractories are expensive, a single firebrick costing from 15 cents to a dollar. On construction sites, when a welder "borrows" a few firebrick on which to do some welding, he invariably selects the dollar bricks, thereafter treating them as common brick.

Refractories are used to line the furnaces that stress-relieve weldments and have so many casual uses in welding that any welder should inform himself about them. Occasionally temporary furnaces can be built of loose firebrick for such purposes as the bending of angle iron. The use of a simple gas or welding torch for the hot bending of steel is a very slow method if it is practical at all. It is wiser to enclose the steel bar in firebrick and to use a propane torch in one end of such a furnace for heating.

A crude (but very effective) such furnace is shown in Fig. 16. If this furnace is built on a concrete floor, the concrete must be protected with firebrick to prevent spalling.

A standard firebrick is called a "9-inch straight," and measures 9 by 4½ by 2½ in. This is larger in all three dimensions than a common brick. Many other shapes and sizes are available besides the 9-inch straight. Firebrick cannot be bonded with ordinary lime mortar but require a refractory cement. The mortar joint is made as thin as possible, usually by making a thin soup of the mortar and dipping the brick into it. Such mortars set up in a very short time compared with sand-lime mortar.

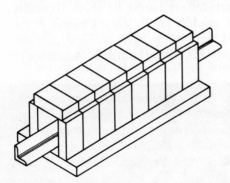

Fig. 16 Temporary furnace made of loose firebrick for heating a length of angle iron.

Refractory castables or concretes do not incorporate ordinary port-land cement or ordinary aggregates, since neither can resist temperature changes without cracking. The castables are sold by the 100-lb bag and are more expensive than ordinary concrete. Both the cement and the aggregate are included in the bag. The contents of the bag are mixed with the correct amount of water, which is always is indicated on the bag, and poured in place. Since castables set very quickly, no more than a few bags should be mixed at a time.

4.6 carbides

The carbides are a group of ceramic materials greatly valued for their abrasion resistance, heat resistance, and hardness, although they are extremely brittle. They do not occur in nature and must be manufactured.

The most familiar of the carbides is silicon carbide, often called by its trade name Carborundum. Silicon carbide was discovered in the late nineteenth century as a result of unsuccessful attempts to make artificial diamonds. This carbide is produced by a reaction between sand (silicon dioxide) and coke at a temperature exceeding 4000 F. Manufacturing at such high temperatures is costly, which accounts for the rather high price of silicon carbide, though it is made from such cheap ingredients as sand and coke.

The other industrial carbides, such as tungsten carbide, have characteristics generally similar to silicon carbide. These materials are fabricated into grinding wheels, Carboloy cutting tools, cutoff wheels, and many other similar tools. In brief, the carbides are used for cutting and grinding other materials and for hard surfacing.

For hard-surfacing roll crushers, conveyor screws, excavator teeth, etc. tungsten and chromium carbides are chiefly used, although tungsten carbide does not tolerate impact. In hard surfacing the abrasion resistance of carbides is desired. Both these carbides are harder by about 10 points on the Rockwell C scale than the hardest steels. (See Chapter 5 for hardness scales.) Many of the hard-facing rods have chemical analyses similar to the following (Liquid Air CX-193 Hardfacing Electrode):

Fig. 17 Tungsten carbide particles in a tungsten high-speed tool steel containing 18% tungsten and 0.78% carbon. (All photomicrographs reproduced in this book have the same magnification, which is approximately 500x, as reproduced.)

3.5% C, 4.2% Mn, 1.9% Si, 26.5% Cr. Such a chemical analysis could be read as 30% chromium carbide (30% is the sum of 3.5% + 26.5%), so that the purpose of the rod is obvious from the analysis. The manganese and silicon do not form carbides in steel and are not considered here.

Almost all metals, including iron, will combine with carbon to form carbides. Nickel and manganese, when alloyed in steel, do not form carbides, but iron, tungsten, chromium, molybdenum, titanium, and columbium, all of which are used in steels, readily form carbides with the ever-present carbon in steel, and it should be no surprise that carbides can be found in steels when examined under a microscope. If the steel is a plain carbon steel, it will contain only carbon and iron (except for minor constituents), and in such a steel there will be no carbon as carbon but only as iron carbide, Fe_3C. If the steel is used for cutting other steels, however, the maximum possible amount of carbides is desirable, and other carbide-forming metals, usually tungsten or molybdenum, will be added. High-speed steels are commonly 18% tungsten and 1% carbon, so that such a steel actually consists of 19% tungsten carbide. This large percentage of carbides ensures that the steel will hold a cutting edge even at high temperatures. As will be noted later, carbon in steel presents difficulties for the welders, as a large proportion of carbides makes the steel difficult to weld without cracking. Figure 17 shows a steel rich in carbides, which appear as numerous spheroids.

4.7 abrasives

An abrasive is a material used to wear away or grind other materials. Any ceramic material might serve as an abrasive, but only a few are so used. None of the naturally occurring ceramics are used in industrial grinding of metals with the minor exception of emery. Emery has rounded grains and is really a polishing material rather than a grinding abrasive. Virtually all grinding of metals is done with either silicon carbide (Crystolon or Carborundum) or fused alumina (Alundum or Aloxite). Alumina is not quite so hard as silicon carbide, but the fused alumina grains are tougher and better able to resist breakage under impact.

Silicon carbide is recommended for the grinding of cutting tools and cast iron. Welding grinders use bonded alumina grit principally. The grit size is designated by sieve size. Thus 24 grit size will pass through a screen with 20 openings per inch (400 per square inch) but will be held on a screen of 30 openings per inch. Grit sizes in the range of 24 are recommended for general-purpose grinding of steel welds in portable grinders, and in the range of 46 or finer for finishing operations. Fine grit must be used for hard materials and coarser grit for softer materials. Thus the grit used for grinding magnesium would be coarser than that for steel. The coarser grit prevents loading of the wheel by the soft material.

The abrasive grain must be cemented together to form a grinding wheel. The bonding material may be a vitrified clay material, a resinoid, a rubber, a shellac, or a silicate. The bond must release the abrasive grains as fast as they wear out, in order to expose fresh cutting edges. Softer bonds therefore are used for grinding harder materials. The vitrified, resinoid, and rubber cements are used for grinding wheels in the welding trade. The vitrified wheels are more easily cracked or broken than those with organic bonds of resinoid, shellac, or rubber.

Grinding wheels should be operated with care. Tapping a wheel with a wooden screwdriver handle indicates whether or not a wheel is cracked; a cracked wheel sounds dead. Wheels should not be operated without guards. Because of the high centrifugal stresses during grinding, wheels are mounted with large steel flanges or washers on each side. These washers hold the wheel as far out from center as possible in order to support the wheel against such stresses.

PROBLEMS

1 Is there a relationship between the melting point of a metal oxide and the difficulty of removing it from a metal surface?

2 Use a file on a piece of clean steel and a piece of rusty steel to decide which is the harder, iron rust or steel.

3 Why is firebrick produced to much closer dimensional tolerances than common brick?

4 Decide from the chemical analyses which of the following rods are hard-surfacing rods:

    (a) 3.0 % C,   1.5 % Mn,   1.5 % Si,   15.5 % Cr,   0.7 % Mo
    (b) 0.09% C,   0.50% Mn,   0.20% Si,   0.03% S,   0.02% P
    (c) 0.01% C,   18.4 % Ni,   7.5 % Co,   4.4 % Mo,   0.30% Ti
    (d) 0.45% C,   4.25% Mn,   19.5 % Cr,   0.60% Si,   9.5 % Ni
    (e) 0.10% C,   1.6 % Mn,   0.90% Si,   0.15% P,   0.03% S
    (f) 0.06% C,   0.70% Mn,   0.65% Si,   0.02% P,   0.02% S
    (g) 0.1 % C,   4.75% Ni,   0.40% Mn

5 A header course of firebrick means that the 4½ by 2½-in. face of the brick faces the interior of the furnace; in a stretcher course the 9 by 2½-in. face is the interior side of the furnace; in a soldier course the 9-in. side of the firebrick is vertical. For a firebrick wall 12 ft long by 75 in. high, how many firebrick are required to cover the wall (a) laid in headers, (b) in stretcher courses?

Most of the seventy-five or so metals of the earth's crust are used in industry, and about one-third of the metals are currently of interest in welding. A use can always be found for the particular configuration of properties represented by any metal. Moreover, the range of available metals has been vastly extended by alloying, and there is no limit to the number of possible alloys. From the one metal iron probably more than 25,000 alloys of steel have been developed; indeed, the uses of pure iron are extremely few in contrast to the vast range of purposes served by the many steel alloys.

The basic characteristics that make the metals so very useful are their weldability, hardness, stiffness, and ductility or ease of being shaped. The other two groups of structural solids, the organics and the ceramics, do not possess all these properties. The organics, such as the rubbers and the plastics, lack hardness and stiffness, and the ceramic materials have neither ductility nor weldability.

There is no such thing as an ideal metal, although nickel perhaps comes closest. For a particular application, the metal that has the least number of unfavorable features is selected, the choice always being a compromise. Probably the two most significant characteristics to be considered are the economic ones of cost and weight. Weight particularly has been given greater emphasis in recent years, as attested by the advances made by the light metals: aluminum for welded truck dump bodies, magnesium for welded warehouse dockboards, titanium for welded supersonic aircraft, and beryllium for welded rocket com-

METALS AND
THEIR PROPERTIES

5

ponents. Cost must be balanced against other characteristics of the metal. It is possible to replace beryllium by metals of only a hundredth the cost, but such substitutes cannot match beryllium's remarkable stiffness and strength, and the industries concerned may decide that the superiority of beryllium warrants the increased cost. Other applications cannot put the same premium on beryllium and therefore do not require this metal.

A remarkably wide range of properties must be considered when selecting a metal for a particular application. The purpose of this chapter is to consider the implications of only the most critical properties of metals, and in particular, those with the greatest bearing on welding techniques.

5.1 crystal structure

All solid materials occur in either crystalline or amorphous (noncrystalline) form. In the crystalline form, the atoms of the material are arranged in a definite fixed pattern with a definite distance between adjacent atoms, which for the metals is from about 2.5 to 5 Angstroms. An Angstrom (A) is 10^{-8} centimeter (one-hundred millionth of a centimeter). This means that any atom in the crystal of the metal is separated from the next nearest atoms by 1 or 2 hundred-millionths of an inch. When the metal melts, the crystal array is lost, the atoms become more mobile, and the metal then becomes an amorphous liquid.

All the metals of significance in welding assume one of the three crystal arrangements shown in Fig. 18. These arrangements are termed crystal lattices. The position of each atom is represented by a circle, and the lines connecting the atoms should be considered to be the forces holding the atoms in place in the crystal lattice. The unit or module of the body-centered cubic crystal is an atom at each corner of an imaginary cube and another atom at the center of the cube. For the face-centered cubic pattern, it is an atom at each corner of the cube and atoms in the center of each face of the cube. The hexagonal close-packed arrangement has a complex hexagonal arrangement of atoms.

The face group of metals are much more ductile than the other two groups are. For example, only the fcc metals are supplied as very thin foil: aluminum, copper, lead, gold, and silver. This group does not become brittle even at very low temperatures, so that very low-temperature applications are reserved for the fcc metals.

The hcp group may be considered to have ductility characteristics intermediate between those of the fcc and bcc metals. The bcc metals are distinguished by lack of ductility below a certain temperature range.

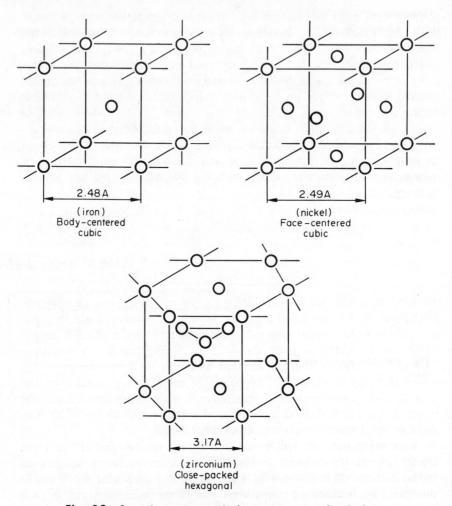

Fig. 18 Crystal structures of the common metals: body-centered cubic, face-centered cubic, and hexagonal close-packed.

2.48 A
(iron)
Body-centered
cubic

2.49 A
(nickel)
Face-centered
cubic

3.17 A
(zirconium)
Close-packed
hexagonal

CRYSTAL STRUCTURES OF THE METALS

bcc	hcp	fcc
chromium	beryllium	aluminum
iron	cobalt	copper
molybdenum	magnesium	lead
columbium	titanium	nickel
tantalum	zinc	gold
tungsten	zirconium	silver
vanadium		

Thus tungsten is brittle several hundred degrees above room temperature, whereas most of the steels begin to show brittleness just below room temperature.

5.2 brittle fracture

Brittleness in metals is obviously a critical matter and has received much study. One of the most stringent and revealing of the tests for low-temperature brittleness is the Charpy test. In a Charpy test samples of the shape and size shown in Fig. 19 are prepared. The figure shows a V notch milled across the specimen, but other types of notches may be employed, such as a keyhole type. The specimen is supported horizontally at its

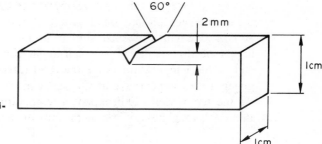

Fig. 19 Charpy impact specimen.

ends in the impact tester and struck on the side opposite to the notch by a swinging hammer that begins its swing with 264 ft-lb of potential energy. When the hammer strikes the specimen at the bottom of its swing, it therefore has 264 ft-lb of kinetic energy. This energy is partially dissipated by fracturing the specimen, the remaining energy carrying the hammer up in the backswing. The Charpy tester records on a scale the amount of energy in foot-pounds required for fracture (it actually measures the amount of backswing energy and subtracts this from the initial 264 ft-lb, since there is no way to measure the fracture energy). Figure 20 shows an impact tester with the pendulum hammer ready for release from the 264 ft-lb position.

Since the specimen has a notch, the Charpy test is really a test of notch toughness under impact. Many materials, steels in particular, will exhibit great resistance to the presence of a notch on a straight tension test at any temperature but will be notch brittle in a Charpy test at the same temperature. The notch acts as a stress concentration to initiate failure of the metal, and the effect of the notch is most severe in the Charpy test. The usefulness of the Charpy test in testing welds is immediately apparent when it is realized that an undercut, or an arc burn,

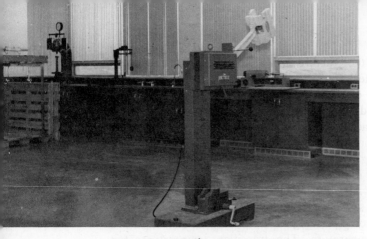

has the same effect on a steel that a milled notch does. Hence for important welds, arc burns and undercuts must be rejected, since these become sites to initiate failure, with or without impact conditions.

Suppose that a number of Charpy specimens of a particular steel are tested over a range of temperatures from +200 to −100 F and the results are plotted on a graph of foot-pounds against temperature. A typical S curve results, similar to the curve 1 in Fig. 21, which is a plot of the results of a notch-tough rimmed mild steel. At the high end of the temperature range the steel offers great resistance to fracture, giving a torn appearance at the break in what is termed a *ductile failure*. As the temperature is dropped, a temperature range is reached in which the notch toughness of the metal falls drastically (for curve 1 of Fig. 21,

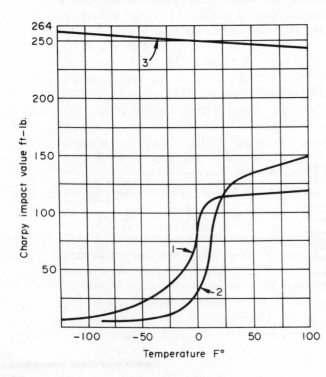

Fig. 21 Impact test results for three metals. Curve 1. A notch-tough rimmed steel. Curve 2. A steel with more carbon (0.35%) and therefore less low-temperature toughness. Curve 3. Pure nickel with unlimited low-temperature toughness.

this range is 0 to −30 F), the fracture appearance changes to a bright crystalline break, and the steel has become brittle.

Figure 22 shows both ductile and brittle fracture. The torn and distorted appearance of the ductile fractures may be contrasted with the clean break of the brittle fracture in the right-hand specimen. The left-hand specimens are pure nickel, a face-centered metal so ductile that it did not approach fracturing. Curve 3 of Fig. 21 presents the results for pure nickel: the remarkable impact strength and the absence of a transition to brittle fracture are notable features.

The minimum impact strength allowed for many applications is 15 ft-lb. The temperature corresponding to this value is called, rather arbitrarily, the transition temperature. The transition temperatures for the two steels of Fig. 21 should be estimated by the reader. For many steels the transition temperature is above 0 F, and failures of steel parts in cold storage rooms maintained at temperatures as high as +30 F are rather common. Weldments such as tanks that will experience sub-zero temperatures must therefore be fabricated and welded from steels with a suitably low transition temperature. It may be objected that such weldments are not subject to impact, but locked-in stresses due to weld cooling have been the cause of brittle fracture cracking, including cracking in several dozen welded ships built during World War II (many of which broke in two), a welded bridge in Three Rivers, Canada, in 1952, pipelines, and welded tanks.

Several methods are available for lowering the transition temperature in steels. Perhaps the cheapest method is that of "killing" the steel with aluminum or silicon in the steel mill. After the steel is melted and

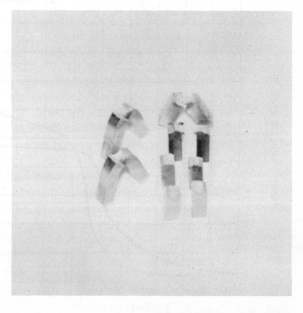

Fig. 22 Charpy test results. On the left two samples of nickel plate which bent but did not crack at −110°F. On the right the progressive deterioration in notch toughness of a rimmed mild steel as the temperature was lowered from +75° (back sample) to −110° (front sample.)

poured into the ladle ready for casting, a few pounds of aluminum or silicon per ton of steel are added to the ladle. These two metals combine with oxygen dissolved in the steel, removing it as alumina or silica inclusions, which for most purposes do not harm the steel. Killed steels have lower transition temperatures, although this cannot be taken for granted for any heat of steel, and Charpy tests should be tried before fabricating such steels.

Another method for lowering transition temperature is to alloy the steel with an fcc metal, since these metals are not notch sensitive at any temperature. Nickel is the metal employed for this purpose, about 3% nickel often being sufficient. If a few per cent of nickel is added to a bcc steel crystal lattice, the crystal remains bcc, the nickel atoms replacing individual iron atoms in the crystal structure. Note from Fig. 18 that the interatomic distances for iron and nickel are similar. In selecting steels for low temperatures, the usual selection procedure is as follows:

1. For operating temperatures as low as -50 F
   (a) killed low-carbon steel
   (b) 3% nickel low-carbon steel
2. For operating temperatures as low as -150 F
   (a) 3% nickel low-carbon steel
   (b) stainless steels with 8% nickel or more
3. For operating temperatures below -150 F
   (a) stainless steels with at least 8% nickel
   (b) 9% nickel steel
   (c) fcc metals such as aluminum or Monel

The transition temperature for any steel plate or welding rod is raised if the carbon content is increased. This explains in part why the carbon content of manual arc welding rods for steel is so low—about 0.1% carbon. Manganese has the opposite effect, and like nickel, lowers the transition temperature. All steels contain some manganese. The importance of a low level of carbon and a maximum of manganese may be seen, for example, in the weld deposits of low-hydrogen 7018 rods. One manufacturer of these rods (Esab Arc Rods) reports the chemical analysis of the deposited metal to be 0.8% C, 1.0% Mn. Such a weld bead should have very satisfactory notch toughness.

Brittle fracture is easy to recognize. The metal appears to have failed like a brittle casting: the break is flat, clean, and shiny, with no evidence of deformation or ductility. Some breaks have a kind of chevron pattern pointing to the origin of the break. Most of these failures do not occur in hot weather but in the fall and winter. Formerly the welder was blamed for such failures, but if the cause is transition temperature, not undercut or welding technique, then brittle fracture is simply beyond the welder's control.

Some metals can exist in two or more solid phases, or conditions. This is especially true of the radioactive metals, such as uranium and plutonium, but the only common structural metal with this characteristic is iron and most of its steel alloys.

At room temperature steel is bcc, and in this condition it is magnetic. At red heats, however, steels change to the face-centered condition, a nonmagnetic phase. (The proper term is paramagnetic.) The temperature at which steel changes from one phase to the other is termed either the *critical temperature* or the *transformation temperature* and is analogous to the melting point that separates the solid phase of a material from the liquid phase. The temperature of transformation depends on the amount of carbon in the steel, although other alloying elements influence transformation temperature. For a steel containing only iron and carbon, the transformation follows the graph of Fig. 23. A pure

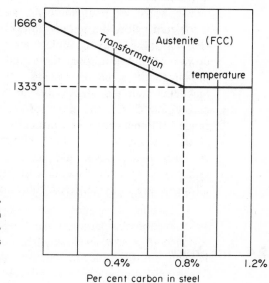

Fig. 23 Transformation temperature diagram for carbon steels. Above the transformation temperature line steel is face-centered cubic.

iron changes its crystal pattern at 1666 F, but with increasing carbon content the transformation temperature falls until at 0.8% carbon it reaches 1333 F. Additional carbon above 0.8% has no influence on transformation temperature. A temperature of 1333 corresponds to a dull red heat.

The importance of the transformation temperature is chiefly in its heat-treating effects. When steel is hardened or softened by heat treating, it is first heated above the critical temperature into the fcc region and then cooled rapidly back into the bcc region for hardening or slowly for softening. When steel is fusion-welded, both the deposited metal and the heat-affected zone will be heated above the critical temperature and cooled, and hence will be heat-treated. If the rate of cooling is rapid, the steel will be hardened, and this severe cooling may be the cause of cracking.

The fcc phase in steels is given the name *austenite*. It is also referred to by metallurgists as the gamma (γ) phase. Austenite has three notable properties:

1. It is paramagnetic (almost nonmagnetic).
2. It is very ductile.
3. It work-hardens.

Work hardening or strain hardening is the process of hardening and embrittling metals by straining them. A familiar use of work hardening is the breaking of a wire by bending it back and forth at one point until it fractures.

If nickel or manganese are added to steel, the critical temperature is lowered below the temperature range indicated in Fig. 23, and if sufficient of these alloying metals are present, the austenitic phase persists down to and below room temperature. It is therefore possible to produce paramagnetic steels by means of these two alloying elements. Paramagnetic stainless steels contain 8% or more of nickel, plus much chromium: this is the series of stainless steels with numbers in the 300 range. Another group of austenitic steels are the austenitic manganese steels, containing about 12% manganese, which are commonly supplied as hard facing rods and have remarkable work-hardening capacity. Otherwise, with the exception of high-nickel and high-manganese steels, all steels are body-centered cubic and magnetic.

5.4 hardness

The hardness of metals is usually found by measuring the resistance of the metal to indentation using some kind of penetrator. The more usual hardness tests are the Brinell and the Rockwell tests. The Brinell tester averages the hardness over an area of the metal by using a large-diameter indentor; the Rockwell tester, using a fine indentor, determines the hardness at a point.

A Brinell tester is shown in Fig. 24. The Brinell indentor is a hardened steel ball 10 mm in diameter. This is forced into the metal to be tested by a 3000-kg load (500 kg for nonferrous metals). The diameter of the indentation left by the ball indentor is then measured under a

Fig. 24   Brinell   hardness
tester.

Fig. 25   Rockwell   hardness
tester.

low-power microscope. By reference to a table, the BHN (Brinell hardness number) is found from the diameter of the impression. Obviously a small indentation diameter means a high BHN, or high hardness.

The ultimate tensile strength of carbon steels can be estimated reasonably well from the BHN, the tensile strength being about 500 times the BHN. The strength of alloy steels or nonferrous metals cannot be estimated by this simple method, however.

Figure 25 is a Rockwell tester. Unlike the Brinell tester, the Rockwell machine indicates the hardness on a dial. Two Rockwell scales are in common use, a B and a C scale, and both are engraved on the dial. The B scale, used for hardness testing of soft steels and nonferrous metals, employs a $\frac{1}{16}$-in. diameter hard steel ball under a load of 100 kg. The C scale, used for harder steels and carbides, has for an indentor a conical diamond, called a Brale, under a 150-kg load. Because of the dial indication, a Rockwell hardness reading takes only a few seconds to execute.

A mild steel plate should give a BHN of about 120. Its tensile strength therefore would be estimated at $120 \times 500 = 60,000$ psi. The corresponding Rockwell reading for the same plate would be about B 75. Tool steels can be hardened to a maximum of C 65 to 67, whereas carbides can give hardness values as high as C 75. Such hardnesses cannot be Brinell-tested without damaging the indentor.

In testing welds in alloy steels, hardness readings often are taken from the heat-affected zone to the parent metal. If the hardness numbers are higher in the heat-affected zone, this may be a danger sign indicating heat-treating effects and the possibility of cracking in this area due to sensitivity of the steel to cooling rate.

5.5 stress and strain

Stress and strain are not the same but are related in that either one will produce the other. Consider the simple example of a manila rope used to tow an automobile. The pull on the rope causes a *stress* or force in the rope fibers. After the pull, or stress, on the rope is relaxed, the rope has been permanently stretched owing to this stress. The increase in length is a deformation or *strain*. The warping that always accompanies fusion welding is a strain and clearly indicates that there are stresses in the metal after welding.

Stresses are calculated in pounds per square inch (psi) just like pressures. The stress in psi is equal to the load P divided by the area supporting the load:

$$s = \frac{P}{A}$$

There are three possible types of stresses (Fig. 26):

1. compression (crushing)
2. tension (pull)
3. shear (cutting)

All materials when loaded or stressed will deform, shorten, or stretch. This change in dimension or shape under a load is occasionally large enough to be visible, as in the case of rubber bands and metal springs, but for metal structural members carrying the loads for which they were designed, the deformations are only a few microinches (millionths of an inch). Being very stiff, metals will strain very little under large stresses. Now it is generally understood that if a material is

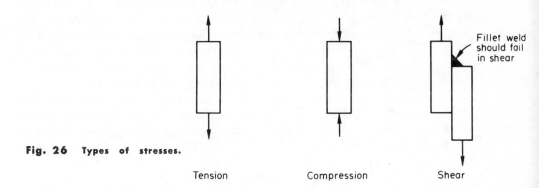

Fig. 26 Types of stresses.

Tension   Compression   Shear

Fillet weld should fail in shear

stressed, it will also strain or deform, but it must be borne in mind, especially in welding, that the reverse applies also, that is, if a metal is strained, it will also be stressed. Basically, strain is the cause of stress. During fusion welding, the metal expands because of the heat of the arc. This expansion obviously is a strain, since the member changes dimension, but this expansion is not free because of tack welds and other restraints against movement. The combination of heat expansion and restraint means that stresses are built into every weldment during fabrication, and if these stresses are not controlled, they are a cause of cracking or even of brittle fracture, sometimes on a dramatic scale.

To demonstrate the relationship between stress and strain, we shall analyze a tension test performed on a weld sample. The weld is a double butt weld with full penetration on ½-in. plate, and a sample 2 in. wide is cut out of the plate for testing the strength of the weld. Although it is not a requirement of all weld tests, we shall note the elongation in a gauge length of 2.0000 in. which includes the weld area. Such elongations are measured by strain gauges. The sample is dimensioned in Fig. 27, and the testing machine is shown in Fig. 28. Such testing machines are simply accurate and instrumented hydraulic presses.

The large dial on the testing machine indicates the tension load applied to the weld test sample. The cross-sectional area of the test sample is 2 in. by $\frac{1}{2}$ in. which equals 1 sq in., and with this cross section the load and the stress are the same. A strain indicator will indicate the elongation over the 2.0000 in. gauge length. The elongation per inch of length is a more useful piece of information: this merely requires that the readings on the strain indicator be divided by 2. This is the actual *unit strain*—the definition of unit strain is the elongation in inches per inch of original length.

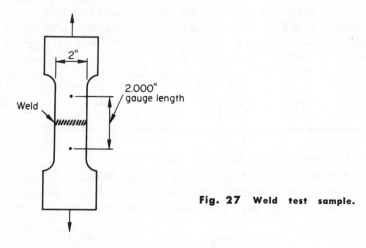

Fig. 27 Weld test sample.

Fig. 28 Universal testing machine. The test load is indicated on the large dial. The operator is controlling the movement of the loading platen by means of an oil valve.

The weld test specimen is held in the grips of the testing machine, and a steadily increasing load is applied to it in tension. Periodically, readings are taken of load and elongation in 2.0000 in. Suppose the results of the test are those given in the following tabulation:

STRESS-STRAIN READINGS FOR A WELD TEST SAMPLE

Load, lb	Stress, psi	Elongation, in 2.0000 in.	Unit Strain, in./in.
1,000	1,000	0.000066	0.000033
2,000	2,000	0.000133	0.000066
4,000	4,000	0.000266	0.000133
6,000	6,000	0.000400	0.000200
10,000	10,000	0.000666	0.000333
20,000	20,000	0.001333	0.000666
30,000	30,000	0.002000	0.001000
42,000	42,000	0.0028	0.0014
42,000	42,000	0.040	0.020
44,000	44,000	0.060	0.030
50,000	50,000	0.170	0.085
60,000	60,000	0.264	0.132
63,000	63,000	0.280	0.140 *Rupture*

The stress-strain graph is plotted in Fig. 29.

Scrutiny of either the tabulated results or the graph discloses much information about the weld sample. First, very large stresses produce only minute strains: 15 tons per sq in. produce a strain of only $\frac{1}{10}\%$,

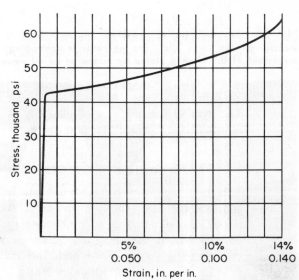

Fig. 29 Stress-strain curve.
See text.

or $\frac{1}{1000}\%$ in. per in. of length. Second, there appear to be two strain regions. For low stresses, up to 42,000 psi, the strain is proportional to the stress. For the higher stresses, the strain is no longer proportional to the stress, and in this region the metal stretches considerably, or *yields*. The stress separating these two kinds of strain behavior is termed the *yield stress,* which for this sample is 42,000 psi. The region below the yield stress is the *elastic* region, and the elastic strain is that part of the strain which disappears when the load is removed. A steel spring, for example, works on elastic strain. Beyond the yield stress, the strain is *plastic,* meaning that it is permanent and remains after the stress is removed.

We can now properly explain the terms *brittle* and *ductile*. A brittle material is any material which shows very little or no plastic strain, and a ductile material develops a long plastic region when stressed. Plasticity is an important requirement of structural materials because plastic deformation gives a warning that the material is being stressed close to its ultimate strength. Brittle materials, having no plastic deformation, give no warning of failure. The weld test sample analyzed above increased in length by 14% before it broke: the total elastic strain was only 0.14%, or one-hundredth as much as the plastic strain. By and large, soft and weak materials behave plastically, and hard and strong materials show little plastic behavior. This is true of steels in particular: the soft or "mild" steels may elongate plastically 25 to 35%.

5.6 modulus of elasticity

In the weld sample cited, strain was proportional to stress in the elastic region. This is usual for elastic strain. The constant that relates elastic strain to stress is termed the *modulus of elasticity,* that is,

$$\text{modulus of elasticity} = \frac{\text{strain}}{\text{unit stress}}$$

The symbol for modulus of elasticity is E, and it is referred to more informally as E value. To find the E value for the weld sample

$$E = \frac{\text{stress}}{\text{strain}} = \frac{1000 \text{ psi}}{0.000033} = 30,000,000 = 30 \times 10^6$$

This is a high E value, characteristic of metals, and indicates a very stiff material that will elongate very little under loads below the yield stress. A material with an infinitely large E value will not strain at all under load. At the opposite end of the range, if, using a spring scale, we stretch a rubber band and find the strain with a 6-in. rule, the E value will work out to about 200.

MODULI OF ELASTICITY OF SOME MATERIALS

glass	9×10^6	lead	2×10^6
wood	about 1.5×10^6	magnesium	6.5×10^6
concrete	about 3×10^6	molybdenum	47×10^6
graphite	0.7×10^6	nickel	30×10^6
aluminum	10×10^6	titanium	16.5×10^6
beryllium	44×10^6	tungsten	50×10^6
copper	16×10^6	zirconium	14×10^6
steel	29×10^6	polyethylene	about 35,000

For industrial work, the round number of 30×10^6, three times the E value of aluminum, is taken as the E value of steel. This means that under the same conditions aluminum can be expected to bend, flex, or stretch three times as much as steel. Notice that the E values of the refractory metals tungsten, molybdenum, and beryllium are the highest in the list: these are the stiffest of all metals.

5.7 fatigue

Different machine members meet with different service conditions. The frame of a machine tool must meet the requirement of great stiffness or minimum deflection. The steel legs of a worktable must be able to carry a certain maximum static load. Some machine members are subjected to repeated stresses, as are springs, truck tires, truck bodies, gear teeth, and aircraft wings.

The effect of loads repeated thousands or millions of times is to reduce greatly the effective strength of the material. This effect is most easily demonstrated by a flag flying in the breeze. The stresses imposed by a strong wind on a flag are rather small, by no means great enough to rip the flag. Yet all flags are eventually torn by wind stresses repeated millions of times. The flag fails in *fatigue*.

The fatigue strength of all materials is lowered as the number of load cycles is increased. If the number of load cycles is one only, then the fatigue strength of the material is its ultimate tensile strength (most fatigue failures are failures in tension). For a greater number of stress cycles, the fatigue strength steadily falls, usually leveling off at a constant value of about 10 million cycles (equivalent to about two cycles a minute for thirteen years). This constant value is termed the *endurance limit* and is of the order of 40% of the ultimate tensile strength.

Changes of section, such as shoulders or notches, drastically reduce the fatigue life of a part. Many welded joints must be designed for fatigue, such as joints in farm equipment or truck bodies. A butt joint has a higher fatigue resistance than any other type of welded joint, simply because there is no change of section in a butt joint. However, for greater fatigue resistance, the butt joint must be welded from both sides and preferably should not be reinforced (that is, built up) since reinforcement provides a change in the cross section. For highest fatigue resistance the reinforcement on butt joints is ground off to leave a smooth flat surface. Any change of shape will impair fatigue resistance, for example, undercut, overlap, lack of penetration, or general roughness of weld surface.

Fatigue failures are perhaps the commonest type of failure, even in welded fabrications. The failure is not always in the welded joint but may be in the parent metal adjacent to the joint, the cause of failure being the change of section produced by the welded joint. To point out the seriousness of fatigue, there have been farm implement manufacturers so badly plagued with fatigue failures that they have gone out of business.

5.8 specific heat

The specific heat of any material is the amount of heat energy, measured in Btu, that will raise the temperature of 1 lb of the material 1 F. The specific heat is therefore a measure of the amount of heat that can be *stored* in a material. We assume, if possible, that the specific heat of a material does not change with temperature, but for most materials the specific heat increases with temperature.

The highest of all specific heats are those of hydrogen, helium, and water, 3.4, 1.25, and 1.0 Btu per lb per degree F respectively at room temperature. In general, specific heats are highest for lightweight materials, lower for heavier materials. Most of the metals have low specific heats.

SPECIFIC HEATS
(Btu/lb/F)

hydrogen	3.4	ceramic materials	about 0.2
helium	1.25	organic materials	about 0.3
water	1.0	copper	0.09
ice	0.5	cast iron	0.12
steam	0.47	steel	0.11
air	0.24	aluminum	0.22

The expansion coefficient of a material is the amount of expansion in 1 in. or 1 ft. produced by a temperature rise of 1 F. Such a coefficient is a thermal strain, though if the material is free to expand without restraints, no corresponding thermal stress exists. Since tack welds, jigs, clamps, and other restraints are always present during welding, any expansion during welding is accompanied by stress.

The following are the most useful coefficients of expansion:

steel	0.000006 in./in.-ft or /ft/F
copper, brass	0.000009
aluminum	0.000012
300-series stainless steel	0.000008

Note that aluminum expands twice as much as steel does for the same temperature rise, and the 300-series stainless steels (18% chromium, 8% nickel) a third more. A large expansion coefficient of course indicates that greater warping must be dealt with during welding. A combination of a high thermal expansion with a large E value may build up very large thermal stresses in a weldment.

5.10 coefficient of thermal
conductivity

The thermal conductivity, or K factor as it is usually called, indicates the effectiveness of an insulation material. If the K factor is low, below 1.0, the material is a heat insulator, whereas a high K factor indicates that the material is a heat conductor.

The K factor is best explained in terms of a board foot of fiberglass, which actually has a K factor of about 0.3 Btu and is therefore an insulating material. Suppose one of the large faces of the fiberglass is maintained at a temperature of 91 F and the opposite face at 90 F, so that there is a temperature difference of 1 F across the inch thickness (see Fig. 30). Then heat will flow through the fiberglass from the hot face to the colder face at 90 F. The actual heat flow through the board foot of fiberglass with a 1 F face difference of temperature will be 0.3 Btu per hr. The K factor of any material is the heat flow through a

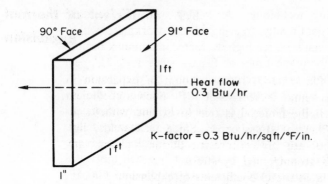

90° Face   91° Face

1 ft

Heat flow
0.3 Btu/hr

K-factor = 0.3 Btu/hr/sq ft/°F/in.

1 ft

1"

Fig. 30 Defining the K factor, or coefficient of thermal conductivity of a material.

material by conduction under these conditions—a square foot of area, an inch thickness, and a degree difference in temperature.

The heat conducted through a thickness of material has been found to be proportional to the K factor, the surface area, and the temperature difference and to be inversely proportional to the thickness. By formula,

$$\text{heat flow in Btu/hr} = \frac{kA(t_1 - t_2)}{L}$$

where $k =$ coefficient of thermal conductivity of the material
        $=$ Btu per hour per square foot per degree F per inch thickness
       $A =$ cross-sectional area of heat flow, in square feet
       $t_1 =$ the higher temperature at the hot side
       $t_2 =$ the lower temperature at the cooler side
       $L =$ the thickness of material between hot and cool side, in inches
Because insulation is sold by the board foot, the area A is calculated in square feet and the thickness is in inches.

K-FACTORS OF SOME COMMON MATERIALS
(At 70 F)

fiberglass	0.25–0.30	copper	2700
corkboard	0.27–3.00	aluminum	1400
common brick	5	nickel	430
ice	15	carbon steel	310
snow	4	stainless steel	100
firebrick	10		

From these representative values of K factor, it is obvious that the metals are outstanding conductors of heat. Those metals that are the best heat conductors are also the best conductors of electricity—copper, aluminum, silver, and gold. The thermal conductivity of the metals of

metals and their properties

course influences the welding technique. A welder who has welded only steel will find his rod continually freezing to the workpiece when he first tries aluminum. Because of its high K factor aluminum drains heat from the weld puddle about ten times as fast as steel does. Copper has such a high K factor that special techniques must be used to hold enough heat in the welding zone. Nothing can be done about the K factor of copper, but the heat flow away from the weld can be reduced by reducing the temperature difference $(t_1 - t_2)$. This is managed by preheating the copper plate before welding to a temperature of about 800 F. The temperature difference $(t_1 - t_2)$ is then not between the weld puddle and room temperature but between the weld puddle and 800 F. Unhappily for the welder, a preheat temperature of 800 F will preheat him too.

5.11 thermal severity number

The thermal severity number, often abbreviated TSN, is not a characteristic of materials, but a welding condition. However, it is most conveniently dealt with in connection with thermal conductivity. The TSN is applied only to steels, not to other metals.

The problem of welding cracks, in either the weld or the heat-affected zone, is largely confined to steel. Though its conductivity is much less than that of copper or aluminum, steel has a K factor of about 310 Btu per hr, depending on the alloy. This is still a very high conductivity and indicates that heat will be rapidly conducted away from the weld area by the surrounding material of the plate, giving a condition of rapid cooling. Rapid cooling always indicates a hardened and embrittled steel and a loss of ductility. Without sufficient ductility, the steel may be forced to take up the cooling strains by cracking.

To reiterate the conduction heat-flow formula, the loss of heat in Btu per unit time is directly proportional to the K factor, the area, and the temperature difference. In, say, a butt weld in a steel plate the K factor is high, as is the temperature difference $(t_1 - t_2)$, being that between the weld and the cold material at a distance from the weld. Now for all fusion welds in steel, let us make the reasonable assumptions that the K factor is the same for all steels and that the temperature difference $(t_1 - t_2)$ is reasonably constant (we again assume that all steels melt at the same temperature and that the plate is not preheated). The area A conducting heat away from the weld is proportional to the thickness of the plate being welded. Hence it is roughly true that the heat flow from the weld, or the cooling rate, *is proportional only to the plate thickness.* All other things being the same, a 14-gauge sheet may not crack, whereas a

3-in. plate may well do so. Thus the thickness of the welded plate is a measure of the *thermal severity,* or rate at which heat is lost.

The unit of thermal severity is the flow of heat through a $\frac{1}{4}$-in. thick plate, this condition being assigned a thermal severity number (TSN) of 1. Two $\frac{1}{4}$-in. plates butt-welded give a TSN of 2, since heat may flow away from the weld in two opposite directions. Two butt-welded $\frac{1}{2}$-in. plates have a TSN of 4. A fillet weld in $\frac{1}{4}$-in plate has a TSN of 6, while a lap weld in $\frac{1}{4}$-in plate has a TSN of 3.

The thermal severity number is a simple concept to understand and provides a ready means of assessing the danger of cracking. Cracking tendencies in alloy steels with high thermal severity numbers are circumvented by preheating or postheating the plate to reduce the temperature difference $(t_1 - t_2)$.

5.12 magnetism

Magnetism, like gravity, is a force that can be propagated through space, whether the space be vacuum or occupied, and the magnetic field of force attracts or repels objects in definite directions. At this point a quick review of the pertinent effects of magnetism in metals, some of which have already been referred to, is sufficient.

Physicists in recent years have developed the bad habit of discovering new kinds of magnetism. However, only two kinds of magnetism are of significance to welding technology at present:

1. *Ferromagnetism,* the powerful magnetic effect shown by most steels
2. *Paramagnetism,* the weak magnetism exhibited by most materials called "nonmagnetic" in everyday conversation

A surprisingly large number of materials are ferromagnetic, including most steels, nickel, cobalt, dysprosium, gadolinium (at low temperatures), many special alloys such as Heusler alloy of copper, manganese, and aluminum, and a number of ceramic materials including most of the iron ores. The austenitic steels, those rich in nickel or manganese, such as the 300 series stainless steels and the austenitic manganese work-hardening steels, are paramagnetic.

Any ferromagnetic metal becomes less magnetic as its temperature is raised. At a certain temperature, about 1000 F for steels, a ferromagnetic metal changes to paramagnetic. This temperature at which the magnetic characteristics change, is termed the *Curie temperature* of the metal. The Curie temperature for a steel is a lower temperature than that of the phase change from face-centered cubic to body-centered cubic.

Metals conduct both heat and electricity, and the best heat conductors—gold, silver, copper, and aluminum—are likewise the best electrical conductors.

In considering the flow of heat or electricity, either the conductivity of a material or its resistance to flow may be measured. One is the inverse of the other, that is, conductivity = 1/resistance or resistance = 1/conductivity. The K factor for heat flow is a conductivity factor, but for flow of electrons, resistance is perhaps the usual concept. The specific resistance to electric current is either.

1. The resistance of a 1-in. cube of a material to the flow of current across the cube, or
2. The resistance of a circular mil-foot, which is the resistance of a wire $\frac{1}{1000}$ in. in diameter by 1 ft long.

Both resistances are expressed in ohms. The circular mil-foot is more convenient for calculating the resistance of electric wiring, but ohms per inch-cube is handier for certain welding applications, such as induction heating and brazing. The circular mil-foot concept is easy to get

ELECTRICAL RESISTANCES

(Microhm-in. or Microhms/In. Cube)

Material	68F	200F	600F	1000F	1400F	1800F	2200F
aluminum	1.12		2.7	4.1			
brass	2.5			4.5			
carbon	1320			720			
beryllium	2.4						
copper	0.7		1.5	2.15		3.7	
iron	4.0	5.5		25.0	42.0	48.5	
lead	8.2	10.8	19.6				
magnesium	1.8						
mercury	3.8						
molybdenum	2.1						13.0
monel	17.4						
nickel	2.7		11.5	15.9		21.4	
silver	0.6						
mild steel	5.0	6.5		23.5	40.0	45.5	48.0
302 stainless	29.0		39.0			51.5	
410 stainless	24.5			40.0		50.0	
titanium	21.0						65.0
tungsten	2.2						15.2
zirconium	16.0						

from any electrical handbook; but here we shall use for electrical resistance the specific resistance in ohms per inch cube. Since such resistances are very small, it is more convenient to use microhms per inch cube. Thus for pure copper, the specific resistance per inch cube is 0.0000007 ohms, or 0.7 microhms.

Notice that the resistance of mild steel is about seven times that of copper. The pure metals are better conductors than their alloys: pure iron has a resistance of 4 microhms, whereas mild steel, which is iron plus 0.2% carbon, has a resistance 25% greater. Similarly brass has three times the resistance of its base metal copper. Note too that the resistance of all the metals increases as the temperature rises.

Since resistance welding depends on I^2R losses, the higher the specific resistance of a metal, the less current required for spot welding and the easier the metal will be to spot-weld. Copper is so highly conductive that in heavier thicknesses it cannot be spot-welded.

The electrical resistance in ohms of any conductor is given by the simple formula

$$R = \frac{\sigma L}{A}$$

where σ = ohms per inch cube
L = length of conductor in inches
A = cross-sectional area of conductor in square inches

The equations for heat flow and for current flow are actually identical mathematically. Consider the following manipulation:

$$\text{for flow of electrons} \quad I = \frac{E}{R} = \frac{E}{\sigma L/A} = \frac{1}{\sigma}\frac{EA}{L} = \frac{1/\sigma\, AE}{L}$$

$$\text{for flow of heat} \quad Q = \frac{kA(t_1 - t_2)}{L}$$

The identity of these two formulas is apparent when $1/\sigma$ is considered as the K factor for electricity and E is the voltage drop $(E_1 - E_2)$ across the resistance.

$$Q = \frac{kA(t_1 - t_2)}{L} \qquad I = \frac{1/\sigma\, A(E_1 - E_2)}{L}$$

5.14 summing up

So far we have examined some of the most important general characteristics of the metals and their bearing on welding techniques. We can now discuss the individual metals and their metallurgical behavior during welding. It should be apparent that the most valued characteristics of metals are strength and ductility, as well as the dimensional stability given by high elastic stiffness (modulus of elasticity) and low-temperature expansion.

1 Draw the graphs of Charpy energy in foot-pounds versus testing temperature, similar to Fig. 21, and find the 15 ft-lb transition temperature from the graph for the following steels:

	+75	+50	+25	0	−25	−50	−75	−100	F
(a) 0.30% C, 0.30% Mn	43	32	20	12	6 ft-lb				
(b) 0.30% C, 0.40% Mn	72	52	34	25	18	10ft-lb			
(c) 0.20% C		58	54	46	37	27	19	10	7 ft-lb

2 Estimate the ultimate tensile strength of the following steels, given their Brinell hardness: (a) BHN 114, (b) BHN 236.

3 A butt weld is made in ⅜-in.-thick plate, the plate being guaranteed for a tensile stress of 70,000 psi. A good weld must meet the tensile stress of the plate. If a weld sample 2 in. wide is cut from the plate, what is the minimum load in pounds at which it can break?

4 A ¼-in.-thick by 8-ft-long alloy steel plate with a shear strength of 50,000 psi is to be sheared on its 8-ft length. What shear pressure in pounds is required?

5 A weld sample measuring ½ by ⅜ in. breaks at a load of 26,000 lb. What is the tensile strength of the weld?

6 A 7018 welding rod has a tensile strength of 70,000 psi. What is the minimum tension force that will pull such a welding rod apart if its diameter is ⅛ in.?

7 If the ⅛-in. rod of problem 6 is 14 in. long, by how much will it stretch if stressed to 30,000 psi?

8 How much will a copper rod 10 in. long stretch if stressed to 20,000 psi?

9 A ⅞-in.-diameter hole is to be punched in ½-in.-thick plate with a shear strength of 40,000 psi. What punch force is required?

10 Mild steel bar ⅞-in. in diameter is cold-drawn in lengths of 20 ft. The yield stress of the bar is 32,000 psi and the modulus of elasticity is 30×10^6. What is the maximum drawing force that can be applied to the bar before it yields and the extension of the bar at this drawing force?

11 An aluminum bar with a cross section of ¾ sq in. sustains a load of 17,000 lb. The elongation in a gauge length of 2 in. measures 0.008 in. What is the modulus of elasticity?

12 A 9-in. firebrick straight weighs 8 lb. If the temperature of the hot face of a firebrick is 1600 F and that of the cool face is 200 F, how much heat above 100 F is stored in the brick?

13 The welded steel drum of a boiler weighs 35,000 lb. It is moved into a stress-relieving furnace, where it is heated to 1200 F. Take room temperature to be 100 F. If 90% of the heat from the burners of the furnace is wasted through inefficiencies, estimate the cost of heat for stress-relieving the drum. Heat is worth 50 cents a million Btu.

14 Mild steel plate weighs 10.2 lb per sq ft in ¼-in. thickness. How much heat must be stored in a 1-in. steel plate measuring 96 by 120 in. to raise the plate temperature 150 F?

15 A certain furnace wall made of firebrick expands ⅛ in. in 4 ft for a temperature rise of 1000 F. What is the coefficient of thermal expansion for the firebrick?

16 A 6-in. O.D. (outside diameter) tube of 300-series stainless steel is butt-welded to a zirconium tube of the same diameter. When this tubing is given a temperature rise of 800 F, the weld cracks. What is the difference in O.D. between the stainless tube and the zirconium tube with a temperature rise of 800 F? Coefficient of expansion of zirconium is 0.000004.

17 The tubing in a large steam generator is 100 ft long. When generating stream, the tubing heats up 800 F from cold. By how much does the tubing expand? Such tubing is always made of steel.

18 An expansion joint must be installed in a pipeline of stainless steel to take up the expansion due to a 350 F temperature rise from cold. How much expansion should be allowed for per hundred feet, including an extra 25% for a safety factor?

19 A water storage tank of 1000-gal capacity is made of ⅛-in. plate and has a surface area of 200 sq ft. The water in the tank is maintained at 40 F, and the outside surface of the steel tank has a temperature of 36 F. Find the hourly loss of heat from this tank.

20 The tank of question 19 loses too much heat and is therefore insulated with 1 in. of fiberglass, K factor 0.30. Take the hot-face temperature of the fiberglass to be 40 F and the cool-face temperature to be 0. Find the hourly heat loss.

21 The tank of question 20 is kept warm in the winter by means of an immersion electric heater, which maintains the water at 40 F. If there is a power failure and consequent loss of heat to the tank, how long do you have to repair the power failure before the water temperature falls to 32 F?

22 Why do Eskimos make igloos of snow instead of ice?

23 Give the thermal severity number for the following welds:
(a) a ¼-in. plate fillet-welded in the middle of a 1-in. plate
(b) a lap weld in ¾-in. plate

metals and their properties
68

(c) a butt weld between a ¼-in. and a ½-in. plate

(d) a butt weld in a 2-in.-thick steam drum

24 (a) Can eight 300-amp welding machines use a common ground line if some machines are operated on straight polarity and some on reverse polarity?

(b) The proposed common ground is a 2-in.-diameter steel bar 50 ft long. Assuming that 300 amp from all the eight welders must be carried the full 50 ft, is this ground properly sized to give a voltage drop of less than 1 v?

25 In a certain MIG welding operation, 80 amp of current is carried through 0.035-in.-diameter steel wire. The wire temperature is 2200 F. What is the voltage drop in 1 lineal ft of wire?

26 What is the increase in the specific resistance of nickel per degree Fahrenheit between the temperatures of 600 and 1000 F?

27 The cross sectional area of a 6-in. pipe is 29 sq in. The pipe is steel. The water in this pipe being frozen, 250 amp of current from a welding generator are passed through 200 ft of the pipe. How much heat in Btu per hour does this arrangement put into the pipe?

28 Substitute copper pipe for steel pipe in question 27.

Steel is the material on which we have built our modern technical civilization. It has been known and used for a few thousand years but not extensively until about a hundred years ago. Since that time steel has maintained its dominant position among the industrial materials, and there is nothing yet to indicate that steel will lose that position in the future. Although other materials, principally aluminum, plastics, and concretes, have recently made inroads into markets served by steel, nevertheless more steel is consumed than the total tonnage of all other metals and plastics combined. Canada uses almost 10 million tons of steel every year, and the United States more than 100 million tons, probably half of this tonnage being used in welded articles.

The sheer versatility of steel explains its popularity. There is a steel for almost every purpose—soft or hard steels; weldable and heat-treatable steels; wrought steels and cast steels, magnetic and paramagnetic steels; and steels to resist heat, cold, corrosion, and wear. Finally, steels can be alloyed with most other metals (even uranium) to give an almost infinite variety of useful metals.

Only limited quantities of iron are used in industry. Instead, iron is alloyed with a small amount of carbon with or without other alloying metals, and the resulting alloy is called a steel. Small percentages of sulfur and phosphorus originating from the iron ore are always present in steel, but these are not counted as alloying elements and indeed are usually undesired elements. In addition, most steels include small amounts of silicon and manganese, and except in larger amounts, these too are

STEEL

6

not counted as alloying ingredients. A carbon steel therefore will contain some carbon and minor percentages of sulfur, phosphorus, silicon, and manganese. A *low-alloy steel* will contain a few per cent of another metal or metals, such as nickel. A *high-alloy steel* will contain more than 10% alloying metals. With few exceptions, both low- and high-alloy steels contain some carbon, which may range from as little as 0.03% to as high as about 2%.

Those steels that contain more than 2% carbon are usually called irons and include gray cast iron, white iron, malleable iron, and ductile iron. These are alloys of iron with about 3% or more carbon and more than 1% silicon and are products of the foundry. Wrought iron does not belong to this group, being a nearly pure iron with a large number of manganese silicate slag stringers scattered throughout it but not alloyed with the iron. Unlike the other "irons" mentioned, it is rolled and not cast.

6.1 the extraction of iron from its ores

Virtually all iron ores of industrial importance are oxides, and most of these are ferromagnetic. Iron ore is found over much of the earth's surface, but the steel industry operates on such a large scale that only the largest ore deposits are mined. Since 2 tons of ore will supply 1 ton of steel, at least a hundred million tons of iron ore must be mined every year on this continent. From one open-pit mine, the Hull-Rust in Minnesota, 1 billion tons have so far been excavated, this famous hole in the ground now being $3\frac{1}{2}$ sq mi in area and a maximum of 535 ft deep. Typical ores are the following three:

1. *Magnetite,* Fe_3O_4, brown, containing about 65% iron. This is a very rich ore and therefore less common than lower-grade types.
2. *Hematite,* Fe_2O_3, reddish (supposed to be the color of blood), containing about 50% iron.
3. *Taconite,* usually green and low grade, containing perhaps 30% iron and much silica.

One ton of ore is worth about $10, or $\frac{1}{2}$ cent per lb. After conversion into iron in a blast furnace, the resulting iron is worth about $66 a ton, or 3.3 cents a lb. When this iron is converted into a steel shape, the steel is worth over 5 cents a lb. When the steel is fabricated by welding into the finished article, it will be worth at least 15 cents a lb. The low price of steel is one more of its outstanding characteristics. Because of the large volume in which it is sold, it is the cheapest of all metals. The next cheapest metal is sodium, about 16 cents a pound. Then come lead, copper, and aluminum and the other metals. Any prices mentioned above are of course only approximations.

It is not yet possible to convert iron ore directly into steel on a commercial scale. At present the transformation from iron ore to steel proceeds in two stages:

1. The ore is converted into hot metal in a blast furnace.
2. The hot metal is refined into steel in a steel-refining furnace.

The largest of all industrial furnaces, the blast furnace is a vertical shaft furnace about 100 ft high, with an inside diameter (I.D.) of about 30 ft. The refractory firebrick lining must be provided by the trainload rather than the carload. A skip car loads the raw materials into the top of the furnace, and the slag and hot metal are tapped off at the bottom. The blast furnace operates continuously until finally the refractory lining is burned out. Production rate is about 3000 tons of iron per day.

The blast furnace is loaded with alternate layers of iron ore, limestone, and metallurgical grade coke. The limestone is of course employed as a slag for removal of sulfur and phosphorus, which are always present in iron ore and coke and have adverse effects upon steel. Romoval of these impurities is not complete, however, and the slagging must be repeated again in the second stage of steel making, refining. The heat for reducing the iron ore is provided by the coke, which burns to carbon monoxide. The carbon monoxide converts to carbon dioxide by taking up oxygen from the iron ore, thus reducing the ore to metallic iron.

The carbon in steel is thus provided from coke in the blast furnace charge. The product of the blast furnace, hot metal, is actually an impure and low-quality cast iron, containing about 4½% carbon plus manganese, silicon, and impurities. This high carbon content in hot metal makes it unsuitable as a steel. With so much carbon it cannot be rolled into sheet, plate, or shapes. This is why the blast furnace iron must be processed further: among other things, the refining furnace must reduce this carbon content.

Some hot metal is cast into pigs, called pig iron, but most of the tapped hot metal is transported in special cars to steel refining furnaces for processing into the final steel product.

6.2 the making of steel

The principal function of a steel furnace is to control the amount of impurities and ingredients in the steel. The delivered hot metal contains more than 4% carbon, which the steel-melting furnace will reduce to less than 1% by burning it out at a temperature of about 3000 F. At the same time, any required alloying ingredients will be added to the molten steel, such as small percentages of nickel, chromium, and manganese. Certain alloying elements have the disappointing habit of disappearing into the slag instead of dissolving in the metal, but these will be added to the molten steel after it is poured from the furnace into a ladle.

Almost all steels are made in one of the following steel-refining furnaces:

1. The open-hearth furnace
2. The oxygen converter, sometimes called the L-D converter, after Linz and Donawetz, two towns in Austria, where this furnace was invented
3. The electric arc furnace

The open-hearth furnace is about 100 years old and melts about 80% of the steel made in the United States and Canada. To some degree, it is being replaced by the oxygen converter, first installed on this continent in Hamilton, Ontario, Canada, in 1954. Both the open-hearth furnace and the oxygen converter can produce steel in large tonnages. For the specialty steels, which are made in smaller amounts, the electric arc furnace is used (Fig. 31). The electric furnace began to come into use about 60 years ago. For still smaller quantities of steel, the electric induction melting furnace, discussed in Chap. 16, is used.

All three types of melting furnaces may be charged with either hot metal or steel scrap, but each has its specialties. Hot metal from the blast furnace is not usually charged into an electric furnace, and the oxygen converter is not well adapted to the melting of steel scrap.

The open-hearth furnace can melt 100 to 300 tons of steel at a time but may take 8 to 10 hours to melt and refine its charge. A large gas burner throws a flame over the bath of steel, which is melted under a lime slag. Compared with the slow performance of the open hearth, the oxygen converter is remarkably fast. It can refine steel before the laboratory can analyze it and pronounce it ready to pour and will melt 150 tons or more in less than an hour. A deep pot lined with firebrick, the converter, after receiving the hot metal charge, is tilted back to vertical position and an oxygen lance, water-cooled, is lowered to the molten steel in the furnace. Pure oxygen at high pressure issues from the lance at high velocity and in minutes burns down the carbon to the required low percentage. Indeed, the converter works so furiously at the job of making steel that it burns out its firebrick lining in about a week, when it is then shut down for repairs.

Specialty steels, such as the stainless steels, are prepared in electric arc melting furnaces. These furnaces do not operate on hot metal but instead use scrap steel. Steel mills that do not have access to blast furnace hot metal must also melt from scrap in electric furnaces. Such furnaces are large-scale arc welders using three graphite electrodes 12 in. or more

Fig. 31 Electric arc melting furnace. The three electrodes are partially withdrawn from the furnace while the furnace crew makes up a slag. (Courtesy American Bridge Division, United States Steel Corp.)

in diameter. Three electrodes are used instead of one as in arc welding because the electric furnace uses three-phase alternating current. The large currents travel through the scrap metal and melt it by resistance heating. The voltage used is almost 200 v for meltdown, being reduced to about 120 during the subsequent refining stage.

The most important function of a steel-melting furnace is to control the carbon content of the steel. If the carbon is too high, it is burned down to the proper level by the sustained heat of the furnace. If the carbon is too low, coke is charged into the furnace. Other melting operations include control of impurities in the metal by means of suitable slagging practice and the addition of alloying metals. When the laboratory has checked the analysis of the steel as satisfactory, the molten steel is tapped out of the furnace into a large ladle and transported by overhead crane to the pouring floor for casting into ingots.

Plain carbon steels are made in three grades: rimmed, semikilled, and killed steel. A killed steel is deoxidized by ladle additions of silicon or aluminum. These two metals are strong oxide-formers and remove the dissolved oxygen in the steel as silicon or aluminum oxide. Since gases are not released when the molten steel cools in the ingot mold, such steels are quiet, that is, killed. A semikilled steel is partially deoxidized. A rimmed steel does not receive this treatment and is named from the characteristic crystals that grow around the rim of the ingot. Killed steels have better notch toughness at low temperatures than rimmed steels do. Rimmed steels are more suitable for drawing and forming.

The killing process of course removes only oxygen from the steel. The oxygen remains as nonmetallic inclusions in the steel only visible under the microscope. For some steels these inclusions are harmful, one of their effects being a reduction in the endurance limit (fatigue life) of the steel. Where inclusions cannot be tolerated and where other dissolved gases such as hydrogen must be removed also, the steel is degassed under vacuum conditions. The improvement in quality gained by vacuum degassing is considerable, and degassed steels have been growing in their acceptance by steel buyers.

The steel, rimmed, killed, or degassed, lies in the ingot mold until it freezes. After freezing, the molds are stripped from the ingots, and the ingots are then reheated in soaking pits until they are at a uniform temperature throughout for hot rolling into final shape. The original hot metal has too much carbon, more than 4%, for hot rolling; it is actually a cast iron without ductility. The final refined steel containing less carbon may be readily rolled or forged. During hot rolling the coarse grains produced by the slowly cooling ingot are broken up to make a fine-grained steel product.

In the rolling mill, the ingot is passed through a succession of rolls until it is reduced to the shape and size required. The final shape may be reinforcing rod, rod or bar, structural shape, rail, skelp (plate for welding into pipe), plate, or sheet. A larger tonnage of steel is rolled into sheet than into any other form, and sheet may be obtained either hot- or cold-rolled. Hot-rolled sheet is cheaper and commoner and can be recognized by its black coat of mill scale. Cold-rolled steel has a bright finish and is less ductile than hot-rolled steel. Cold-rolled steel is rolled at a somewhat lower temperature for the final pass than hot-rolled steel is. The smaller gauges of steel sheet are produced only in the cold-rolled condition.

As a result of rolling, steel becomes anisotropic, that is, its mechanical characteristics are not the same in all three directions. The tensile strength and notch toughness are greatest in the direction of rolling and not quite so favorable in the other two directions. Figure 32 is a photomicrograph of a rolled steel, in which the direction of rolling can be seen. If an isotropic metal is desired, with uniform characteristics in three directions, it may have to be forged, cast, or sintered from metal powders.

Fig. 32 Directionality in rolled steel. The rolling direction in this sample is the vertical direction.

6.3 shapes and sheets

Small quantities of rolled steel must be ordered from a steel warehouse. Larger quantities, 40,000 lb or more, are ordered directly from the steel mill. Steel, like most articles, is sold on a per pound basis.

Warehouse prices are about a third higher than mill prices, so that steel fabricating companies must operate at a production volume that permits mill orders.

All structural steel, plate, and sheet conform to the requirements of certain ASTM specifications (American Society for Testing and Materials), and in Canada, to CSA (Canadian Standards Association) specifications. These specifications run to some elaboration, setting out such matters as tolerances, chemical analysis, tensile properties, elongation and bending properties, surface condition, and so on.

Regular structural shapes include WF (wide-flange) I beams, channels, angles, T's, and Z's. WF beams are designated thus: 8 WF 24. The first number indicates the approximate depth of the beam, and the second number indicates the weight in pounds per lineal foot. Wide-flange beams are not usually rolled larger than 36 in. deep, but automatic welding machines are used to produce larger sizes from three plates, and these permit the manufacture of beams of any depth and weight. Angles are designated by the length of the two legs and the thickness, thus 6 by 4 by ⅜. T's are not rolled but are made by cutting I beams in two by means of rotary shears.

To differentiate between a plate and a sheet, note that a plate is more than 6 in. wide and ¼ in. and over in thickness, or more than 48 in. wide and ³⁄₁₆ in. or more thick. Any thinner material is classified as sheet. Plate can be expected to be half an inch oversize in length as delivered from the mill but is never undersize in any dimension. It is normally supplied very close to the nominal width. For estimating purposes, a very useful figure to remember is that a square foot of ¼-in. plate weighs 10.2 lb, or if accuracy is unimportant, 10 lb. From this figure the weight of any plate can be calculated mentally, but this figure does not apply to special alloys such as stainless steel. The following table gives the weight and thickness of the standard gauges of steel sheet:

SHEET STEEL GAUGES

Gauge	Weight psf	Thickness
6	8.125	0.1943
7	7.50	0.1793
8	6.875	0.1644
9	6.25	0.1495
10	5.625	0.1345
11	5.000	0.1195
12	4.375	0.1046
14	3.125	0.0747
16	2.500	0.0598
18	2.000	0.0478
20	1.500	0.0359

SHEET STEEL GAUGES

Gauge	Weight psf	Thickness
22	1.250	0.0299
24	1.000	0.0239
26	0.750	0.0179
28	0.625	0.0149
30	0.500	0.0120

Note that the sheet metal gauges are based on weight, not thickness. Eleven gauge is often considered to be ⅛ in. thick for convenience.

6.4 carbon in steel

It is obvious by now that the most important alloying ingredient in steel is carbon, and like garlic on steak, not very much carbon is needed to serve its purposes. Those steels in which carbon is the only significant alloying material are termed carbon steels, plain-carbon steels, or straight-carbon steels. Low-carbon steel, also called mild steel, is produced in greater tonnage than all other steels combined: it is cheap, remarkably ductile, and easily welded. Steels are designated according to their carbon content in the following classification:

1. low-carbon or mild steel   0.08–0.30% carbon
2. medium-carbon steel   0.35–0.55% carbon
3. high-carbon steel   0.60–1.5% carbon
4. cast iron   over 2% carbon

The low-carbon steels are fabricated into bridges, ships, tanks, pipe, automobile bodies, and sheet. The medium-carbon steels go into such products as harrow teeth, concrete form ties, and hangers for wooden joists. Finally, the high-carbon steel are used for knives, files, springs, concrete reinforcing bars, piano wire, hammers, and axes.

A small increase in the carbon content of a steel, even as little as a tenth of a per cent, has a potent effect on the properties of the steel. Virtually all the characteristics of the steel are changed. If the carbon content is increased, then:

1. The melting point of the steel is lowered.
2. The steel becomes harder.
3. The steel becomes stronger.
4. The steel becomes more brittle.
5. The steel becomes more wear resistant.

6. The steel becomes more difficult to weld without cracking.
7. The steel becomes more difficult to machine.
8. The steel is more easily heat-treated.
9. The steel becomes more expensive.

There is no change in the modulus of elasticity. If a mild steel and a strong steel are both loaded to the same stress, both will exhibit the same strain. The difference between the two steels is simply that the stronger steel can sustain a higher stress before the deformation becomes plastic, and it will require a higher load for fracture.

Carbon has a powerful effect on the melting point of steels. A pure iron melts at 2800 F; increasing carbon reduces the melting point until at 4.3% carbon the melting point is down to 2065 F. The high melting point of pure iron makes very severe demands on the firebrick linings of melting furnaces, and this is part of the reason why pure iron is seldom used in industry. By leaving a little carbon in the steel the melting point is lowered, and so is the cost of the steel.

The effect of carbon on the hardness of steel is shown in Fig. 33. Steels may be hardened or softened by heat treatment; the graph shows

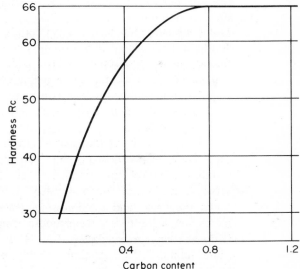

Fig. 33 Rockwell C hardness versus carbon content for steels heat-treated to their highest possible hardness.

the hardest possible condition for any carbon content. It will be noted that the hardness increases to a maximum at a carbon content of 0.8%. This poses the question: Why then increase the carbon above 0.8%? The reason for doing so is that still higher carbon content gives an improvement in the wear resistance of the steel, an important factor for such articles as pocket-knife blades, wood-turning tools, and certain hard-facing electrodes, all of which contain more than 0.8% carbon.

Although carbon dissolves in molten steel, it cannot dissolve in cold metal, in which the carbon is combined with iron as iron carbide, Fe_3C, distributed through the steel. If therefore a hard or wear-resistant steel is needed, the steel is given a high carbon content to increase the amount of hard ceramic carbide.

On this subject of carbon in steels, two practical observations must be set out:

1. The easily welded steels have not more than 0.30% carbon.
2. The steels that can be heat-treated must have a minimum of 0.30% carbon.

An easily welded steel cannot be heat-treated, and a heat-treatable steel will present welding difficulties—cracking caused by heat treatment incidental to the welding.

6.5 alloying elements other than carbon

Other alloying elements are commonly added to carbon steels in order to obtain characteristics not obtainable in straight-carbon steels. We have already mentioned some of these additions.

Silicon and aluminum, when added to steel in the small amounts required for killing, are not considered to be alloying additions. Small amounts of aluminum provide an additional benefit in promoting small grain size in steels.

Figure 23 shows that carbon produces an expansion of the temperature range over which austenite can exist. Carbon then is an austenite stabilizer. Nickel and manganese are likewise austenite promoters but serve several other functions also. Both these alloying metals improve notch toughness and toughness in general. Nickel, like aluminum, promotes small grain size. Manganese removes sulfur from steels by taking it up as manganese sulfide, MnS. Few steels are rolled without at least small amounts of manganese. Finally, one other austenite promoter may be mentioned: the gas nitrogen. A few grades of stainless steel use nitrogen to obtain the austenitic phase at room temperature.

Most of the other alloying additions to steel are carbide formers and therefore contribute hardness, wear resistance, and high strength. Tungsten, chromium, molybdenum, and vanadium are included in this group, and all are found in tool steels used to cut and form other metals. Tungsten and chromium carbides are a common feature of hard-surfacing rods for wear resistance. Chromium also contributes corrosion resistance and is the dominant alloying ingredient in stainless steels.

The commonest type of cast iron is gray cast iron, a steel containing about 3 to 3½% carbon, and more than 1% silicon. These are large amounts of carbon and silicon, and in these proportions all the carbon is not taken up by the iron as iron carbide. A part of this carbon separates out as graphite flakes distributed throughout the cast iron. These graphite flakes give a characteristically dark appearance to a freshly broken surface of gray cast iron. Figure 34 shows the microscopic appearance of the graphite network.

Fig. 34 Gray cast iron showing the network of graphite flakes in a lamellar pearlite structure.

Gray cast iron has little ductility, and if heated or cooled too quickly during welding, it tends to crack. The graphite flakes present other difficulties for the welder. Graphite is one of the solid lubricants, and it is obviously impossible to make weld metal adhere to graphite. Grinding the surface to be welded does not assist the welding process, since the grinding wheel will smear the graphite over the area to be welded. Scorching the surface with a torch will remove any graphite smears.

Gray cast iron can sustain high compressive loads. Its low tensile strength is explained by the presence of the graphite flakes. The strength of graphite in cast iron is no different from its strength in a lead pencil, and in effect each graphite flakes acts as a crack in the metal, reducing the tensile strength. However, the graphite network must not be viewed as offering nothing but disadvantages. It does contribute resistance to corrosion and high temperature, plus a little-known virtue, vibration damping. Gray cast iron is often used as the material for crankshafts in large diesel engines. The reason for this seemingly odd choice of metal is that the graphite network acts like microscopic springs to damp out vibrations in the crankshaft and prevent shaft "whip." Vibration-damping characteristics are part of the thinking behind the choice of gray cast iron for machine bases also. Gray cast iron has a modulus of elasticity of only about 18×10^6, however, considerably less than steel's 30×10^6, and since minimum deflection is a critical requirement in a machine base, sometimes a cast machine base is rejected in favor of a welded steel machine frame. If the frame of a punch press deflects 0.008 in. under load when made of gray cast iron, then it should deflect only 0.004 in. when made of welded steel (assuming that 18 is half of 30, approximately). Such deflections are not trivial simply because they are small. By and large, then, we can sum up the case for gray cast iron by saying that it is a mixture of good and bad characteristics.

Most cast iron is melted in foundry cupolas, which are miniature blast furnaces. Cupolas measure from about 3 to 6 ft in inside diameter and use limestone, coke, and scrap iron for the charge. Gray cast iron, white cast iron, or nodular iron may be made in a cupola.

White cast iron, which will not be discussed here, is the hardest type of cast iron. It is unweldable. Nodular iron, for which International Nickel Company holds the patents, is a variation of gray cast iron, and has a microscopic structure that overcomes most of the limitations of gray cast iron. Nodular iron likewise contains graphite, but the iron is inoculated with a small amount of magnesium while being poured into the ladle. As a result the graphite becomes nodular or approximately spherical. The result is a cast iron with excellent ductility and tensile strength. The operation of inoculating the iron is one of the most dramatic in industry. When the hot iron contacts the magnesium, the latter of course produces a brilliant flare.

6.7 clad steels

Today a strong trend toward the use of mild steels coated with another metal exists. The mild steel core provides strength and ductility, the surface cladding providing other service characteristics, usually corrosion resistance. Galvanized steel was one of the first of the clad steels. Another is stainless steel cookware, which is made of a mild steel clad on two sides with stainless steel. Such a sandwich of metals is better than solid stainless steel for cooking purposes because of the poor thermal conductivity of stainless steel. Cadmium-plated hardware items, chrome-plated automobile bumpers, and hard-surfacing welding electrodes come to mind as other examples of cladding. Whereas many of these clad metals have little importance for welding, others require some mention here.

Zinc coating, or *galvanizing,* is a cheap and effective method of protecting steel from corrosion. The steel is dipped into a bath of molten zinc, and the usual minimum weight of this coating is 1.25 oz per sq ft, which is of course the sum of the coatings on the two sides of the steel sheet. Galvanized sheet is readily spot- or seam-welded, but arc or gas welding will boil off the zinc coating. The fumes produced may make the welder ill, but no permanent harm is done to his health. It is more usual to complete the weldment first and then to galvanize it.

Terne sheet is steel sheet coated with an 80-20 alloy of lead and tin. The tin is required because lead will not wet steel and therefore cannot bond to it. Most terne sheet is used for fuel tanks and other welded and soldered components of automobiles, construction equipment, and portable lawn mowers. Seam welding and soldering are the best welding methods for terne-coated steel. Note that the terne coat is actually a soldering alloy.

Aluminized steel is sheet steel with an aluminum coating on both sides produced by a hot-dip process and resembles aluminum somewhat in appearance. It is available in as high as 16 gauge in two grades. Heat-resistant aluminized steel has an aluminum coating of 0.001 in. per side, and corrosion-resistant aluminized steel has a coating of 0.002 in. per side. Uses include a variety of welded sheet products such as automobile mufflers, ducts, hot water heaters, domestic furnace heat exchangers, chimneys, and roofing sheets.

Resistance welding is the preferred method of welding aluminized steel, since the high temperatures of torch or arc welding will damage the coating. Somewhat higher spot-welding currents are needed than are used for unclad steel because of the low electrical resistance of the aluminum cladding.

Arc and gas welding may be used to join aluminized steel, but unless an inert gas blanket is used, the aluminum coating will oxidize to aluminum oxide, a refractory oxide that can be removed only with special fluxes.

Stainless-clad steels consist of a low-carbon plate with some type of stainless steel rolled onto one or both sides. The thickness of the stainless cladding is greater than that of the zinc or aluminum coatings mentioned above. The stainless-clad steels (and the Monel-clad steels that are used in the potash industry) are normally arc-welded and present special welding problems. One of these problems is the dilution of the cladding by the core metal.

6.8 weld dilution

Weld dilution is a common feature of welded joints using filler metal. Sometimes dilution does not matter; at other times it may be critically important.

If a steel plate with a particular alloy is welded with a filler rod of different composition, as is usual, the deposited metal would be expected to be a compromise between the two compositions. To illustrate, we take the following example. The steel plate is 0.2% carbon, and the welding rod 0.1% carbon.

Now suppose that in depositing 1 lb of rod metal we melt 1 lb of the plate metal. This is not a very likely proportion, but it makes an easy case to analyze. For manual arc welding the proportions would be closer to 3 deposited metal to 1 of plate, and for submerged arc welding there would be more plate metal per pound of deposited metal. However, we are assuming equal proportions and 0.2% and 0.1% carbon. The deposited metal should be 0.15% carbon, the average composition of plate and rod metal. This assumes that no alloy constituents of the rod are lost in the arc or dissolved in the slag. A small amount of carbon in the rod will presumably disappear as carbon monoxide gas. In a high-chromium rod, much of the chromium will be lost in manual arc welding.

Consider next the welding of a 0.5% carbon plate with a 0.1% carbon rod, in which three times as much metal is deposited as base metal melted. The total melted metal is four parts, and the difference in carbon is 0.4%. The analysis of the deposited bead will thus be 0.2% carbon. Suppose that a second bead is laid on top of the first bead, and the first bead, not the plate, is the cause of dilution. Then the second bead will be 0.125% C, or one-quarter of the difference between 0.2 and 0.1%.

Dilution is a significant feature of hard surfacing. The first deposit of a high-manganese, high-carbon hard-facing rod on a mild steel will be heavily diluted by the base metal. It may be necessary to lay down a second or a third deposit in order to obtain the proper composition for best wear resistance. Since for a variety of reasons it is usually impossible to match the welding rod with the base metal, the only sure cure for dilution is a welding method that does not require the deposition of metal. Electron beam welding is such a method.

Probably the trickiest dilution problems arise in the welding of the stainless and Monel-clad steels. Suppose that we must weld a stainless-clad plate, clad one side only. Figure 35 shows the edge preparation. The base metal is ordinary low-carbon mild steel, and the beads 1, 2, and 3 are deposited with the usual manual arc welding rods, taking care that the first bead does not melt through into the cladding. Any dilution in the first three beads presumably has no practical significance. The plate is then turned over and bead 4 deposited, as shown in Fig. 35(b).

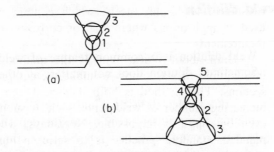

Fig. 35 Welding sequence for
stainless-clad steel.

(a)

(b)

The welding process is manual arc, and we shall assume that we are depositing 3 lb of weld metal for every pound of plate metal melted. We shall assume the base metal to be 0.16% C, and 0 Cr. The cladding and the deposited stainless rod if undiluted are 0.08% C and 18.0% Cr. Then bead 4 should be about 0.10% C and 13 ½% Cr. The dilution could of course be a three-way dilution problem between the rod, the cladding, and the base material; this would make for a complicated analysis not really worth the trouble. Bead 5 should have 17% or more chromium and low carbon, which presumably is acceptable.

Suppose, however, that the welding method is submerged arc welding, discussed in Chapter 12. Submerged arc welding uses very high currents and filler metal is deposited at remarkably high rates, but in so doing more base metal is melted than filler metal. Submerged arc welding will necessarily cause greater dilution of the filler metal. If submerged arc is used to deposit bead 4, assuming 2 lb of base metal melted for every pound of deposited metal, than bead 4 must be 0.133% C and 6.0% Cr, a brittle and undesirable weld, for it will form hard chromium carbides and may crack during welding or in service. If bead 5 is also laid down by submerged arc welding, then it may not have sufficient chromium in it for adequate corrosion resistance, the reason why the plate was clad originally. For a submerged arc weld, the analysis of the bead is determined largely by the base metal rather than the filler metal, simply because more base metal is melted.

The above discussion assumes that the same number of beads are laid down for submerged arc as for manual welding. This is not true, however, but can be ignored for the present.

6.9 low-alloy steels

Low-alloy steels are those steels that do not contain more than 5% of any alloying metal or in which the total alloy content does not greatly exceed 5%. Such steels are used principally for applications requiring either toughness or great strength, or sometimes for heat or corrosion resistance. High-alloy steels, which contain more than 10% alloy, are used in applications where heat or corrosion resistance are the dominant requirements.

Until about World War II the method of building great strength into equipment was simply to make the equipment of thicker and heavier sections. This method is both inefficient and uneconomical, and for an increasing number of weldments, such as submarines, ships, rockets, and even buildings, is impossible. Nowadays, when greater strength is demanded, standard practice is to select a high-strength material. High-strength steels, especially, are growing rapidly in popularity. These must be low-alloy steels. Every year a number of new low-alloy steels are introduced, and the result is a continuing pressure for more skill and knowledge on the part of welding operators and superintendents, for these steels call for careful attention to welding procedures. To some degree low-alloy steels are replacing the former mild steels in such applications as structural steel and truck dump bodies. If, for example, the weight of a truck body can be decreased by 1 ton by the use of low-alloy steels, then an extra ton of payload can be carried on each truck haul for the life of the truck. Again, suppose that by the use of high-strength low-alloy steel the beams in a building frame can be made shallower by 2 in. Then for a 20-storey building 20 in. of height is saved. Each inch of height saved may mean a cost reduction of perhaps $2000 and represents 20 in. less of steel framing, curtain wall, fireproofing, ducting, piping, insulation, and other building components, including labor.

The standard structural steel in use for the last 60 years is made to ASTM specification A7. It is a low-carbon steel but does not have a definite chemical analysis. Yield strength is 33,000 psi, ultimate tensile strength is 60,000 psi, and welding rods with a guaranteed strength of 60,000 psi must be used for welding it.

The newer low-alloy steels are making inroads into the applications formerly filled by A7 steel. They are all lean steels, that is, very low in alloy content, with ultimate strengths as high as 120,000 psi. They must be welded with high-strength welding rods. One of the most familiar of these steels to welders is United States Steel's T-1, with the following composition typical of low-alloy structural steels: 0.10–0.20 C, 0.60–1.0 Mn, 0.15–0.35 Si, 0.70–1.0 Ni, 0.40–0.65 Cr, 0.40–0.60 Mo, 0.03–0.08 V, 0.15–0.50 Cu, 0.002–0.006 B. This analysis looks like a recipe for Irish stew, but it fulfills two conflicting requirements: high strength and weldability. United States Steel can make a much simpler steel with the same strength of 120,000 psi simply by using 0.45% carbon and nothing else. But the higher carbon content would mean brittle fracture, serious welding problems, cracking, plus the marketing problem that no honest salesman would be willing to sell it.

Another group of low-alloy steels are the chromium-molybdenum (chrome-moly) steels used for high-temperature piping of steam. In general, plain carbon steels are not used for piping at temperatures exceeding 750 F. The chrome-moly steels replace them for service conditions in the temperature range 750 to 1050 F. Joints in such piping require special welding procedures.

A very large number of the low-alloy steels come under the number-coding system of the AISI (American Iron & Steel Institute) and the SAE (Society of Automotive Engineers). In this coding system, a steel is designated by four digits. The system is best explained by an example such as SAE 2345 (AISI 2345). The latter two digits, 45, indicate the carbon content, 0.45%, the second number indicates the percentage of the principal alloy, 3%, and the first number gives the type of steel, in this case nickel. This is a 3% nickel steel with 0.45% carbon. The coding follows this system:

AISI OR SAE CODE FOR LOW-ALLOY STEELS

10xx	plain-carbon steels
2xxx	low-nickel steels
3xxx	nickel-chromium steels
40xx	molybdenum steels
41xx	chromium-molybdenum steels
43xx	nickel-chromium molybdenum steels
5xxx	chromium steels
6xxx	chromium-vanadium steels
7xxx	tungsten steels
8xxx	nickel-chromium-molybdenum steels
9xxx	manganese-silicon-nickel-chromium-molybdenum steels

An SAE 1015 steel contains 0.15% carbon only, a 2330 has 0.30% carbon and 3% nickel, a 3150 contains 1% nickel, 0.50% carbon, and some chromium, and a 4037 less than 1% molybdenum (because of the zero) and 0.37% carbon. The following are typical applications for these steels:

1030	soft wire
1060	gardening tools and agricultural equipmemt
1070	cold chisels
1080	hammers and punches
10110	twist drills and threading taps
3435	rear axles and gears for trucks
4130	motor casings for the Black Brant rocket
4340	undercarriages for aircraft

In Canada, Atlas Steel Company's SPS 245 is a popular general-purpose low-alloy steel which does not fit the AISI-SAE system: 0.40% carbon, 1.25% nickel.

6.10 high alloy steels

The high-alloy steels, like the low-alloy steels, cover a broad range of alloys, some of which are of limited interest to welding technology. Many of the hard-facing welding rods are high alloy. The austenitic manganese hard-facing materials have already been mentioned. These contain about 1% carbon and a minimum of 12% manganese, are austenitic (fcc) at room temperature, and have the highest work-hardening capacity of all the metals.

A great many of the tool steels—steels for manufacture into cutting and forming tools—are high alloy. These are not usually welded except for repair and maintenance. Their hardness is explained by the presence of large amounts of carbide-forming alloying ingredients in the steel, such as tungsten, molybdenum, and cobalt. Figure 17 is a photomicrograph of one type of tool steel, a high-speed steel containing 18% tungsten, 4% chromium, 1% vanadium, and about 1% carbon. Such steels remain hard up to temperatures of about 1200 F, a dull red heat, whereas the plain carbon steels begin to soften just over 300 F.

The two most important groups of high-alloy steels are the alloy tool steels and the stainless steels. Special attention must be directed to the stainless steels.

6.11 stainless steels

The use of stainless steels has been growing at a more rapid rate than that of other types of steels, annual consumption in the United States being now about a million tons. The cost per pound depends on the quantity, shape, and type, and can range from 40 cents to over a dollar. Actually the stainless steels are a rather large group of low-carbon high-alloy steels that offer the advantages of great corrosion resistance, oxidation resistance, high strength at either high or low temperature, attractive appearance, and cleanliness.

The electrical and thermal conductivity of the stainless steels is considerably lower than the conductivity of the carbon steels. Despite a popular faith in the stainless steels as virtually faultless materials, it must be pointed out that, like all other materials in industry, the stainless steels have their deficiencies too. They are not *always* more corrosion resistant than cheaper steels are. They are heavy, so that in buying stainless steel there is actually a double price premium: a greater cost per pound and a greater weight per cubic inch or per square foot. Finally, the 300-series stainless steels have an expansion coefficient about a third higher than steel.

A supermarket used mild-steel reinforcing rods to hold the refractory concrete in place in the charging door of its incinerator. Because of the high temperature, these rods used to burn out after three months, allowing the refractory lining to fall out of the door. To eliminate this maintenance problem, the decision was naturally made to replace the carbon steel with stainless rods. The stainless rods were expected to last indefinitely.

Expectations were fulfilled. The stainless rods were undamaged by the heat. But the maintenance problem became worse. After a week the refractory lining cracked and began to fall out. A replacement lining poured around the stainless rods likewise fell out. What everyone had overlooked was the high expansion coefficient of the stainless rods, causing them to bow and thus crack the refractory concrete. Actually the real moral of this story is simply that personnel ought to have some minimum knowledge of stainless steels, for, out of about forty kinds, there are types of stainless with low expansion.

Being high-alloy steels, the stainless steels are not included in the AISI-SAE coding system. Instead, they have their own numbering system, which uses three digits instead of four. Except for the first digit, there is not much system or significance to the system. Neglecting a few 200 and 500 series stainless, which will be discussed presently, all stainless steels are assigned numbers in either the 300 or 400 range, such as 304, 310, 405, 446.

The 400 series contain a minimum of 12% chromium and a maximum of 0.15% carbon. Actually one or two 400 series have more carbon

Fig. 36(a) Type 416 stainless steel, martensitic.

than this, but 0.15% will serve for a general rule. The 400 series are body-centered cubic steels. In addition the 400 stainless contain 1% manganese and 1% silicon. Certain problems of brittleness are associated with the welding of the 400 series. The expansion coefficients for the 400 series are about the same as for carbon steels. The 400 series are also not quite so resistant to corrosion or heat as the 300 series are but can be used up to a dull red heat (1200 F or more) without scaling. They are usually cheaper than the 300 series. They are ferromagnetic.

Two types of 400 series are available: *ferritic* and *martensitic*. Martensitic steels can be hardened by heat treatment; ferritic steels cannot be thus hardened but are sometimes hardened by cold working. If only the corrosion resistance of stainless 400 were needed, then a ferritic stainless would be selected, but if it is necessary also for such a steel to carry high stresses, then a martensitic stainless steel would be chosen and heat-treated to a sufficiently high yield stress. The difference between the ferritic and the martensitic 400 stainless steels is approximately this: the martensitic stainless steels contain less chromium and more carbon than the ferritic steels do. Type 410 stainless is the commonest and cheapest of the martensitic hardenable types, and 430 is the most used of the ferritic stainless. Their analyses are:

410   12% chromium, 0.15% carbon
430   18% chromium, 0.12% carbon

It was established previously that to make hard and strong steels it is necessary to form carbides in the steel. It is not possible to do this in the 430 steel. Part of the reason is that there is insufficient carbon, but this subject will be discussed further in Chapter 7.

The 400 series are straight-chromium steels. The 300 series, however, are chromium-nickel low-carbon steels. Since the latter contain a minimum of 18% chromium and 8% nickel, they are occasionally referred to as 18-8 stainless, though this is a misnomer since many of the 300 series contain more chromium and nickel than this, especially the 300-series welding rod alloys. The peculiarities of the 300 group can be thus summed up:

1. They are paramagnetic.
2. They are austenitic, face-centered cubic owing to the presence of face-centered cubic nickel.
3. They cannot be hardened by heat treatment.
4. They have an expansion coefficient a third higher than carbon steels or the 400-series stainless steels.
5. They work-harden when formed or sheared.

The most frequently used steels of the 300 group are 302 and 304, containing the following:

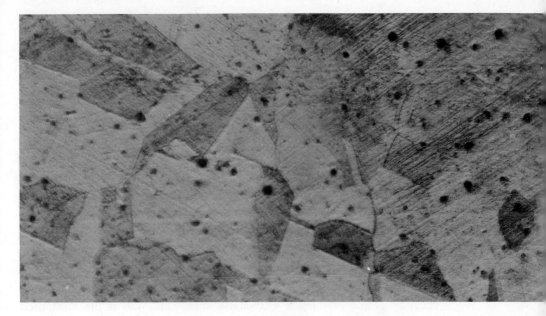

Fig. 36(b) Type 316 stainless steel, austenitic.

302   18% chromium, 8–10% nickel, 0.15% carbon
304   19% chromium, 8–12% nickel, 0.08% carbon

Thus 304 is a slightly richer alloy than 302, with only half the carbon. The 302 may in time be withdrawn and replaced by 304 as it has too much carbon for a stainless austenitic steel.

6.12 carbide precipitation
in austenitic stainless steels

A rather interesting metallurgical problem develops in austenitic stainless steels heated into the temperature range 800 to 1600 F.

The stainless steels, both 300 and 400 series, obtain their stainless and corrosion-resistant properties from a thin and tightly adherent skin of chromium oxide, just as aluminum is protected by its oxide coating. To develop this protective oxide, a minimum of 12% chromium is required. If the stainless steel should lose sufficient chromium, the stainless quality would be lost too.

An austenitic stainless steel always contains some carbon. At temperatures between 800 and 1600 F this carbon rapidly combines with chromium to form chromium carbide. Chromium carbide is no longer

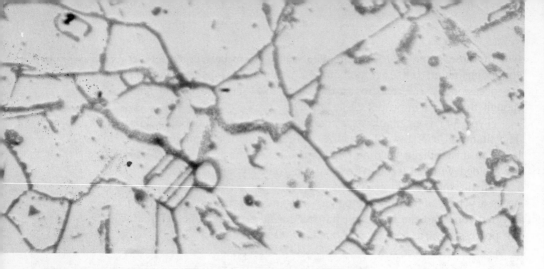

Fig. 36(c) Type 316 stainless steel showing pronounced chromium carbide deposits as black material at the grain boundaries. In this condition this steel is no longer stainless. The sets of parallel lines distributed through the crystal structure are called "twins" and are found in all wrought face-centered cubic metals.

chromium metal, and the effect of the chromium is lost. The effect is powerful, for carbon can combine with seventeen times as much chromium. This chromium carbide is deposited in the grain boundaries of the steel, hence the term *carbide precipitation*. Areas adjacent to the grain boundaries are chromium-depleted and can be corroded, depending on the aggressiveness of the corroding medium.

When a 304 or other 300 stainless is fusion-welded, some region in the heat-affected zone must necessarily be heated between 800 and 1600 F for some length of time. For a weldment to be used in a pulp mill, say, this could be serious, and some method must be available to prevent carbide precipitation. Actually, two methods of prevention are available.

Obviously if there were no carbon in the stainless steel, there could be no carbides and no precipitation problem. Steel with no carbon is not possible, but grades of austenitic stainless steel are produced with sufficiently low carbon to reduce carbide precipitation to acceptable levels. Such steels are designated L or ELC (extra low carbon), thus 304L or 316ELC. The carbon content of such stainless steels does not exceed 0.03%, approximately a two-thirds reduction in carbon. Stainless 302, containing 0.15% carbon (highest of all the 300 series), obviously cannot be used in critical applications in which precipitation is a factor.

Reduced carbon is one solution to the problem. The other solution is metallurgically more shrewd: a metal with a greater affinity for carbon than chromium has, is added to the stainless steel so that it, instead of chromium, takes up the carbon. The austenitic stainless steels that include a special carbide-former are termed *stabilized* austenitic steels. There are two of these: type 321 containing about 0.4% titanium and type 347 containing about 0.8% columbium or columbium plus tantalum. These are occasionally referred to as the "weldable" grades of 300 stainless, though this is an improper description.

Type 347 is available as a manual arc welding rod, but 321 is not. The titanium in 321 would oxidize in the arc or disappear in the slag to leave an unstabilized welding bead. Therefore both 321 and 347 stainless are welded with 347 rods. Low-carbon rods are also available.

In the martensitic grades of 400 stainless, carbide precipitation is a necessary part of the hardening process and is expected. Both the heat-affected zone and the bead will harden during welding, whether the welding process be arc, gas, or resistance.

6.13 200 and 500 stainless steels

The stainless types 201 and 202 are substitutes for 301 and 302, and like them, are austenitic. These are chromium-nickel-manganese steels, developed during World War II and the Korean conflict, when there was a serious shortage of nickel. The nickel content is reduced to the range of 3.5 to 6%, and 5 to 10% manganese is substituted. The chromium content is the same as that in the corresponding 300 stainless, but nitrogen up to 0.25% maximum is added. Both nitrogen and manganese, like nickel, are austenite promoters.

Stainless types 501 and 502 are low-chromium steels used chiefly by the oil industry, where a lesser degree of corrosion resistance will suffice. They include only 4 to 6% chromium and are not true stainless steels.

6.14 summary of alloy elements in steels

1. *Carbon*. Present in all steels in the form of carbides of iron and alloy elements. In gray cast iron and in ductile iron, some carbon is in the form of graphite.

2. *Silicon*. Added to steel in small quantities as a deoxidizer. In greater amounts, silicon dissolves in ferrite and strengthens it. Silicon is added to cast irons in amounts greater than 1% to promote the formation of the graphite network. Silicon is present in virtually all steels.

3. *Aluminum.* Used in small quantities as a deoxidizer and promoter of small grain size.

4. *Manganese.* Like silicon, is present in virtually all steels. It removes sulfur from steel by combining with it as manganese sulfide. Manganese also has some tendency to act as a deoxidizer and to form carbides.

5. *Nickel.* Dissolves in ferrite, chiefly producing a toughening effect.

6. *Copper.* Added to steels in small amounts for resistance to atmospheric corrosion.

7. *Molybdenum.* Forms hard carbides for tool steel and high-speed steel uses. In smaller amounts, molybdenum improves strength at high temperatures, and in stainless steels, such as 316, improves the resistance to acid corrosion.

8. *Tungsten.* Like molybdenum forms hard carbides which preserve the hardness of tool steels at high temperatures.

9. *Titanium.* A powerful carbide-former, used in type 321 stainless steel to prevent chromium depletion due to chromium carbide formation.

10. *Columbium.* A strong carbide-former, used in type 347 stainless steel for the same reason that titanium is used in type 321. Also found in small amounts in low-alloy structural steels.

11. *Vanadium.* Carbide-former used in high-speed steels. In smaller quantities promotes fine grain size.

12. *Chromium.* A carbide former if there is sufficient carbon in the steel also. Therefore in heat-treatable (martensitic) stainless steels the carbon content exceeds $\frac{1}{100}$ of the chromium content; in non-heat-treatable stainless steels (ferritic and austenitic) the carbon content is less than $\frac{1}{100}$ of the chromium content. In small amounts chromium improves the hot strength of low-alloy steels. About 5% chromium will produce an air-hardening steel. A minimum of 12% chromium results in a stainless steel.

PROBLEMS

1 What is the minimum number of mild steel plates required to make up a mill order of steel of 40,000 lb, if the plates are the following size:
(a) ¼ by 48 by 96 in.
(b) ¼ by 96 by 240 in.
(c) ½ by 36 by 96 in.
(d) 1 by 48 by 144 in.

2 What is the weight of a mild steel sheet 48 by 120 in. in the following gauges: 10, 14, 20, 24.

3 The analysis of a tool steel is 18% W, 4% Cr, 1% V, 0.90% C, 0.5% Si, 1.0% Mn. Give weight per ton of all elements in the steel including iron.

4 What procedures might be adopted to reduce dilution when manual-arc-welding a stainless steel plate to a mild steel plate? Consider such matters as high or low current, large or small rods, etc.

5 Mild steel of 0.2% carbon is being welded to stainless steel of 0.08% carbon. It is estimated that 3 lb of deposited metal is melted per pound of base metal melted. Estimate the amount of carbon in the bead. The joint is a butt weld, the rod has the same composition as the stainless base metal, and chromium is not lost to the slag. Dilution is from both sides of the joint.

6 Low-alloy 2% chromium piping is being butt-welded with an 18% chromium rod. Assume no loss of chromium. For every pound of piping melted, 3 lb of rod metal are deposited. Estimate the amount of chromium in the bead.

7 Give the carbon and nickel analysis of the following steels: AISI 1040, 2315, 10110.

8 Suppose that we state generally that a standard stainless steel does not contain more than 0.12% carbon.
(a) What is the advantage of less carbon?
(b) For what purpose would more carbon be used?

9 When stainless steel is welded with an oxyacetylene torch, why would you expect the original chromium content of the steel to be reduced somewhat by this method of welding?

10 Would a martensitic stainless steel have less or more carbon than a ferritic stainless steel. Why?

11 List three elements that promote the austenitic phase in steels.

12 If holes must be drilled in an austenitic stainless steel, would a fine feed or a coarse feed be used in drilling? Why?

13 The edge of a sheared plate of stainless 304 is harder than the rest of the plate. Why?

14 To produce nodular cast iron, a small amount of magnesium is added to the molten iron when it is poured into the ladle. Why is the magnesium not added to the iron in the melting furnace?

We have previously defined a weld as "a casting surrounded by a heat treatment." The statement is perhaps flippant but unfortunately also true. Perhaps half of all welding difficulties arise from heat treating. Without a knowledge of heat treating, it is not possible to understand the welding process nor to avoid many of the difficulties that accompany the welding of many metals. Previous sections of this book have made frequent reference to heat-treating—carbide precipitation in austenitic stainless steels for example; in this chapter a more systematic approach to heat treating must be undertaken.

To heat-treat means to change the physical properties of a metal by means of temperature. The properties usually changed are hardness, ductility, and toughness; yield strength and ultimate tensile strength; wear resistance; corrosion resistance; and machineability. The heat treatments that produce these changes go by a variety of names, such as hardening, annealing, normalizing, tempering, stress relieving, spheroidizing, drawing, and austempering. To understand these processes, it is necessary to direct attention first to the heat treating of steels, despite the fact that few metals are heat-treated in the same manner that steels are.

HEAT TREATING
AND
WELDING OF STEELS

7

Figure 23 shows the phase changes in plain carbon steels as the carbon content and the temperature vary. For a pure iron, the phase change from body-centered cubic at lower temperatures to face-centered cubic austenite occurs at 1666 F. The bcc state is termed *ferrite*. This ferrite phase is commonly found in carbon and alloy steels and cast irons. It can be considered to be pure iron, but in plain carbon steels it is actually a solution of 0.008% carbon in iron at room temperature (though iron can dissolve somewhat more carbon than this at higher temperatures). The carbon atoms are small enough (0.77A) to fit between the iron atoms in the body-centered cubic crystal lattice.

But even an extra low-carbon stainless steel contains much more carbon than 0.008%, so that the carbon in steels must be in the steel in some form other than this. The irresistible chemical attraction between most metals and carbon has been a recurrent theme in this book: virtually all the carbon in steels is taken up as carbides of iron, tungsten, chromium, molybdenum, vanadium, titanium, and other metals. Here we come to the heart of the matter. *We can heat-treat any steel that contains sufficient carbides.* Pure iron cannot be heat-treated. Carbon steels with less than about 0.3% carbon have carbides insufficient for any significant heat treating to be possible. Thus the 300-series stainless steels, in which carbon is generally less than 0.15%, cannot be heat-treated. The martensitic stainless steels are given enough carbon to produce sufficient carbides of iron and chromium for heat treating. The non-heat-treatable ferritic stainless steels must be discussed later.

To heat-treat then, we need carbides plus one other steel characteristic—a phase transformation from austenite at higher temperature to other phases at lower temperatures. Again, the 300-series austenitic stainless steels do not have this second characteristic, but most steels do.

Iron carbide, Fe_3C, is called *cementite*. Like other carbides, it is hard, strong, and brittle, the hardest constituent in carbon steels. Cementite has a carbon content of 6.6%. At room temperature, all carbon steels are mixtures of ferrite and cementite. To harden a carbon steel, the steel is first heated to just above its critical temperature into the austenite phase. It is held at this temperature long enough for cementite and other carbides to dissolve in the austenite. The steel is then cooled at a rapid rate. This fast cooling is obtained by quenching the hot steel in water or oil, or, in the case of a weld, the cooling is fast because of a high thermal severity number. Because of the rapid cooling, the austenite does not have time to dissociate into the usual ferrite and cementite. What comes down with drastic cooling is a supersaturated solution of carbon trapped in a body-centered tetragonal (i.e., rectangular) crystal structure, this frozen solution being given the name *martensite*.

The transformation from austenite to martensite does not occur at the transformation temperature between ferrite and austenite. Instead, the martensite transformation occurs over a *range of temperature*. Austenite may begin to transform to martensite at 800 F in a low-alloy steel. As the temperature continues to fall, more martensite is formed, until at room temperature the structure of the steel may be 99% martensite. With added alloy ingredients the martensite transformation begins at a lower temperature, and the transformation is also less complete. In a high-speed steel, martensite may not begin to appear until a temperature of 600 F is reached, and perhaps only 80% of the austenite will have transformed when room temperature is reached. The untransformed fraction will still be austenite. All these changes take place only during a fast quench of an alloy steel or a carbon steel of 0.3% carbon or more. In welding terms, a fast quench might mean a thermal severity number as low as 2.

Figure 33 shows the hardness of carbon steels in the martensitic condition.

Martensite is hard, brittle, and nonductile, so that the danger of cracking due to thermal stresses is ever present. Worse still, there is a volume expansion when martensite appears. The part of the steel that is merely cooling is contracting, while the fraction that is transforming is expanding. This makes the cracking possibilities even greater.

In carbon steels, the brittle martensitic condition is obtainable only with a very rapid cooling rate. Additions of any alloying ingredients affect this cooling rate. The greater the proportion of these ingredients in a steel, the slower the cooling rate that will still give a martensite condition. This statement holds true whether the alloying metals are carbide-formers like tungsten and molybdenum or those that dissolve in ferrite, such as nickel and manganese.

7.2 tempering

Tempering, an operation that heat-treaters often call "drawing," is a softening and toughening heat treatment performed immediately after hardening operations.

It is not usually practical to leave a steel in the full-hardened, or martensitic, condition. Most martensitic steels will crack, and to prevent this, the steel is tempered immediately after hardening. Tempering a hardened steel is done by heating it to some temperature below the transformation temperature, in the range of 300 to 1200 F (Fig. 37).

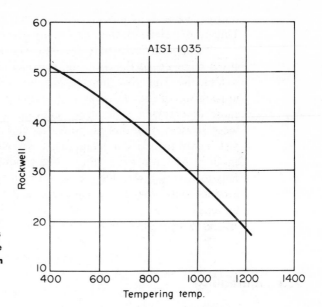

Fig. 37 Rockwell C hardness versus tempering temperature for an AISI 1035 plain carbon steel.

Since the transformation temperature is not passed, the rate of cooling back to room temperature is not important. The higher the tempering temperature, the softer and tougher the steel will be. A scriber for marking steel must be hard but need not be tough: it would be tempered at about 350 F. On the other hand, a screwdriver requires considerable toughness as well as some hardness: it would be tempered at about 650 F. The purpose of tempering may be understood from the following reasoning. In hardening, we obtain the maximum possible hardness in a steel but no toughness. In tempering, we sacrifice some of this hardness in order to get toughness. If a great deal of toughness is required, then much of the hardness must be given up. If toughness is not required, then most of the hardness can be retained, although some tempering is always required to relax the severe hardening stresses and prevent cracking of the steel.

Tempering is well known because of the beautiful colors that appear on carbon steels at various temperatures. (These colors do not always show on alloy steels.) Such colors serve as a built-in thermometer. The following is the relationship between color and temperature:

straw yellow	400 F
brown	460
bright purple	500
dark blue	550

Progressively lighter blues develop at increasing temperatures, until at 700 F the colors disappear. No more colors appear until the temperature of the steel reaches 1200 F, when a dull red heat begins to show. This is the start of the red-hot range.

Tempering is in part a stress-relieving operation but is not called stress relieving. *Stress relieving*, so-called, is a common heat treatment for weldments. The distortion caused by welding creates locked-in stresses in such weldments as tanks and pressure vessels. Such stresses may be a cause of cracking. The stress-relieving operation is carried out to relax these stresses. For this purpose the weldment is heated to a temperature just below the critical temperature, or about 1200 F, followed by slow cooling. At these temperatures the modulus of elasticity of the material falls to a very low value. As a result, the thermal strains of welding can produce only low values of stress, and the material can relax or move to relieve these stresses. Since stress relieving is carried out below the critical temperature, it is really a kind of tempering.

7.3 annealing

This is a softening process, actually bringing a steel to its lowest possible hardness. To anneal a steel, it is heated to just above its critical temperature into the austenite range and allowed to cool slowly. The cooling is done by leaving the steel in the annealing furnace after the heat is shut off, or in annealing after welding, a post-heating operation would be required to prevent the steel from cooling too quickly. Note that the difference between hardening and softening of steels lies only in the cooling rate. Fast cooling hardens; slow cooling softens, but both must begin from the austenite phase.

Tempering and annealing are both softening operations. However, tempering does not involve a phase change. Further, tempering is only

Fig. 38 (a) Ferrite. There is almost no carbon in this steel.

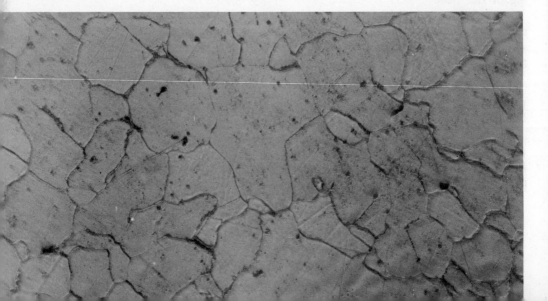

Fig. 38 (b)   Pearlite in a 0.8 per cent steel.

Fig. 38 (c)   Tempered martensite in a medium carbon
steel.

performed after a hardening operation, and its purpose is not to soften
but to toughen.

The slow rate of cooling through the transformation temperature
allows the carbides in austenite to transform to a structure called *pearlite*.
Pearlite, as Fig. 38 indicates, is a laminated structure resembling finger-
prints. In metallurgy it is trade practice to call pearlite "lamellar" rather

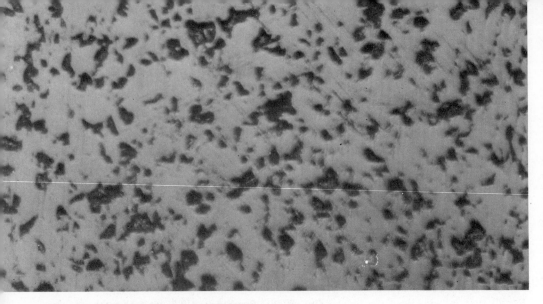

Fig. 38 (d)   A normalized medium carbon steel.

Fig. 38 (e)   White ferrite and dark pearlite in a plain
carbon steel.

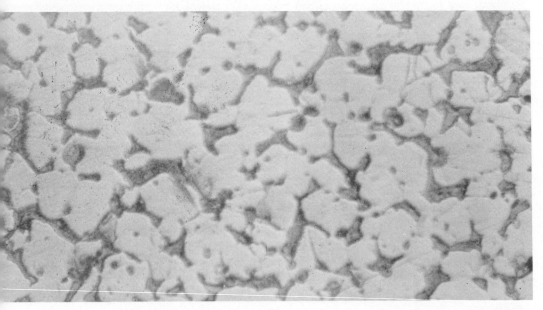

than "laminated." The white constituent of pearlite is ferrite, almost
pure iron, and the dark constituent is iron carbide, Fe₃C. The carbon
content of ferrite is almost zero, the carbon content of iron carbide is
6.6%, and the carbon content of pearlite is 0.80%.

Now if pearlite contains 0.8% carbon and an AISI-1080 steel likewise contains 0.80% carbon, the steel, if in the annealed condition, will

consist of pearlite only. At the opposite extreme, a pure iron contains no carbon, therefore shows no pearlite grains under the microscope, and must be 100% ferrite grains. A medium-carbon steel containing carbon between the limits of 0.8% and 0 will in the annealed condition contain some ferrite and some pearlite. If it is a 1040 steel, half the grains will be ferrite and half pearlite. Using this reasoning, the reader should estimate the carbon content of the steel shown in Fig. 38(e).

The figure of 0.8% carbon is something of a magic number for carbon steels. This is the carbon content at which the hardness of hardened steels reaches the maximum value (Fig. 33). It is also the carbon content at which the transformation temperature reaches its lowest value (Fig. 23). A carbon steel containing 0.8% carbon is called a eutectoid steel, steels with less carbon are termed hypoeutectoid, and steels with more carbon than 0.8% are termed hypereutectoid.

Another heat-treating process similar to annealing is *normalizing*. Recall that in annealing the steel is taken slightly above the critical temperature and then furnace-cooled or otherwise cooled very slowly. To normalize a steel, it is heated about 100 F above the critical temperature and then air-cooled. The cooling rate for normalizing is between the cooling rates for hardening and for annealing. The purpose of normalizing is to produce a harder and stronger steel than annealing can give and to refine the grain. Certainly the grain size of the steel ought to be finer with a faster cooling rate. As seen from Fig. 38(d), the pearlite structure is finer than that obtained by annealing, and the lamellar structure of the pearlite is no longer visible under the microscope.

Normalizing is a characteristic feature of multipass welds. Suppose a welded joint is to be completed in several passes. A root pass is first laid down, and let us suppose that this first pass cools slowly enough for a fairly coarse-grained structure to form in the weld metal. When the second pass is laid down on top of the root pass, the heat of the second pass commonly normalizes the root pass, the result being grain refinement in the root pass and a coarser grain in the second pass. If a third pass is then laid down, the second pass will be normalized. Hence all passes except the last one become normalized and fine-grained, an advantageous feature of multipass welding.

7.4 summary of the microconstituents of carbon steel

ferrite   essentially bcc pure iron; soft and ductile
cementite   iron carbide, Fe_3C; hard and brittle
pearlite   lamellar mixture of ferrite and cementite; 0.8% carbon
austenite   face-centered iron or steel; ductile
martensite   hard and brittle quenched steel

This is a remarkable range of constituents, each with its own set of properties. Even so, the list is not complete but is restricted to those constituents that have significance in the welding processes. No other metal can match the heat-treating possibilities of steel.

7.5 carburizing and decarburizing

Carburizing, or case hardening as it is also termed, consists of contacting the steel surface with a carbon-rich material, such as a gas, a cyanide, cast-iron chips, a proprietary salt, or a carburizing flame, under conditions that cause the carbon to migrate into the steel to form a high-carbon "case" on the steel surface. Such carbon-rich cases are not usually thicker than 0.100 in. The case may or may not be subsequently heat-treated. Case hardening is performed on low-carbon steels to provide a wear-resistant case with a soft and tough core. Since steel in the body-centered cubic phase does not dissolve carbon or iron carbide, case hardening must be carried out at a temperature above the transformation temperature, the steel being in the austenitic condition.

The opposite of carburization is decarburization, the loss of carbon from the surface of a steel. Decarburization is an undesirable effect of heating upon steel and is to be expected to some degree if steel is heated to a red heat in air or oxygen. The high temperature combined with oxygen burns out some of the carbon to form carbon monoxide gas. The extent of decarburization is not too great in the plain carbon steels but is often more pronounced in alloy steels.

7.6 alloy steels

The basic method of heat-treating the plain carbon steels is rather complex. When this method is extended to alloy steels, the basic operations of hardening, annealing, stress relieving, and so on remain, and there are no new phases to consider beyond those already set out. For the alloy steels, however, the heat-treating processes are somewhat modified and often of more restricted scope than those possible with the carbon steels.

The alloy ingredients added to steels are grouped generally into two broad classes: ferrite-strengtheners and carbide-formers. The ferrite-strengtheners are those elements which dissolve in ferrite; these strengthen and toughen the ferrite. Most alloying elements are carbide-formers.

The addition of any alloy alters the transformation diagram from that of the carbon steels shown in Fig. 23. It has been noted earlier that both nickel and manganese lower the transformation temperature and in sufficient amounts will produce an austenitic steel. The carbide-formers, titanium, columbium, molybdenum, chromium, tungsten, and others, move the transformation temperature to higher values. Large amounts of tungsten, for example, will move the transformation temperature to about 2000 F; this is why high-speed steels of 18% tungsten must be heat-treated at temperatures from 2100 to 2400 F.

The plain carbon steels must be cooled very quickly to obtain a martensitic condition. The addition of any alloying elements, whether ferrite-strengtheners or carbide-formers, permits a much slower cooling rate for hardening. Many of the alloy steels are even air-hardening types. In practical terms, if a steel is air-hardening, then it is likely to be hardened if it is heated or welded, unless the rate of cooling is slow. Such steels will require a preheat or postheat when welded if they are not to be brittle. Besides the thermal severity number the temperature of the steel before welding probably is the greatest factor in the cooling rate. Still another method of slowing the cooling is to use a larger welding rod and a higher welding current. The larger the weld bead deposited, the greater the amount of heat energy that must be removed and the slower the rate of cooling.

Although a few alloying metals such as nickel enlarge the austenite field, many metals restrict it. Chromium is one of the most common of the metals added to steel, and its effect on austenite is shown in Fig. 39. The lines marked 0% Cr are the boundaries of the austenite field for a plain carbon steel. A steel may be hardened or annealed from any temperature within this area, but only the lowest possible temperatures, those just above the critical temperature, are used. The higher tempera-

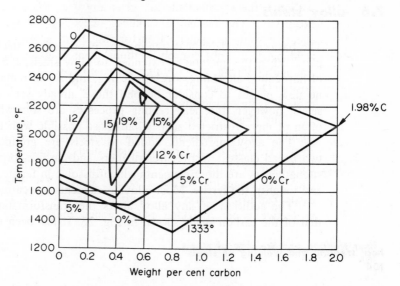

Fig. 39 The austenite range in chromium steels. Since chromium is a ferrite promoter, increased chromium reduces the austenite range.

tures will produce excessive loss of metal by oxidation, grain growth, and decarburization. With the addition of 5% chromium, several effects are produced. The eutectoid carbon composition is moved from 0.8% to 0.5% carbon. The transformation temperature is increased to about 1500 F. Finally, the whole austenite region is narrowed. The next boundary shown is for 12% chromium. Again the austenite field is reduced, the transformation temperature is raised to the neighborhood of 1600 F, and the austenite region pinches out at about 0.9% carbon. Type 410 stainless steel contains 12% chromium and 0.15% carbon, and Fig. 39 shows that this steel is martensitic, that is, hardenable, since it has a transformation temperature. Its transformation temperature is about 1650 F; therefore it must be hardened from at least 1700 F to ensure that the transformation temperature is crossed and the steel is definitely in the austenite range.

The boundary diagram for a 15% chromium steel shows that a steel containing 15% chromium, 0.15% carbon, and no other alloying elements would not be martensitic. The ferrite region persists at all temperatures up to the melting point, and there is no transformation temperature. Finally, the boundaries for a 19% chromium steel show that the austenite region has nearly disappeared: if such a steel is to be hardened, the carbon content must be very closely controlled, and so must the heat-treating temperature. Type 430 stainless steel, containing 14 to 18% chromium and a maximum of 0.12% carbon is without an austenite region and the accompanying transformation temperature. It is a ferritic stainless steel and cannot be hardened by heat treatment.

Because chromium raises the transformation temperature, all the martensitic stainless steels have hardening temperatures in the range 1700 to 1850 F. The ferritic stainless steels cannot be hardened, since they lack an austenite phase. The austenite stainless steels cannot be hardened because they lack a ferrite phase. The martensitic stainless steel, like the plain carbon steels, have two phases and may thus be hardened. Although these statements are generally true, there are, as always, some exceptions. The austenitic stainless steels will work-harden: this is the effect of some martensite transforming from austenite. Again, austenitic weld beads are not entirely immune from cracking without a small percentage of ferrite, and welding rods and wires are supplied with a composition to produce just the right amount of ferrite in the weld bead to protect against cracking.

The phase change from austenite to ferrite promotes a fine-grained structure in any steel. This phase change is absent with ferritic stainless steels. Heating or welding of such steels produces large grains, which contribute to brittleness.

The austenitic stainless steels, being very low-carbon steel, are easily carburized by contact with foreign material. If such materials as protective paper, marking paint, pencil marks, soap film, grease, oil, or dirt are left on the surface of these steels while they are being welded, the steel will be carburized, leading to loss of corrosion resistance and to carbide precipitation. The same effect can be produced by cleaning such stainless steels with carbon steel brushes, since small particles of the brush wire may remain on the surface. Only stainless steel brushes should be used for such cleaning.

Although carbon steels are stress-relieved at temperatures around 1200 F, this temperature, being in the range that produces carbide precipitation, is not suitable for austenitic stainless steels. Temperatures of 1600 F or higher must be used for stress-relieving these steels. Such operations as brazing must be performed above the precipitation range of 800 to 1600 F and the steel cooled as quickly as possible through this range.

7.7 heat treatment of nonferrous metals

Summing it up, we may say that to heat-treat a steel is to change the form of its carbides, a process possible because steel undergoes a phase transformation. Steels without a phase transformation, such as the ferritic and austenitic stainless steels, in general are not susceptible to heat treatment. Again, pure iron cannot be heat-treated, for although it has a phase transformation, it is without carbides.

A great many metals and alloys do not undergo phase transformation on heating. It is not possible to heat-treat them, at least in the sense of controlling the hardness, strength, and ductility of the metal. Such metals, however, may be annealed after cold working. Heat treating for hardness and strength is not possible; the only hardening methods available are cold working and alloying, two methods not available to the fabricator. Unalloyed copper, beryllium, aluminum, nickel, magnesium, titanium, zinc, and lead are without phase changes below their melting points.

Other unalloyed metals have more than one solid phase. Zirconium, one of the metals used to enclose nuclear fuels, is close-packed hexagonal up to 1570 F and body-centered cubic above this temperature. Cobalt, chromium, thorium, and uranium all have two or more phases. Plutonium, with six phases between room temperature and 900 F, is a chameleon of a metal. In general these phase changes are not useful for heat treating. These metals will form carbides, but this characteristic too is of little assistance for heat treatment; the carbides are insufficient and unstable, the metal-carbon alloy is too brittle, or there are other reasons.

Only one industrial alloy of importance can be heat-treated similarly to the steels—aluminum bronze with a composition 10% aluminum, 90% copper. With furnace cooling this alloy gives an annealed structure like pearlite and may be quenched to a martensitic structure for strength and hardness.

Most of the nonferrous metals and alloys are not heat-treatable. The few that are are heat-treated in a process different from those applicable to steel, with the exception of 10% aluminum bronze just mentioned. The most important of these heat-treatable nonferrous alloys, aluminum bronze excepted, are

> beryllium copper (2% beryllium)
> aluminum 4% copper
> aluminum zinc
> magnesium 6% aluminum
> magnesium zinc
> alloys of titanium

The method of hardening these alloys is termed *age hardening*. Two stages are required to produce the hardening, solution heat treatment and aging. Like most metals, these alloys may be softened by annealing. The method of age hardening will be explained for aluminum alloy 2024 (in Canada 24S), a high-strength aluminum containing 4.5% copper plus lesser constituents.

Figure 40 is a part of the phase diagram for copper alloys of aluminum. At 1018 F aluminum can dissolve a maximum of 5.65% copper. On slow cooling, aluminum can dissolve progressively less copper, as shown by the bottom phase line. The κ (Greek letter kappa) phase is a solution of copper in aluminum. The θ (Greek letter theta) phase is

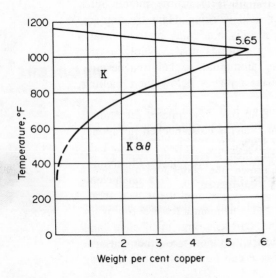

Fig. 40 Phase diagram for aluminum alloyed with copper.

the intermetallic compound $CuAl_2$. Now suppose that the 2024 aluminum with 4.5% copper is heated to 1000 F into the kappa region. The 4.5% copper is held in solution in the aluminum, a solid metal dissolved in another solid metal. If the alloy is then slowly cooled back to room temperature, almost all the copper must come out of solution, or "precipitate," dispersed throughout the alloy. For maximum hardness, however, the alloy must be solution-heat-treated, or quenched rapidly. This freezes the solution, holding the copper as a supersaturated solution. But the metal is not in its hardest condition after solution heat treatment. The hardening comes in the aging, when over a period of hours or days the supersaturated copper gradually comes out of solution to form copper aluminide, $CuAl_2$. Aging occurs naturally at room temperature and may be delayed by the use of low temperatures. By means of age hardening, the ultimate tensile strength of 2024 aluminum may be doubled, from 32,000 to 64,000 psi.

If 2024 aluminum were to be fusion-welded (not a recommended practice), age hardening would take place somewhere in the heat-affected zone. This might be advantageous. In the area of the weld, however, the metal would be taken beyond the proper temperature for age hardening, or as the term is, be "overaged." For age hardening, close control over temperature is necessary, because overaging would soften the alloy. If such an alloy were welded and maximum strength was a requirement, the whole weldment would have to be age-hardened after fusion welding.

The other age-hardenable nonferrous alloys have the same characteristics and follow the same heat-treating procedures. All show a decreasing solubility curve with lower temperatures. As an example, copper with 2% beryllium may be age-hardened to the remarkable strength level of 220,000 psi, but this is an unusual figure. Some of the titanium alloys may be age-hardened to similar strength levels.

PROBLEMS

1 The village blacksmith had an interesting method, which is still occasionally used, of heat-treating a cold chisel. He heated the chisel to a cherry red, then quenched it about one inch back from the cutting edge. The rest of the chisel remained red hot. This heat then reheated the point of the chisel. When the cutting edge turned brown, the chisel was quenched a second time. Explain how this process heat-treated the cold chisel.

2 In what respects are the hardening of steels and the hardening of nonferrous heat-treatable alloys similar?

3 Explain why a plain carbon steel is not suited for cutting tools at temperatures above 300 to 400 F.

4 A carbon-steel drill bit has a Rockwell C hardness of 60. Suppose that during a heavy drilling cut the point of the drill turns purple. Using the graph of Fig. 37, estimate how many points of hardness the bit has lost.

5 What difference in cooling treatment will produce a hardened, a normalized, and an annealed carbon steel?

6 What is the ratio of ferrite grains to pearlite grains in a 0.60% carbon steel?

7 A steel was heated at much too high a temperature for hardening, and after quenching the hardness was Rockwell 58 instead of 65. Explain what happened.

8 A steel contains 15% chromium, 0.2% carbon, and no other alloying elements. Explain why this steel cannot be hardened by heat treatment.

9 Estimate the hardening temperature for the following steel, using Fig. 39: 15% chromium, 0.4% carbon.

10 Magnesium will dissolve 12.7% aluminum at 818 F, decreasing to 3.2% at 400 F. Can a magnesium-6% aluminum alloy be heat-treated?

Aluminum is second to steel in annual consumption. Further, the market for aluminum expands at a faster rate than that for any other metal, except possibly the stainless steels. This market growth is explained by the favorable properties of aluminum, the most important of which are light weight, excellent corrosion resistance, excellent formability, variety of finishing effects, high electrical conductivity, and for some of the aluminum alloys, great strength. Pure aluminum melts at 1215 F, and its numerous alloys at slightly lower temperatures. The crystal structure of aluminum is face-centered cubic, indicative of great ductility.

Compared with steel, aluminum has a third the modulus of elasticity, weighs a third as much, and costs about three times as much per pound. Its coefficient of expansion is twice that of steel, a disadvantageous characteristic and the cause of warping during fusion welding.

No doubt aluminum is at its very best in transportation equipment. Aircraft, buses, railroad, cars, and dump-truck bodies are now made of aluminum, and even the use of an aluminum submarine is being assessed. Transportation equipment must carry its own dead weight plus a revenue-producing load. If the equipment itself is made of aluminum, it will be lighter, and the saving in weight can be passed to the revenue-producing cargo.

ALUMINUM,

THE

TRANSPORTATION METAL

8

8.1 extraction of aluminum

The most abundant material in the earth's crust is silica, and next to silica, alumina. Alumina comprises about 15% of the earth's crust and is even present in clay in the form of about 8% aluminum metal. It is therefore not possible for the human race to become short of aluminum ore, since every farm is a potential mine.

Aluminum extracted from clay is not the cheapest, however. Extraction costs are lowest for bauxite ore, a type of alumina found in tropical areas such as Jamaica. Alumina is a much more stable oxide than iron oxide, which accounts for the greater cost of aluminum as compared with steel. Coke will not reduce alumina to aluminum in a blast furnace; instead, electrical refining methods which require enormous amounts of electric energy, about 10 kwhr per lb of aluminum produced, must be used. Although Canada is completely without economical aluminum ores, it has a plentiful supply of hydro power sites, making it the site for large aluminum smelting industries.

About four pounds of alumina are needed to produce a pound of aluminum. The reduction of the alumina is carried out in electrolytic cells. Alumina does not conduct electricity, but cryolite, a conductive aluminum ore, is added to the alumina for conductivity. A mixture of these two ores is thus the electrolyte for the cell. Carbon electrodes made from petroleum coke bring current into the electrolytic cell, and under the influence of the electric current, the alumina separates into aluminum and oxygen. The molten aluminum is tapped off from the bottom of the cell periodically.

8.2 designation
of aluminum alloys

The aluminum alloys are classified into two groups: the casting alloys and the wrought alloys. The wrought alloys can be rolled, extruded, drawn, and forged. For the wrought alloys, two numbering systems are in use in Canada and the United States, both, however, based on the principal alloying element. In Canada a one- or two-number system is common, the number being followed by the letter S to designate a wrought alloy. In the United States a four-digit system is preferred. The following tabulation compares the two systems:

99.6% minimum aluminum purity	1S	1060
99.0% minimum aluminum putity	2S	1100
manganese alloy	3S–9S	3xxx
copper alloy	10S–29S	2xxx

silicon alloy	30S–39S	4xxx
magnesium alloy	50S–69S	5xxx
magnesium and silicon alloy	50S–69S	6xxx
zinc alloy	70S–79S	7xxx

Pure aluminum is a soft metal of low strength and remarkable ductility. The manganese alloys contain about 1% manganese, which has the effect of increasing the ultimate tensile strength about 50%. The magnesium and silicon alloys are not heat-treatable and have strengths of about 40,000 psi. The magnesium alloys are also the best weldable grades. Finally, the copper and zinc alloys are the very high strength heat-treatable grades of aluminum. In general, corrosion resistance is impaired by alloying, though the magnesium and silicon alloys have good corrosion resistance. The high-strength alloys are not especially ductile unless specially heat-treated for ductility and cannot be bent sharply.

The heavier aluminum weldments are often fabricated from plate of 5154 (C54S) or 5056 (56S). The following alloys are available as welding wire or rod:

1100 (2S)		
4043 (33S)	4.5–6.0	silicon
3035 (35S)	11–13	silicon
5056 (56S)	4.5–5.5	magnesium

Special wire is also available in 1060 and 5154 (54S) alloys.

The temper designation follows the alloy designation, 65S-T6 for example. A "temper" in this case is a condition produced in the metal by mechanical working or thermal treatment; the aluminum tempers are produced either by cold working or age hardening or both. Only the zinc and copper alloys may be heat-treated by age hardening.

The wrought alloys that are not heat-treatable may be supplied in the "O" or annealed temper, or the "F" or as-fabricated temper. The mechanical properties are not guaranteed in the "F" temper. Other tempers are

H1 work-hardened only
H2 work-hardened and partially annealed
H3 work-hardened and stabilized

There may also be a second digit in the temper designation, such as H14. This second digit indicates the degree of work hardening:

1. eighth-hard
2. quarter-hard
4. half-hard
6. three-quarters hard
8. hard
9. extra hard

Thus H14 indicates that the aluminum is work-hardened only and is in the half-hard condition.

The heat-treatable alloys such as 24S (2024) may also be supplied in heat-treated condition. The heat-treated tempers are indicated by "T." Except for resistance welding, the heat-treatable alloys are almost never welded, and filler metals for these alloys may be considered to be unavailable.

Aluminum casting alloys are available for sand casting, permanent mold casting, and die casting. The casting alloys are designated by a two- or three-digit number, such as 43 or 355. The usual alloying elements in the casting alloys are silicon, copper, and magnesium, and the amount of the alloying elements usually is greater than that in the wrought alloys, a factor that makes the casting alloys more difficult to weld in

Fig. 41 (a) Heating small aluminum alloy billets for extrusion.

Fig. 41 (b) A silicon alloy of aluminum, in the as-cast condition. The gray crystals are silicon.

general. Alloy 108, 4% copper, 3% silicon, accounts for about a third of all sand castings produced, and alloys of about 7% copper, 2% zinc, 2% silicon represent another third. About a third of all permanent mold castings are represented by alloy 132 with 12% silicon, and another third are 319 with 6% silicon. About 80% of aluminum die castings are alloy 380, an $8\frac{1}{2}\%$ silicon alloy. The difference between a sand casting, a permanent mold casting, and a die casting can usually be determined from the general appearance of the casting.

Most of the wrought alloys are produced as sheet, plate, tubing, pipe, wire, rod, bar, and extrusions. Structural aluminum extrusions are available at least as large as 8 by 8 by $\frac{5}{8}$-in. angle, 12-in. channel, and 12-in. I beams. The extruded aluminum shapes as used on buses, aluminum windows and doors, and building entrances are perhaps the most familiar and widespread applications of aluminum. Most of these extruded shapes are made of alloy 6063 (50S), 0.45 to 0.85% Mg, 0.20 to 0.60% Si.

The heat-treatable alloys such as 2024 (24S, 4.5% copper) are not especially corrosion resistant, and for better resistance to corrosion are often supplied as "Alclad" in sheet form. An Alclad alloy sheet has a thin surface layer of pure aluminum on one or both sides of the sheet. The Alclad layer is about 5% of the sheet thickness. Occasional scratches in the Alclad layer do not impair the resistance to corrosion of the sheet.

8.3 anodizing of aluminum

Anodizing is a finishing process applied to aluminum and magnesium and their alloys. Since anodizing raises some problems for the welder, it merits discussion here.

Because all aluminum has a naturally acquired coating of aluminum oxide, the metal has an excellent corrosion resistance. Anodizing is an electrochemical process of thickening the oxide film on aluminum and may be done for a variety of reasons, such as improved abrasion and corrosion resistance or decoration. A plain anodized coat, such as is often used on architectural sheet and extrusions, causes very little change in the appearance of the aluminum and would not be noticed by uninformed persons. Often, however, the anodized surface is impregnated with pigments to give decorative effects; the large, self-supporting aluminum ashtrays found in reception areas in public buildings may be anodized and pigmented with gold.

The electrolytic bath for anodizing is usually sulfuric acid, and the aluminum article is the anode. Large currents at low voltages are used.

The resulting appearance of the anodized coating depends to some degree on the alloy, thus if there is much silicon in the aluminum, the article will anodize to a darker shade. If aluminum is welded with a filler metal of different composition from the parent metal, this difference will appear as a color contrast to which buyers and architects take exception. The heat of welding will also produce tinting in the heat-affected zone. In addition to the above difficulties, anodizing does not hide imperfections such as scratches, and these must be buffed out before submitting the article for anodizing.

Fabrication of aluminum articles to be anodized should therefore not be commenced before consultation with the anodizer. Failure to comply with the anodizer's requirements may require that the anodized coating be removed and that the article be refabricated and reanodized. Heat tints due to welding may sometimes be removed by heating the whole anodized article. If possible, welding should be done only on the underneath or hidden side.

We have already discussed the two major structural metals, steel, with its strength, hardness, and stiffness, and aluminum, the lightweight structural metal. This chapter includes all the other nonferrous metals, the uses of which may be summed up in the following capsule statements. *Nickel* and *lead* are at least as versatile as steel, their applications ranging widely throughout industry. The uses of *copper* stem chiefly from its high conductivity for heat and electricity. *Magnesium* and *titanium* are light metals competing with aluminum in application. *Zinc* is found in brasses, die castings, and galvanized steel sheet. The *refractory metals*, beryllium, columbium, molybdenum, tantalum, tungsten, zirconium, and others, are useful for their high melting points. Certain of the *radioactive metals*, notably iridium-192 and cobalt-60, are used to photograph welded joints. Finally the *rare earths*, which are metals and not earths and are not really rare, are only now finding industrial uses.

9.1 nickel and its alloys

The place of nickel in our technical civilization may be summed up by the statement that this metal takes care of a very wide range of problems in corrosion resistance, instrument work, metal joining, cryogenics (very low-temperature work), and high-temperature applications. It is a most unusual metal in that it is equally useful both at extremely low and

METALS

FOR

SPECIAL PURPOSES

9

extremely high temperatures, being found in pressure vessels containing lox (liquid oxygen) on the one hand and in gas turbine engines at 1800 F red heat on the other (Fig. 42). Nickel is a face-centered cubic metal, quite ductile and workable, corrosion- and heat-resistant. Tensile strength, modulus of elasticity, melting point, specific heat, and magnetic properties of nickel are roughly the same as the corresponding properties of steel.

Canada supplies about 80% of the nickel consumed by the non-Communist world, about two-thirds of this production being shipped to the United States. The largest ore bodies are the nickel-copper sulfide ores of the Sudbury district of Ontario. Sulfur compounds are corrosive

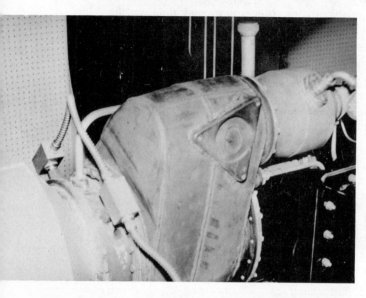

Fig. 42 (a) Welded nickel alloy combustion chamber on a 60 hp gas turbine engine. The soundproofing on adjacent walls should be noted.

Fig. 42 (b) Monel (nickel-copper alloy). The presence of groups of parallel lines (called "twins") identifies this alloy as face-centered cubic.

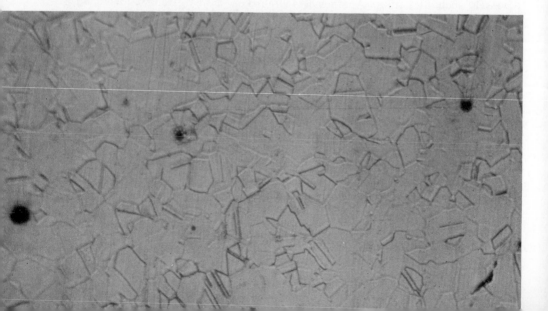

to nickel, and it is interesting that the Sudbury ores are sulfides of nickel. About 80% of annual nickel consumption is used for the production of ferrous and nonferrous alloys, such as the austenitic stainless steels, the low-nickel steels, nickel coppers, and others. Because nickel readily forms solid solutions with other metals such as copper and iron, it is a highly useful alloy metal.

Nickel and the high-nickel alloys are embrittled by minute amounts of lead, sulfur, and phosphorus. Before welding or heating such alloys, all grease, oil, lubricants, paint, marking crayons and inks, and cleaning compounds and dirt must be removed, since any of these may include harmful elements. The paint may have a lead base, and many cutting oils have a sulfur base. Some of these high-nickel alloys may also be embrittled if contaminated by small amounts of iron. In addition, the high-temperature alloys of nickel must be completely free of welding slag, because at red heats nickel is rapidly corroded by nickel slag.

The low-nickel steels such as AISI 2300, 4300, T-1, and others, have already been discussed. In these steels the nickel addition acts as a ferrite strengthener and toughener. The most important group of high-nickel steels is the 300 series stainless steels, in which the nickel stabilizes the austenite against phase transformation. There is a considerable range of other high nickel steels, including 9% nickel steel plate for low-temperature pressure vessels, and cast stainless steels with 1 to 65% nickel for heat or corrosion resistance. By and large, it is difficult to imagine a steel technology without nickel.

Among the considerable number of high-nickel alloy metals the following are perhaps the most important:

1. The nearly pure nickels, used for corrosion-resistant plate, castings, and bar, and instrument parts such as vacuum tube components, magnetostrictive transducers, and springs. Nickel 200 (A Nickel) is a commonly used member of this group, particularly in the chemical and soap industries for the construction of heating coils and heating vessels such as kettles. Another is Duranickel, a high-strength low-alloy nickel that is age-hardenable.
2. The Monels, about two-thirds nickel and one-third copper. Both copper and nickel occur together in the ore, and the Monels are directly produced from the ore without separation of the two metals.
3. The Hastelloys, alloys of nickel, molybdenum, and iron, for resisting acid attack. Recently the Hastelloys have been fabricated into combustion chambers for gas turbine engines.
4. The Nimonics, approximately 80% nickel and 20% chromium, chiefly used as superalloys for gas turbine engines.
5. Electrical, magnetic, and instrument alloys, which need not be discussed here. These include the famous Invar, an alloy of 36% nickel and 64% iron, with a coefficient of expansion of almost zero.

6. Filler metals for welding purposes, which will be discussed in the next chapter.
7. The Inconels, usually age-hardenable, outstanding in their ability to resist temperature cycling between 0 and 1600 F without thermal cracking. Inconel X-750 was used to build the fuselage of the Bell X-15 rocket plane.
8. The high-nickel superalloys, which would include the Inconels. The so-called superalloys are complex alloys designed for strength at temperatures above 1500 F. Many, but not all, the superalloys are nickel-based. None of them have as good a performance as industry would like. The large number of superalloys developed is simply an indication of the urgency of the need for high-temperature metals and the failure to solve this pressing metallurgical problem. Probably the outstanding metallurgical failure of our times is our inability to make an alloy metal serviceable above 2000 F for extended periods of time. Here, however, nickel again provides outstanding performance, for the nickel superalloys are used within a few hundred degrees of their melting points, an achievement no other metal can match.

NICKEL-BASE ALLOYS

	Ni(+Co)	C	Mn	Fe	Al	Ti	Others
Nickel 200 (A Nickel)	99.45	0.06	0.25	0.15			
Duranickel	93.9	0.15	0.25	0.15	4.5	0.45	
Monel 400	66.0	0.12	0.90	1.35			31.5 Cu
Monel K-500 (K Monel)	65.0	0.15	0.60	1.0	2.8	0.50	29.5 Cu
Hastelloy X	50.0			22.0			28.0 Mo
Inconel 600	76.0	0.04	0.20	7.2			15.8 Cr
Inconel 718	52.5	0.04	0.20	18.0	0.6	0.8	3.0 Mo, 5 Cb, 19 Cr
Inconel X-750	73.0	0.04	0.70	6.75	0.9	2.5	0.9 Cb
Rene 41	65	0.09			1.5	3.0	11 Cu, 10 Mo, 19 Cr
Nimonic 75	75	0.10		5.0		0.4	20 Cr
TaZ-8	78.5	0.12	4% W		6.0		1 Zr, 2.5 V, 8.0 Ta

The small amounts of manganese in these alloys provide some increase in strength through the formation of manganese carbide. The more complex nickel-base alloys listed also include for carbide formation columbium, molybdenum, and tungsten, besides manganese.

The heat-treatable alloys, such as Duranickel, K-500, Rene 41, Inconel 718, and Inconel 750, are made heat-treatable by the addition of titanium and aluminum. After solution heat treatment in the range of about 2000 F (a very high temperature for heat treating), quenching, and aging, a hard intermetallic compound, $Ni_3(Al-Ti)$, precipitates. The strength of these alloys at high temperatures may be considered to be proportional to the sum of the aluminum and titanium additions. The new alloy TaZ-8 is included in this table of representative alloys, since it represents a new development, the alloying of refractory metals such as zirconium and tantalum to nickel for strength at high temperatures.

In 1962 the International Nickel Company announced an entirely new type of steel, *maraging steels* (pronounced mar-ageing). This innovation represents an ingenious development in nickel metallurgy, and discussion of it belongs here rather than in the chapter devoted to steels. Although the maraging steels have been in use only a short time, they are rapidly being accepted for a wide range of uses, including such exacting applications as aerospace vehicles and the experimental high-speed hovercraft being built for the Royal Canadian Navy. For most purposes, the maraging steels require welding.

Although it is possible to produce structural steels with tensile strengths beyond 500,000 psi, about 200,000 psi has been the practical limit for steels, because strength levels higher than this have almost no ductility whatever. The maraging steels will provide strengths at least to 300,000 psi with the limited but sufficient ductility of about 10% elongation in a 2-in. gauge length. This is made possible by a most unusual heat-treating method. To review heat-treating principles, ferrous metals are hardened by quenching to martensite from austenite, and nonferrous metals are hardened by precipitation hardening and aging to precipitate out a submicroscopic hard intermetallic compound dispersed through the softer metal, such as $Ni_3(Ti-Al)$ in the hardenable nickel alloys. The term *maraging* is an abbreviation of "martensite" and "aging," which suggests that these high-alloy steels use both methods of heat treating for strength.

The maraging steels contain at least 18% nickel (manganese may also be used in the near future), a maximum of 0.03% carbon, about 8% cobalt, about 4% molybdenum, 0.5% titanium, and 0.10% aluminum. To heat-treat a maraging steel, it is first quenched to a martensitic condition from 1500 F. Air cooling is a sufficient quench. But because of the low carbon, 0.03% maximum, an unusual martensite is produced: it is a ductile martensite, does not crack or distort during heat treating, and is actually soft enough to be machined, cold-worked, or welded. The steel is next precipitation heat-treated (maraged) at 900 F for about three hours to produce the $Ni_3(Ti-Al)$ intermetallic compound dispersion. The resulting metal will have a strength of about 300,000 psi, 10% elongation, and a hardness of about Rc 50.

Welding filler wire is commercially available for joining the maraging steels. However, experience with the welding of these steels is still limited, and procedures are still being developed for welding them. The problem is that some welding methods do not provide ductility in the weld equal to that of the parent metal. The tungsten inert gas method and the welding methods that use very high currents, such as submerged arc and electrogas welding, seem to produce the best ductilities. Maraging steels will not crack during welding, even in the maraged condition.

9.2 copper and copper alloys

The high thermal and electrical conductivity of copper makes this metal the logical choice for bus bars and other electrical conductors and for chill bars and resistance welding electrodes. Thermal conductivity of copper is almost ten times that of carbon steel. This high conductivity makes copper a difficult metal to weld, since the welding heat cannot be concentrated. Spot and seam welding on copper frequently require that the surfaces of the copper be tin-plated. The electric current-carrying grades of copper are 99.9% pure, usually electrolytic tough pitch copper (ETP) with 99.9% copper plus 0.04% oxygen. Any alloying elements increase the electrical and heat resistance of copper, but may be necessary for reasons of heat resistance, higher strength, or other requirements. Thus electrodes for resistance welders are usually alloyed with other metals to gain improved compressive strength.

Copper, like nickel, is one of the highly ductile face-centered cubic metals. It cannot be heat-treated, but strain-hardens when worked. It is annealed by quenching from a low red heat. Copper and its alloys offer the unique feature of a range of colors, from the red of copper through the yellow of high zinc brasses to the silver color of nickel brasses.

Electrolytic tough pitch copper contains about 0.04% oxygen in the form of copper oxide (Fig. 139). In wrought form, this oxide is distributed through the metal as small particles and has little effect on the properties of the copper. However, if such an oxygen-bearing copper is melted or fusion-welded, the copper oxide deposits in the grain boundaries, resulting in a weak and brittle copper. Worse still, if such a copper is gas-welded, hydrogen in the welding gas will combine with the oxygen in the copper to form steam, leaving actual voids at the grain boundaries. There is no method of rehabilitating copper that has been deteriorated by hydrogen penetration. Because of these welding considerations, tough pitch copper must be considered as unsuitable for fusion welding. For welding purposes oxygen-free or deoxidized copper is preferred, phosphorus being the most used deoxidizer.

Copper is alloyed with zinc, tin, aluminum, silicon, nickel, and beryllium to obtain higher strength levels and specific types of corrosion resistance. In particular some of these copper alloys, such as the phosphor bronzes (actually tin bronzes) and the beryllium coppers, have outstanding fatigue strengths. The beryllium copper and some of the aluminum bronzes are heat-treatable by age hardening.

The alloys of copper have a rather confusing nomenclature, which sometimes is also misleading. The phosphor bronzes contain minor amounts of phosphorus but are actually tin bronzes. Likewise, the nickel silvers are alloys of copper, nickel, and zinc containing no silver. Beryllium copper should really be termed beryllium bronze. In general, a *brass* is an alloy of copper and zinc, whereas a *bronze* is an alloy of copper and some metal other than zinc, although alloys of copper and nickel also go by the name cupronickel.

Beryllium coppers can be solution-heat-treated and aged to high strengths and hardness, 220,000 psi ultimate tensile strength and Rc 45. Such hardness makes these alloys suitable for resistance-welding electrodes. The alloys contain from 0.25 to 2.0% beryllium, often with some cobalt. Oxidizing conditions during welding or brazing will convert some of the beryllium to highly refractory beryllia.

Copper will dissolve 2.1% beryllium at 1600 F, and less than 0.25% at room temperature. By quenching from 1200 to 1600 F, a supersaturated solution of beryllium in copper, which can be aged to give the high-strength levels mentioned above, is developed at room temperature.

Copper and nickel are completely soluble in each other, so that an unlimited number of copper-nickel alloys containing from zero to 100% nickel are possible. Such alloys go by a variety of names. If the percentage of nickel exceeds the percentage of copper, the alloy will be called a *Monel*. If the nickel content ranges from 12% to 30%, the alloy will then be termed a *cupronickel*. Aluminum bronzes contain 4 to 11% aluminum. The aluminum bronzes with 8 to 11% aluminum can be heat-treated like the steels, giving a pearlitic condition on slow cooling and a hand martensitic condition on quenching, with tensile strengths exceeding 100,000 psi.

The silicon bronzes, sometimes using the trade names Everdur and Herculoy, usually contain less than 5% silicon. These are the strongest of the work-hardening copper alloys. Under welding heats, oxidation of the silicon to silica must be prevented.

The *tin bronzes* are called phosphor bronzes. These have a phosphorus content of less than 0.5% and 1 to 11% tin.

The *silver solders* are alloys of copper, silver, and zinc. These will be discussed in the chapter devoted to soldering and brazing.

9.3 the brasses

A part of the phase diagram for the copper-zinc brasses is shown in Fig. 43. The crystal structure of copper is face-centered cubic, and that of zinc is hexagonal close-packed. The alpha brass phase is a solution of up to 39% zinc dissolved in copper, and being predominantly copper, is face-centered cubic. The beta phase, richer in zinc, is a body-centered cubic solution, in which copper and zinc atoms are randomly disposed at the various locations in the bcc space lattice. On cooling below 849 F, an ordered beta prime structure appears, still bcc but with copper atoms at the corners of the unit cubes and zinc atoms at the centers of the cubes. This is called a superlattice and cannot be used for heat-treating purposes.

The addition of zinc increases *both* the strength and the ductility of the metal: note that it is usual for the ductility to decrease if the strength is increased in a metal. The zinc is a low-boiling-point metal,

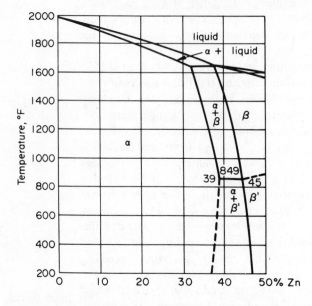

Fig. 43 (a)   Copper-zinc phase diagram for red and yellow brasses.

Fig. 43 (b)   Cast copper. This dendritic (treelike) structure is characteristic of cast metals. If this casting is rolled or otherwise wrought, it will then show the grain structure of the other photomicrographs in this book.

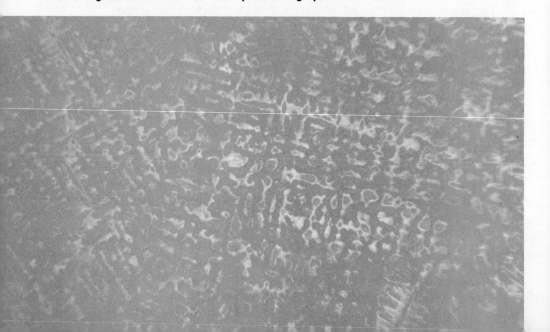

and to prevent loss of zinc the brasses must be oxyacetylene-welded, resistance-welded, or brazed.

The alpha brasses vary in color from red for high copper alloys to yellow at about 35% zinc. The red alpha brasses have the better corrosion resistance. The alpha-plus-beta brasses are more difficult to cold-work than the alpha brasses but are easily hot-worked.

COMPOSITION OF THE BRASSES

	Copper	Zinc	Tin
Alpha Brasses			
electrolytic tough pitch copper	99.9 +	0.04%	oxygen
oxygen-free copper	99.9		
gilding metal	95	5	
commercial bronze	90	10	
red brass	85	15	
low brass	80	10	
admiralty metal	71	28	1
cartridge brass	70	35	
yellow brass	65	30	
Alpha Plus Beta Brasses			
muntz metal	60	40	
naval brass	60	$39\frac{1}{4}$	0.75
forging brass	60	38	2% lead
architectural bronze	57	40	3% lead

9.4 zinc and lead

Zinc melts at 787 F and boils at 1665 F. These low temperatures call for control of heat inputs during the welding of zinc. Gas welding with a small tip on the torch is the usual method. The chief structural use of zinc is in die castings, the most important of the die casting alloys being the Zamaks with about 4% aluminum.

Pure lead melts at 621 F. Like nickel, lead has a wide variety of special applications which arise from its unusual properties. The most outstanding of its characteristics are its great density, softness, ductility, low strength, low melting point, corrosion resistance, and the ability to lubricate. The fatigue strength of lead is poor, and failure by fatigue cracking is to be expected under vibration conditions. The principal uses of lead include

1. biological shielding against X-rays and gamma radiation
2. lead sheathing for electric cable

3. corrosion-resistant tank linings
4. storage batteries
5. pipe and plumbing fittings
6. solder
7. bearing materials
8. low melting alloys for such uses as pipe bending

Pure lead provides better corrosion resistance and better radioactive shielding than its alloys. The presence of lighter metals in lead radioactive shielding would reduce shielding efficiency.

Most of the low-melting-point solders are alloys of lead and tin, with a maximum of 95% lead. Lead by itself cannot be used as a soldering material because of its inability to wet the surface of metals.

To increase the strength of lead, two types of lead alloys are in use: tellurium lead and antimonial lead. The addition of less than 0.1% tellurium improves the work-hardening capacity of lead. An addition of 1 to 12% antimony increases the hardness and doubles the tensile strength, but at some sacrifice in melting point.

The thickness of sheet lead is usually referred to by weight in pounds per square foot. One square foot of lead $\frac{1}{64}$-in. thick weighs 1 lb.

9.5 magnesium and its alloys

Magnesium is one of the group of light metals, which includes also aluminum, beryllium, and titanium, and like these others it combines adequate strength with its light weight. A typical industrial article of magnesium is the welded magnesium dockboard shown in Fig. 44, a warehouse article that provides access for fork-lift trucks between a loading dock and a boxcar.

In addition to its ores, magnesium is also extracted from sea water,

Fig. 44 Welded magnesium dockboards and ramps are familiar equipment in material-handling and warehousing operations. (Courtesy Magline of Canada, Ltd.)

which contains 0.5% magnesium chloride. Magnesium weighs 1 oz per cu in. and is two-thirds the weight of aluminum or one-quarter the weight of steel. Commercially pure annealed magnesium has a tensile strength of 27,000 psi, about double that of pure annealed aluminum, but has less ductility (magnesium is hcp, aluminum is fcc). The melting point of pure magnesium is 1202 F, the melting point of aluminum being only slightly higher, 1220 F. With alloying, magnesium may be used at temperatures as high as 700 F, whereas aluminum alloys have a temperature limit of about 300 F. The modulus of elasticity of magnesium, like its density, is two-thirds that of aluminum, 6.5×10^6. Crystal shape is hcp, the same as zinc, titanium, beryllium, and zirconium. Magnesium is pyrophoric when finely divided, burning with an intense white flare.

The corrosion resistance of the magnesium alloys is rather poor. Low-temperature alloys contain aluminum, zinc, manganese, or zirconium. The high-temperature alloys, for use above 300 F, contain rare earth metals such as didymium, or contain thorium, a radioactive metal; though the amount of thorium, and therefore the radioactivity, is very slight. Some of the alloys are heat-treatable. The method of designating temper in magnesium alloys is the same as that used for aluminum alloys. The alloy designation method is different, however. Alloy designations for magnesium use one or two letters representing the alloying elements present in the greatest amounts, followed by the respective percentages rounded off to whole numbers. A serial letter follows the alloy letters and numbers. Thus AZ31B indicates 3% aluminum, 1% zinc, and AM100A means 10% aluminum, less than 1% manganese. The letter representations are these:

A	aluminum	K	zirconium
C	copper	M	manganese
E	rare earths	Z	zinc
H	thorium		

Welding methods for magnesium are similar to those used with aluminum. Failure of a welded joint is usually in the heat-affected zone rather than in the weld, perhaps because of grain growth conditions.

9.6 titanium

Titanium became an industrial metal about 1954, and since then has had some ups and downs in the competitive market for metals. Chiefly used for aerospace applications, it is slowly finding other uses, such as racks for anodizing tanks and small storage tanks. It is one of the light

Fig. 45 (a) Titanium racking for supporting aluminum parts in anodizing tanks.

Fig. 45 (b) The upper bundle of rods is a group of zirconium fuel rods for a nuclear reactor. These short lengths can be connected together to produce a full-length fuel rod. (Courtesy Whiteshell Nuclear Research Establishment.)

metals for special purposes

metals, offering the highest strength-to-weight ratios in the temperature range from about 500 to 1000 F. It can often be recognized by its bluish metallic color. Figure 45(a) shows titanium racking at an anodizing plant.

The high price of titanium, over $5 a pound, is explained by the difficulties of producing the metal from its ores. The melting point is 3035 F, higher than that of steel. The liquid metal is a universal solvent for any material that comes in contact with it, solid, liquid, or gas, with the exception of the inert gases such as argon and helium. It dissolves atmospheric gases readily, all of which ruinously embrittle the metal. Molten titanium will even extract oxygen from a firebrick, and the metal cannot thus be welded on a firebrick. Welding must be done under vacuum or inert gas, and the surface of the metal must be clean of all dirt and contaminants of all kinds, including fingerprints.

Tensile strength of titanium is as high as 90,000 psi in the annealed condition, and the E value is 15×10^6 or half that of steel. Large increases in strength are possible by alloying and heat treatment, though the pure metal is not heat-treatable.

Titanium has a hcp structure at room temperature, known as alpha titanium. At 1625 F there is a change to beta titanium, which is body-centered cubic. Titanium is a powerful carbide-former in steels, but carbon in more than minute amounts seriously embrittles titanium metal. Certain alloying additions have a high solubility in the beta phase and produce a lowering of the transformation temperature to alpha. Such additions are called beta stabilizers and include hydrogen, beryllium, and silicon. Beta stabilization is similar to the action of carbon dissolved in gamma austenite, which in the same manner lowers the transformation temperature. Aluminum, carbon, oxygen, and nitrogen are alpha stabilizers; these strengthen the base metal by solid-solution strengthening, giving single-phase, non-heat-treatable alloys. Their behavior is similar to that of nickel in steel. Quenching from the beta condition gives a type of martensite. Rather large amounts of alloying additions, even exceeding 10%, are added to titanium.

9.7 beryllium

This metal has the highest strength-to-weight ratio of any metal. It is slightly heavier than magnesium, but its strength ranges up to 100,000 psi. Its modulus of elasticity is unusually high, $40–44 \times 10^6$, making it 50% stiffer than steel. Beryllium is hcp at room temperature, with a phase change to bcc at 2300 F, only 32° below its melting point. Titanium and zirconium also experience a phase change from hcp to bcc at higher temperatures.

Beryllium has some disadvantages to balance against its strength and stiffness. It costs about $60 a pound, and its dusts and compounds are dangerously toxic. Ductility is extremely low at room temperature. It must be shaped by sintering beryllium powder into billets.

One of the important properties of beryllium is its low absorption of X rays, gamma rays, and neutrons. The metal therefore serves such purposes as a "window" for X-ray tubes. Like so many other metals, beryllium obtains its corrosion resistance from the film of beryllium oxide that forms on its surface. For welding techniques, filler rod methods are not as good as desired, and brazing is the best joining method.

9.8 zirconium

Zirconium also has a hexagonal close-packed structure at room temperature—alpha zirconium—becoming body-centered cubic at 1590 F —beta zirconium. The melting point is 3366 F. The tensile strength of commercial zirconium ranges up to 100,000 psi, and its E value is 14×10^6. Sheet zirconium has somewhat the same appearance as stainless steel. Cost is of the order of $10 a pound. This metal too protects itself with its own refractory oxide, zirconia, and is especially resistant to acids. However, the metal is seriously embrittled by minute amounts of hydrogen, which collects in the heat-affected zone during welding. When fusion-welded in the presence of oxygen, bright-yellow zirconium oxide forms on the metal, even when spot-welded.

Most zirconium is fabricated into welded or brazed "cans" (i.e., container tubes) for nuclear fuels (Fig. 45b). Nuclear uranium, being a reactive metal, cannot be exposed, and zirconium makes a suitable canning material because it does not to any significant degree absorb the neutrons released by the uranium to carry on the nuclear process. Or, in the language of the nuclear trade, zirconium has a low "neutron absorption cross section."

The two most important zirconium alloys are Zircaloy-2 and zirconium-niobium. (Columbium is called niobium by scientists.) Zircaloy-2 contains 1.2 to 1.7% tin for improved corrosion resistance in nuclear applications. Since nickel promotes the absorption of hydrogen by zirconium, it is kept to the low level of 0.05%. Boron and cadmium have high neutron absorption cross sections (i.e., high absorptivity for neutrons) and are restricted to a maximum of half a part per million in zirconium alloys. Hafnium is always present in zirconium ores, up to 7%. This metal too has a high neutron absorption and likewise must be held to a low level.

Like so many of the newer metals, zirconium has a very low coefficient of expansion (0.000004). It does not present any serious warping problems when fusion-welded.

Hafnium, boron, and *cadmium* are used as alloying elements in the control rods of nuclear reactors. Because of their high absorption of neutrons, these metals remove neutrons from the nuclear reaction. Such captured neutrons are not then available for fissioning atoms. By lowering control rods containing these absorptive metals into the nuclear reactor, the operation is slowed down by starving it of neutrons.

9.9 the precious metals

Silver is used both for corrosion-resistant tank and vessel linings and as an alloying component in copper-silver-zinc brazing alloys, often called silver solders. Silver also plays a highly important role in welding inspection in the form of photosensitive silver compounds on X-ray film.

Much microwelding is done on gold, silver, platinum, palladium, and iridium wire and foil for electronic circuitry, using small desk-mounted microwelders, actually miniature spot-welding machines. Platinum and rhodium are also micro-butt-welded to form thermocouples.

9.10 the refractory metals

The refractory metals are so named because of their high melting points, tungsten leading the list with a melting point of 6170 F. In general the melting points of these metals are so high that they exceed the melting points of their oxides, a characteristic unfavorable for high-temperature operation.

THE REFRACTORY METALS

		Melting Point, F	Structure
Chromium	(Cr)	3407	bcc
Columbium	(Cb)	4474	bcc
Hafnium	(Hf)	4032	hcp
Molybdenum	(Mo)	4730	bcc
Rhenium	(Rh)	5755	hcp
Tantalum	(Ta)	5425	bcc
Tungsten	(W)	6170	bcc
Vanadium	(V)	3450	bcc

metals for special purposes

Note an intriguing mathematical relationship: melting points in general increase with alphabetical order.

Such metals can be and are welded, but the problems of ever casting them are virtually impossible. Melting on a small scale, as in welding, may be done by arcs and electron beams. Usually such metals are chemically reduced from their ores, then crushed to powder and sintered. Despite their high melting points, the refractory metals cannot be used much above 1000 F in air because they react rapidly with oxygen and other gases. Much research, largely unprofitable, has been devoted to the problem of preventing oxidation of these metals at high temperatures, since if this problem can be overcome, they offer remarkable strengths and high E values (up to 50×10^6) at all temperatures from room temperature to perhaps 3500 F.

Tungsten is a familiar member of the refractory group. Like others of the group, it is a carbide-former in tool steels. Nonconsumable electrodes for tungsten-inert gas welding are made of tungsten, either commercially pure or alloyed with zirconium or thorium. The targets (anodes) of X-ray tubes are commonly made of tungsten to take advantage of this metal's great heat resistance in a vacuum.

Molybdenum, like tungsten, has to date found a greater variety of industrial applications than the other refractory metals have. It too has remarkable strength at high temperatures but is subject to oxidation if unprotected. It does not dissolve hydrogen, an unusual characteristic. Molybdenum has a low coefficient of thermal expansion, 0.000003, and the high modulus of elasticity of 50×10^6, virtually the same as tungsten in both properties. Commonly used alloys of molybdenum are TZM with 0.5% titanium and 0.08% zirconium, molybdenum with 0.5% titanium, and Mo-30W with 30% tungsten. Among the many uses for molybdenum are injection molding dies and welding tips for spot welding.

Tantalum and *columbium*, although produced by way of powder metallurgy, are ductile at room temperature. Tantalum has almost identical corrosion resistance to glass, and most of its applications are for chemical equipment. Both metals may be resistance-welded or arc-welded with inert gases.

To complete the roster of available metals, casual mention should made of the rare earths. This group of metals actually includes about one-quarter of all the metallic elements. Their names need not be listed here, but they include such relatively unknown metals as the ferromagnetic gadolinium, neodymium, thulium, lanthanum, and others. Mixtures of the rare earths are called mischmetal, an additive to stainless steel melts to make such steels easier to roll. Some of the rare earths are in use as doping materials for lasers. Others have had limited use as radioisotopes for photographing castings and welds.

Previous references to corrosion have been only general. By corrosion we mean the deterioration or loss of metal by chemical action, and in any strict sense no metal is corrosion resistant. So-called corrosion-resisting metals such as aluminum and stainless steel, obtain their resistance by the establishment of a thin adherent oxide film developed by an actual corrosion process with oxygen. This oxide film retards or prevents further corrosion. Those metals such as carbon steel that are not corrosion-resistant develop a bulky and porous surface oxide that provides no barrier to further corrosion. Generally metals tend to revert back to their ores by means of corrosion processes, that is, an ore is a corroded metal.

Many kinds of corrosion have been distinguished. One of the commonest types of corrosion, however, is *galvanic corrosion,* the cause of which is electrical. In any wet or storage battery an anode and a cathode are connected by a liquid called an electrolyte. The anode is the one that is corroded, and this process is termed galvanic corrosion. In a storage battery galvanic corrosion is employed as a means of generating electric power. Now suppose that a small rectangular water tank using steel angle iron for the frame and sheet aluminum sides is welded up. Here we have the conditions for galvanic corrosion. The water in the tank will act as an electrolyte, one of the metals as an anode and the other as a cathode. The anode will be subject to corrosion. In this particular tank, the aluminum will act as anode and corrode away, probably near the angle iron. The corrosion proceeds by means of small electric currents circulating through the metal from the aluminum to the steel and back to the aluminum by way of the water. Just as in a storage battery, there will be a difference in voltage between the anode and the cathode in the presence of an electrolyte, and this voltage will be different for every pair of metals. Thus a dry cell and a lead battery use different pairs of metals and therefore do not produce the same voltage. The greater this voltage difference, the more rapid the corrosion will be.

The range of metals can be arranged in a galvanic series, from the most anodic to the most cathodic, this series then giving in tabular form the relative corrodability of the metals. If two metals are coupled in a galvanic pair, the most anodic will be corroded. Thus if zinc is plated on iron, such as galvanized iron, in the presence of rainwater as an electrolyte, zinc being the more anodic will corrode, and the iron will not corrode until the galvanizing is corroded away. In any strict sense a galvanic series must be set up for different electrolytes, but the differences are rather minor, and the following series for sea water may be considered to be universal in application:

Anodic, or corroded end	high copper brass
magnesium	copper
zinc	aluminum bronze
aluminum	copper and nickel alloys
cadmium	nickel
aluminum alloys	stainless steel (passive)
carbon and alloy steels	monel
cast iron	titanium
stainless steel (active)	Cathodic, or protected end
high zinc brass	

Thus the pairing of titanium and magnesium will lead to rapid corrosion of the magnesium, since the two metals are widely separated in the series. Coupling of zinc and magnesium will produce slow corrosion of the magnesium, since the two metals are very close together in the series.

If, however, the metal develops an adherent and impervious oxide, such as chromium oxide on stainless steel, this oxide will act as an electric insulator stopping flow of the galvanic current, and corrosion may then cease. On the other hand, galvanic corrosion may appear in less obvious circumstances. A deposited weld bead may have a slightly different composition from the heat-affected zone or the parent metal, less chromium perhaps, and this may cause the weld area to corrode. In carbide precipitation in austenitic stainless steels, the grain boundary regions are depleted of chromium as compared with the metal grains, and thus galvanic corrosion removes the grain boundaries. Note, however, in both the corroded weld bead and the stainless grain boundaries, in addition to being more anodic, the corroded areas are much smaller than the cathodic areas. Weld bead is only a small area of a plate, and a grain boundary is only a small portion of grain. Galvanic corrosion proceeds only very slowly if the anodic or corrodable areas are made very small in comparison with the cathodic or protected areas. In practical terms this means that if a low-chromium weld bead will be corroded, the solution to the problem is to lay down a bead rich in chromium as compared with the surrounding plate. This results in a small anodic area simply by reversing the composition. Similarly, steel rivets in a copper plate will be rapidly eaten away, but the galvanic corrosion of a steel plate with copper rivets will be a slow process.

Another type of corrosion promoted by bad welding design and technique is called concentration-cell corrosion. An example is the lap joint in the tank plates shown in Fig. 46. A bead is run on one side of the lap joint, but the bead on the inside is omitted. As a result of this omission, there is a small crevice between the plates into which the corrosive liquid will be drawn. Corrosion may subsequently appear at the entrance to the crevice.

The tendency of the metal plates to go into solution in the liquid will be influenced by the concentration of the metal in the liquid in immediate contact with the metal. If in a certain area this metal concentration is low, tendency of the metal to dissolve will be greater, or more specifically, the voltage will be higher, tending to promote corrosion. Since the liquid at the bottom of the crevice does not circulate, the concentration of metal ions will be high in the crevice and corrosion will not be promoted in the crevice as a result. At the entrance to the crevice, circulation and other factors will all tend to reduce the metal ion concentration, and it is at this point that corrosion can be expected.

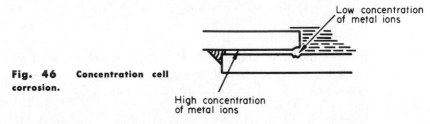

Fig. 46 **Concentration cell corrosion.**

This is concentration cell corrosion arising from a difference in metal ion concentration between two areas of the metal. This type of corrosion can arise in structures such as the above single-welded lap joint, in slip-on flanges, and in socket-welded fittings in pipe. Such corrosion is obviously prevented by welding both sides of the lap. This will not prevent corrosion but will prevent the corrosion from being concentrated at a single area and will produce a slower rate of corrosion.

The usual methods of combating corrosion are these:

1. Use of high-purity metals.
2. Proper design, as in the lap joint mentioned.
3. Cathodic protection, such as the insertion of a magnesium anode in a domestic hot water tank or the burying of a magnesium anode beside an underground steel pipeline.
4. Use of inhibitors, such as phosphate coatings on steel, chromate treatment of aluminum, Alcladding of aluminum alloys, and other such treatments.
5. Surface coatings such as paints.

9.12 toxicity of metals

A number of metals may produce toxic dusts, fumes, or compounds, and therefore fabrication of such metals is governed by regulations, statutory or otherwise. Even so, the best and most effective safety practice is a trained and informed worker.

The radioactive metal *thorium* is used as an alloying element in tungsten inert gas electrodes, in certain magnesium alloys, and in a few other applications. The amount of radioactivity produced from these small amounts of thorium is inconsequential and should be less than that received from the surrounding building, soil, and atmosphere. The matter of radiation safety is dealt with more comprehensively later in this book.

The most toxic of all metals is *beryllium,* including the oxide beryllia, and even in low concentrations its fumes and dusts are exceedingly toxic. Inhalation of minute amounts of beryllium or its compounds may produce no symptoms of poisoning for months or years, making a diagnosis of berylliosis most difficult for the physician. Beryllium has the effect of interfering with the passage of oxygen between the lungs and the blood system. Symptoms are loss of weight, coughing, and shortness of breath. A few antibiotic drugs will produce remissions of the disease, but there is no cure. Careful and exceedingly thorough ventilation is required to prevent exposure to beryllium, because, to quote the sober medical phrase, "the prognosis is grave."

Cadmium compounds, including the oxide produced in welding or brazing, are poisonous. The use of cadmium in brazing alloys is prohibited in food-processing equipment and so is cadmium plating. Welders can be poisoned by inhaling cadmium fumes, a circumstance that often arises because cadmium plating is assumed to be a galvanized zinc. There are no effects for a few hours, and without symptoms a worker may persist in breathing the fumes. Finally, he will cough and have difficulty in breathing. Complete recovery from cadmium attack is to be expected, except of course for cases resulting from long-continued or very heavy exposure. Suitable ventilation is a sufficient protection.

Considerable exposure to *lead* fumes over a long period of time is required before symptoms of lead poisoning will develop. However, this is no argument against the use of proper ventilation and other protective practices. Inhaled lead may be deposited in most types of body tissue: blood, muscles, kidneys, and nervous system are most seriously injured. Certain chemicals are available for the treatment of lead poisoning. These form compounds of lead which can be excreted by the body.

The breathing of *zinc* fumes is a rather familiar accident in welding. The welder becomes temporarily ill but recovers the next day. There are no lasting effects.

Unfortunately, many of the exhaust ventilation arrangements in welding shops are inadequate. The relative effectiveness of air supply and air exhaust openings is shown in Fig. 47, which is taken from *Industrial Ventilation* by the American Conference of Governmental Industrial Hygienists. The figure shows that air can be blown thirty

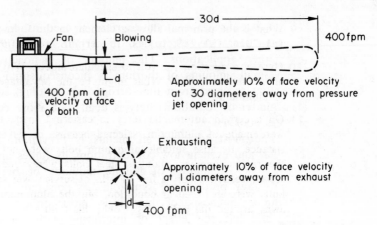

Fig. 47 Relative effectiveness of ventilation by supply and exhaust openings.

times farther than the distance from which it can be exhausted. If an exhaust hood is to exhaust the fumes of arc welding, it is unlikely to be effective unless positioned not more than about a foot from the arc.

PROBLEMS

1 List as many uses of nickel in industry as you can think of.

2 A material obtains its stiffness from its modulus of elasticity, and for structural metals a modulus of elasticity of 15×10^6 or more is desirable. How many metals do you know of which meet this requirement?

3 In what respect could you argue that the following metals are misnamed?
(a) commercial bronze   (c) beryllium copper
(b) nickel silver   (d) architectural bronze

4 What difficulties would you expect in resistance-welding lead?

5 How thick is 8-oz sheet lead?

6 Why must lead used for radioactive shielding be commercially pure?

7 Alpha brass is face-centered cubic like copper, and beta brass is body-centered cubic. If the zinc content of brass is enriched in zinc beyond the zinc content of beta brass, what would you expect the crystal structure to be?

8 Give the alloy content of the following magnesium alloys:
(a) ZH42   (d) A3A
(b) EX33A   (e) ZK60B
(c) AZ61A

9 What is the principal alloying element in the following aluminum alloys: (a) 2014, (b) 28S, (c) 6061, (d) 71S, (e) 7079.

10 Here is a question for you to speculate about. Why have you never seen an aluminum bridge? What might be the advantages of building bridges of aluminum?

11 On a certain automobile ferry in eastern Canada the automobile ramps were made of aluminum, selected because of its excellent corrosion resistance. Because suitable aluminum bolts were not available for bolting the ramps together, stainless steel bolts were used, again for corrosion resistance. After only a few months of service over salt water, the stainless bolts were in excellent condition, but the aluminum frame was corroded away around the bolt holes. Could this failure have been predicted?

The subject of the previous several chapters has been welding metallurgy, the necessary foundation for the understanding of the welding processes since it explains the reasons behind the varied techniques of welding. Having dealt with the complex behavior of metals under the influence of welding heats, we turn from the metal to be welded to the electrodes and filler metal that makes the welding bead. Sometimes the electrode and the filler metal are one and the same, sometimes not:

carbon arc welding	carbon nonconsumable electrode and metal filler rod
gas welding	filler rod, no electrode
manual arc welding	the filler rod is the electrode
tungsten inert gas welding	tungsten nonconsumable electrode and metal filler rod
metal inert gas welding	continuously fed wire is both the electrode and the filler metal
submerged arc welding	continuously fed wire is both the electrode and the filler metal
electron beam welding	no filler rod used

10.1 nonconsumable electrodes

Ideally, a nonconsumable electrode is not melted away by the heat of arc welding. In practice the intense heat of the arc causes continued

WELDING ELECTRODES,
RODS,
AND WIRES

10

slow loss of a nonconsumable electrode. The usual materials employed for such electrodes in arc welding are carbon and tungsten, both of which remain in the solid state beyond a temperature of 6000 F, and in resistance welding, copper alloys.

Carbon electrodes are employed in such welding and cutting methods as carbon arc welding and the Arcair cutting method. Either one or two carbon electrodes, ranging in diameter from $\frac{5}{32}$ to $\frac{5}{8}$ in. may be used. Although the carbon is not deposited as filler metal, these electrodes are not true nonconsumable electrodes since protection of the weld metal is obtained from the carbon monoxide and carbon dioxide generated by the slow oxidation of the carbon electrode. Straight polarity is used. Two-thirds of the arc heat is produced at the anode; in reverse polarity this intense heat would carry considerable amounts of carbon into the weld metal and produce extreme brittleness. For the same reason the carbon electrode must not touch the weld metal: the result is always a hard spot. Carbon arc welding is chiefly employed in welding thin sheets, with or without a filler rod.

Tungsten electrodes find their chief employment in atomic hydrogen welding and TIG welding. In atomic hydrogen welding the arc is drawn between two tungsten electrodes in an atmosphere of hydrogen. The use of hydrogen, a reactive gas, restricts the usefulness of this welding method. Tungsten inert gas welding, also called gas tungsten arc welding, uses one tungsten electrode and the workpiece as the other electrode in an inert atmosphere of argon. Carbon dioxide cannot be used as the shielding gas because it converts the tungsten electrode to tungsten carbide. The tungsten electrodes are sold usually ten to a carton, in lengths of 3, 6, 7, or 18 in., and in diameters 0.020, 0.040, $\frac{1}{16}$, $\frac{3}{32}$, $\frac{1}{8}$, $\frac{5}{32}$, $\frac{3}{16}$, and $\frac{1}{4}$ in. They are supplied either cleaned or ground, since the presence of any processing lubricants or compounds, even in very small amounts, would cause difficulties, such as porosity in the weld, contamination, and arc sputter.

One of the problems of TIG welding is the contamination of the weld metal by tungsten from the electrode and of the electrode by the weld metal. The presence of weld metal in the tungsten electrode will have an alloying effect that will lower the melting point, in effect making the electrode consumable, and of course make for poor arc characteristics. Tungsten electrodes are available in at least four types. Pure tungsten is cheapest but is most susceptible to contamination. The alloyed electrodes with 1% thorium oxide, 2% thorium oxide, or 1% zirconium oxide are much more resistant to contamination and in addition can carry higher currents. Thoriated tungsten has a higher electron emissivity, resulting in easier arc starting and a more stable arc. This material gives best results with DCSP and has about 20% higher current capacity than pure tungsten, though it is not suitable for welding aluminum. Zirconiated tungsten is used chiefly for a.c. welding.

Resistance welding electrodes The electrodes used in resistance welding must carry current to the sheet metal being spot-welded and must also apply considerable pressure to hold the welded sheets together and forge the weld nugget. Such electrodes must combine two incompatible requirements: highest electrical conductivity and high compressive strength and hardness to avoid deforming. Electrode forces may run as high as 3000 lb for spot-welding heavy gauges of sheet, and currents may be as high as 100,000 amp or more. Now it is true that the pure metal provides the best electrical conductivity and alloying provides the greatest strength. For spot-welding electrodes, it is thus necessary to use alloys of copper that offer the best compromise between these two requirements.

In addition to wear and abrasion, these electrodes can pick up dirt and oxides. Such impurities interfere with current flow, leading to local overheating and subsequent deterioration. Alloying of the electrodes can result from pickup of zinc, tin, and other metals from the material being spot-welded. Such alloying increases the electrical resistance of the electrode and is thus another cause of overheating.

Copper-alloy electrodes for resistance welding are produced in three types. Class 1 alloys are cold-worked to obtain their strength and hardness. Cadmium copper is a typical class 1 alloy. Such alloys if overheated to a high enough temperature will be annealed. Class 2 alloys have electrical and strength characteristics intermediate between class 1 and class 3, an example being chromium copper. Class 3 alloys are heat-treatable and have the highest strength and hardness, combined necessarily with the lowest electrical conductivity. Heat-treatable cobalt-beryllium copper is the most usual of class 3. The class 2 group are more commonly used than the other grades are. All spot-welding tips have No. 1, 2, or 3 Morse taper shanks for attachment and internal water passages for cooling.

In addition to the copper-alloy electrodes, the refractory metals are used for extreme service conditions. Such electrodes may be sintered copper-tungsten, copper-tungsten carbide (the carbides are electrical conductors), and commercially pure tungsten and molybdenum. Where heating and alloying will give excessive deterioration in service, tungsten-tipped or molybdenum-tipped electrodes may be used. These have a $\frac{3}{16}$- or $\frac{1}{4}$-in.-thick facing of refractory metal.

10.2 welding rods for the manual arc welding of mild steels

Manual arc welding is still the most widely used of the many welding processes. For this process excellent flux-coated rods that can normally produce weld having physical properties exceeding those of the parent metal are available. Such rods are available for almost all conceivable circumstances, including poor fit-up, underbead cracking, fast freeze, fast deposition rate, thin sheet and thick plate, and for all types of position welding.

In earlier times manual arc welding was done with bare wire, including barbed wire. Edward R. Pierre of Miller Electric Manufacturing Company suggests that the use of coated rods may have developed from the discovery that a more stable arc was obtained from rusty wire. The flux coat supplies required arc characteristics and is the source of the slag usually necessary in any melting of metals. The flux coat further provides various inert atmospheres, such as the carbon monoxide in cellulose coatings. Sometimes alloying elements are added to the flux, and certain rods also have iron powder in the coating for the purpose of increasing the rate of deposition of metal. Thus the electrode coating nowadays must serve a very great number of functions. Other requirements of the coating are that it must have a slightly lower melting point than the rod and that the slag must have a low enough specific gravity to float on the molten metal. For position welding, the slag must have a fast-freeze characteristic. By and large, then, the differences in the welding characteristics of manual arc electrodes must be attributed to the different types of coatings used, since any differences in the core wire are rather minor by comparison. Such wire is approximately SAE 1010 steel, and the carbon content usually less than 0.15%.

The American Welding Society classifies the carbon steel electrodes for arc welding in a four-digit numbering system preceded by the letter E for "electric." The first two digits give the minimum tensile strength of the deposited metal in thousands of pounds. Thus an E6010 rod will deposit metal exceeding 60,000 psi ultimate tensile strength; E7018 will exceed 70,000 psi. The third digit is a 1 or a 2; Exx10 to Exx19 signify all-position rods for flat, horizontal, vertical, or overhead welding, whereas Exx20 to Exx29 signify a rod suited only to flat or horizontal welding. E6030 rods are sometimes available, and here the 3 signifies the flat position only. Since 6030 rods are in competition with automatic submerged arc welding in heavy plate, their use is not common nowadays.

The fourth digit does not indicate any single piece of information but must be explained by the following tabulation of properties:

Last Digit	0	1	2	3	4	5	6	7	8
power supply (a)	a.c. or DCRP	a.c. or d.c.	a.c. or d.c.	a.c. or d.c.	DCRP	a.c. or DCRP	a.c. or d.c.	a.c. or DCRP
coating (b)	organic	rutile	rutile	rutile	low H	low H	mineral	low H

Last Digit	0	1	2	3	4	5	6	7	8
type of arc	medium	digging	digging	soft	soft	medium	medium	soft	medium
penetration	(c)	deep	medium	light	light	medium	medium	medium	medium
iron powder in coating	0–10%	none	0–10%	0–10%	30–50%	none	none	50%	30–50%

(a) 6010 is DCRP, 6020 is a.c. or d.c.
(b) 6010 is organic, 6020 is mineral.
(c) 6010 is deep penetration, 6020 is medium penetration.

The 6010 and 6011 types of rod obtain their deep penetration from hydrogen in their cellulose coating. These are called "fast-freeze" rods because of their ability to deposit metal which freezes rapidly, an important characteristic for vertical and overhead welding. The 6010 rods are DCRP for general-purpose work requiring deep penetration; for tack welding; and for general pipe, tank, and shipbuilding work and butt welds in plate. They deposit a light slag since the cellulose in the coating is all converted into gas after welding. The weld itself has a characteristic coarse ripple that might be objected to in work requiring the very best appearance. Strengths as high as about 70,000 psi and elongations of about 25% in 2 in. are obtainable from 6010 or 6011 rods. The 6011 is the equivalent of 6010, though it may also be used with DCRP. The deposit has a smoother ripple than the metal deposited from 6010 rods.

The 6012 electrodes are the best choice for joints with poor fit-up and are a good rod to learn to weld with. This rod has a rather quiet arc, and penetration is not so deep as that of 6010 or 6011. The still shallower penetration of 6013 rods makes these suitable for welding thin sheet metal without burning through. Both 6012 and 6013 have a dense slag, though slag removal is easier with 6013 rods. The 6012 rods do not produce metal as ductile as other rods do, nevertheless 6012 is a popular rod with welders. Straight polarity is preferred on d-c operation.

The coating on 6014 electrodes is thick because of the inclusion of iron powder in the coating. Deposition rate is high because of the iron powder, and the amount of deposited metal exceeds the weight of the core wire burned off. Higher currents are used on 6014 rods.

The 6015 and 6016 rods are similar, 6015 being a DCRP rod and 6016 being a.c. or DCRP. These were the first of the low-hydrogen rods, discussed below. The 6018 rods are also a low-hydrogen type, with iron powder in the coating for greater deposition rates, and are more commonly used than 6015 or 6016. The low hydrogen coating consists chiefly of calcium carbonate and silicates.

The 6020 rods are not all-position but are restricted to downhand and horizontal fillet welding. These rods are usually used with a.c. or DCSP, though some may be used with DCRP. A heavy slag is produced, but it is readily removed. Penetration is medium but is deeper at higher currents and travel speeds. Like the other xx2x rods, this rod is chiefly used for heavier work.

AWS E6024 electrodes are high-deposition-rate rods for production fillet welding. With iron powder coatings, they have a deposition rate that exceeds that of most other rods. The arc is soft and quiet and gives minimum spatter, and a smooth bead can be produced. Power supply may be a.c. and DCRP, or DCSP.

In addition to the E60xx grades, electrodes are produced in 45xx, 70xx, 80xx, and higher strengths. The most commonly used of the higher-strength rods is the low-hydrogen E7018. This electrode is used when underbead cracking in the heat-affected zone, brittle fracture, or cold-weather welding are matters of concern. The strength, ductility, and Charpy impact values of this rod are excellent. The low-hydrogen coating is chiefly lime, which in the arc releases carbon monoxide and carbon dioxide as shielding gases. The coating, however, can pick up hydrogen from moisture in the air if left exposed. Therefore these rods are packaged in sealed steel containers. If left exposed to the atmosphere for more than a short time, they must be heated to about 400 F for at least an hour. Special electrode drying ovens are available, though any suitable oven can be used for drying. It is foolish to pay for low-hydrogen rods and then allow them to pick up atmospheric water vapor. The amount of water vapor absorbed will depend on the relative humidity, but may be as much as twelve times the moisture allowed by certain specifications if humidity is high. To further avoid hydrogen pickup, the shortest possible arc should be used to avoid drawing atmospheric gases into the arc. Prevention of underbead cracking is virtually assured if all these precautions against hydrogen pickup are employed.

Selection of welding rods In brief, rod selection for various operations on mild steel is governed by the following general rules:

1. deep penetration   6011
2. pipe welding   6010
3. maximum deposition rate for horizontal fillets   6024
4. poor fit-up   6012
5. thin sheet metal   6013
6. assurance of good welds under adverse or doubtful conditions   7018

Identification of mild steel rods The AWS grades of rods can be identified by a color code marked on the end of the rod. As indicated in Fig. 48,

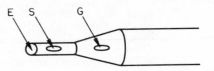

Fig. 48 Coding of manual arc rods for mild steel. See text.

two or three color spots, an end color (E), a spot color (S), and a group color (G), are used.

	E	S	G
6010	none	none	none
6011	none	blue	none
6012	none	white	none
6013	none	brown	none
6014	black	brown	none
6015	none	red	none
6016	none	orange	none
6020	none	green	none
6024	none	yellow	none
6027	none	silver	none
7010	blue	none	none
7016	blue	orange	green
7018	blue	orange	green
8020	white	green	silver
9018	violet	blue	green
9020	brown	green	silver
10020	green	green	silver
11018	red	blue	green

The higher-strength rods in this table are actually low-alloy, not mild, steels. These rods are used for welding high-strength, low-alloy steels, though the composition of the rod does not necessarily match the composition of the steel: there are too many low-alloy steels to make this a practical arrangement.

Deposition and burn-off rates A deposition rate is the rate in pounds per hour of arc time at which rod metal can be laid down in the weld bead, consistent with quality welds. For continuously fed wire instead of stick electrodes, it is usual to refer to a *burn-off rate,* the rate in pounds per hour or in inches per minute at which the wire is burned off in the arc, again consistent with quality welding. Both the deposition rate and the burn-off rate will increase with current, though if the current is excessive, weld quality will suffer from a variety of defects, such as spatter and undercut. The best method of increasing burn-off or deposition is to change to larger-diameter rods (or wire) if this is possible. Larger diameters have the additional advantage that they are cheaper per pound, since the amount of cold reduction in wire drawing during manufacture is less for large diameters.

welding electrodes, rods, and wires
145

The electrode flux coating to a large degree determines the burn-off or deposition rate. The following table shows the approximate burn-off rates for $\frac{3}{16}$-in. rods of various AWS classes:

	lb/hr
6010	4
6012	4.3
6020	5.5
6024	7.6

The rods with the highest rates have the heaviest coatings.

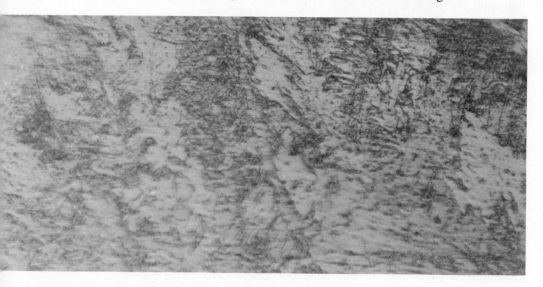

Fig. 49 (a) Deposited metal from an E 6011 welding rod. This fast-freeze rod produces fine columnar grains.
Fig. 49 (b) Deposited metal from an E 7018 rod. The grains are coarser and less sharp than those of the 6011 rod.

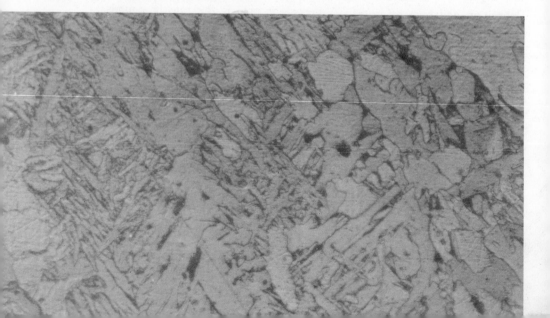

Because of stub losses and other factors, the burn-off rate for stick electrodes is higher than the rate of metal deposition. Deposition efficiency relates deposition rate to burn-off rate; if the deposition rate were equal to the burn-off rate, the deposition efficiency would be 100%, a figure not obtainable by any welding method. However, deposition efficiency can mean two things: deposition efficiency including the inevitable stub losses, or the same thing not including the stub losses. The latter method would give a considerably higher apparent efficiency, since stub losses are not small. By either method of calculating deposition efficiency, that efficiency is higher for larger diameter rods, and for the larger rods it may be as high as 75%, including stub loss.

RANGE OF ELECTRIC CURRENTS FOR MILD STEEL ELECTRODES, AMPERES*

Rod Diameter, in	6010	6011	6012	6024	7018
3/32	50– 90	50– 75	30– 90	110–160	70–110
1/8	90–130	80–130	70–130	140–180	100–160
5/32	110–160	110–160	110–180	180–250	130–220
3/16	140–250	160–190	130–260	180–250	180–260
7/32	180–260	190–250	170–380	225–300	210–320
1/4	220–300	200–300	200–425	260–355	230–360
5/16	250–440			300–410	350–440

*The rods showing the higher currents are of course those with the higher deposition rates. The highest values of current shown may not be practical for position welding.

10.3 arc welding rods for repair of tool steels and cast irons

Tools, dies, and punches can be repaired and altered with the use of arc-welding rods of appropriate alloy composition. However, the variety of tool steels is great, and the welding rod must be suited to the tool to be repaired, though it is unlikely to match the alloy composition of the tool. After deposition of the weld metal, a heat treatment will usually be required to produce the Rockwell hardness needed for service conditions. Such tool steel rods are sold under various trade names like those of the tool steels themselves, and the supplier must be consulted for information on welding techniques. As a general guide, however, the hundreds of tool steels may all be grouped into five general types, and for each type electrodes are available to match its requirements:

Fig. 50 Welded fuel rod transfer machine for the WR-1 research nuclear reactor at the Whiteshell Nuclear Research Establishment. The machine pulls out spent fuel rods and inserts new rods into the reactor vessel (which also is a weldment).

1. water hardening
2. oil hardening
3. air hardening
4. hot working (used for such purposes as hot-forging dies)
5. high-speed steels

The heat-treating methods for the first three types are suggested by their names. The last two types require heating to 2000 F or higher for hardening.

In addition to the standard tool steels, work-hardening austenitic manganese rods are often used for the repair of such items as clutch dogs, gear teeth, and pneumatic tools. Repair welding on tools is done with small electrodes, $3/32$ in. being a suitable size. Current settings are always below 150 amp, for the less heat put into a tool or die the more serviceable the repair will be.

Rods for the repair of cast iron are supplied in machineable and nonmachineable steel types. The machineable rods are high nickel, up to 60%. Rods for cast iron require low-penetration characteristics to minimize pickup of carbon from the cast iron, an effect that would produce brittleness in the weld.

10.4 hard-facing rods

Hard-facing rods are deposited for the purpose of resisting impact or abrasion, or both. *Abrasion* is a type of wear caused by the movement of an abrading material such as sand parallel to the surface of the tool, causing scoring of the tool. *Impact* is the type of wear that results from hammering or battering perpendicular to the tool. Wear by abrasion removes metal by scoring or scratching: impact removes metal by peening, mushrooming, cracking, spalling, and chipping. These two types of wear call for different types of metal to resist them. Resistance to abrasion is provided by a very hard surface, such as carbides give. Resistance to impact requires toughness, which could be provided by some type of austenitic material, for example. No material possesses both characteristics to as high a degree as we would like, though reasonable compromises have been developed.

The hard-facing materials can be rated as follows in their resistance to abrasion and impact. The rating is from the most abrasion-resistant at the top to the most impact-resistant at the bottom. Materials in the middle of the group can be expected to have reasonable resistance to both impact and abrasion. Typical analyses for hardfacing rods are given for each type of material.

most resistant to abrasion	
tungsten carbides	tungsten carbide rod
chromium carbides	26.5% Cr, 3.5 % C
semiaustenitic steel	15 % Cr, 2.25% C
austenitic manganese	13 % Mn, 0.6 % C
austenitic stainless steel	18 % Cr, 8 % Ni, 0.08% C
most resistant to impact	

In addition to these five types, various martensitic rods, such as high-speed steel rods, offer a fair degree of resistance to both impact and wear. For both heat and wear resistance, the Stellite hard-facing alloys deserve mention. These are cobalt rods highly alloyed with chromium, tungsten, and carbon.

A hard-facing rod that has given good service in the iron ore industry is Eutectic Alloys Ultimium 112. This is a flux-coated rod with an ingenious construction. The filler material itself is pure tungsten carbide, but since this material has too high an electrical resistance to be used as a manual rod, it is sheathed in thin steel and the flux coats the steel tubing.

Since hard-facing rods are frequently deposited on materials of a different composition, the problem of dilution must be considered. Deep penetration is not desired when surfacing. The fact that the base metal and the hard facing do not have the same coefficient of expansion can also cause problems, possibly spalling of the facing material. Deposition of a layer of austenitic stainless steel between the base material and the hard facing can overcome differences in expansion. The austenitic stainless rod, by its ductility and toughness, can act as a spring to compensate for small dimensional differences between the two materials.

The selection of a suitable facing rod for any specific application can be difficult and often only made by much trial and error. To cite an example, the same hard-facing rod may not perform equally well in two identical limestone crushers in two different quarries if the moisture content of the two types of limestone is not the same. This difference has been explained as due to corrosive action of the limestone with the higher water content, which may be absent in the limestone with less water.

10.5 stainless steel rods

Stainless steel rods are of course used to join the stainless steels, but have a variety of other uses also. The usefulness of these rods is primarily due to the high nickel content, which establishes a tough and ductile austenitic phase at room temperature without the danger of hardening in the weld bead. The use of austenitic stainless steel as an underbead for overlays has already been noted. For similar reasons, austenitic stainless rods are used to join stainless to carbon and low-alloy steel, and for some types of low-temperature work.

The low-hydrogen or mineral type coatings are the only kind used on stainless steel rods for manual welding. To preserve the low-hydrogen condition and prevent absorption of water vapor, such rods are sealed in steel containers and should be protected after the container is opened. The mineral bases of the coatings are either *lime* or *rutile*. The lime coating is used for DCRP and the rutile coating for a.c. or DCSP. The rutile coatings require additives to promote a stable arc with an a-c power source, and such additives may produce metal somewhat more sensitive to cracking than weld metal from lime-coated rods. As a result, the lime-coated rods are preferred if the very best weld properties are desired, especially in position welding. Most welders, however, prefer to use the rutile-coated rods, which have a more easily removed slag. The lime coating is designated by the number 15 after the alloy number, and rutile coating by 16, 308-16 for example. Hence 15 indicates DCRP and 16 a.c. or DCSP.

Lime coatings produce a slightly convex weld bead, and rutile gives a slightly concave bead. Finally, the rutile coatings tend to lose more chromium in transfer across the arc, and to compensate for these losses, they may require additional ferrochromium in the coating.

The composition of a stainless rod does not necessarily correspond to that of the stainless steel to be joined. One reason is economics: there are too many types of stainless steel, just as there are too many types of tool steel, and to make a corresponding number of alloy rods, in both lime and rutile, would mean a high price for the rods. An equally important reason is that alloying elements, particularly chromium and titanium, are lost in the welding slag. If, say, 18% chromium is desired in the deposited metal, then perhaps 19½% chromium must be put into the rod to allow for melting losses. Similar losses occur in furnace melting of stainless steels. Titanium is so reactive that it is uncertain how much of it would cross the arc as titanium metal. Much of it would oxidize and go into the slag. For these reasons, stainless welding rods have special compositions, normally richer than the stainless materials they are to weld.

The 300 series austenitic welding rods have a slight tendency toward cracking in some circumstances, hot cracking for instance. The reasons are not well understood, but it is known that the cure is to deposit a few per cent of ferrite in the austenitic bead. Rod compositions are adjusted to provide this small amount of ferrite.

Typical compositions of the deposited metal from the commonly used stainless steel rods are given in the table. These compositions represent the deposited metal, not the rod itself.

TYPICAL COMPOSITION OF COMMONLY USED STAINLESS STEEL RODS

				(Deposited Metal)			
Rod	C	Cr	Ni	Mn	Si	Cb-Ta	Mo
308	0.08	18–21	9–11	2.5	0.90		
308 L	0.04	18–21	9–11	2.5	0.90		
309	0.15	22–25	12–14	2.5	0.90		
309 Cb	0.12	22–25	12–14	2.5	0.90	0.7–1.0	
310	0.20	25–28	20–22	2.5	0.75		
310 Mo	0.12	25–28	20–22	2.5	0.75		2.0–3.0
316	0.08	17–20	11–14	2.5	0.90		2.0–2.5
316 L	0.04	17–20	11–14	2.5	0.90		2.0–2.5
318	0.08	20	11–14	2.5	0.90	0.80	2.0–2.5
347	0.08	18–20	9–11	2.5	0.90	1.0	
410	0.10	11–13		1.0	0.60		0.5
430	0.10	15–18	0.6	1.0	0.90		
502	0.10	4–6		0.75	0.75		0.5

The 308 rods are general-purpose rods for joining the common grades of stainless steel such as 301, 302, 304, 305, and sometimes other grades such as 201, 202, and the martensitic grades 403, 410, and 420 when a highly ductile weld is demanded. The low-carbon 308L rods have an extremely low carbon content to reduce carbide precipitation. Types 309 and 310 are used to weld both the martensitic and ferritic

400 series steels and for welding carbon and low-alloy steels to stainless steel. The columbium types 309Cb and 310Cb contain columbium plus tantalum to prevent intergranular corrosion due to formation of chromium carbides. For certain types of nuclear reactor work the tantalum content must be less than 0.10% because of the absorption of neutrons by tantalum. The 310 rods are especially useful for the welding of stainless-clad plate, since their higher alloy content allows for dilution by the carbon steel backing metal.

Type 316 and 316L rods are used on parent metal of the same type. Type 347 rod is a stainless steel stabilized with columbium (and some tantalum) like any other stainless 347, for joining stainless types 321 and 347. Rods of 321 composition are not available, since 321 contains titanium, a metal too reactive to cross the arc without being converted into slag.

Stainless 410 rods are martensitic and may be used to join most of the martensitic grades of stainless steel, such as 403 and 410. Since 410 is air-hardenable, the weld will be hardened on cooling, however, if the carbon content does not exceed 0.12%, heat treating may not be required. The weld will not have the ductility of an austenitic deposit. If the carbon content should exceed 0.12%, then preheating will almost always be necessary, possibly as well as slow cooling or annealing at 1600 F.

Type 430 rods are ferritic for joining the ferritic stainless steels such as 430, the commonest. A ferritic deposit ought to have excellent ductility and present no problems, for ferrite is a ductile phase in steels. However, arc-deposited 430 can be brittle, owing to grain growth (which cannot be prevented in arc welding) and the formation of some martensite. Although the deposit is ferritic, it is not 100% ferrite. Post-weld annealing is usually necessary.

Electrodes of type 502 contain no nickel. They are used for the joining of the 500 series stainless steels. Such steels are chiefly used in oil-refining work, in which sour petroleums containing sulfur compounds must be handled. The explanation for the absence of nickel is simply that sulfur compounds are very corrosive to nickel and nickel alloys. The 500 series are air hardening like the martensitic 400 types and require preheating to 300 to 500 F and post-weld annealing at 1350 to 1400 F.

Certain special welding techniques are advantageous in depositing stainless steel weld metal. The metal must be clean of all oxide, oil, grease, dirt, and carbon steel, all of which are the cause of porosity and carbon pickup. Only stainless steel wire brushes should be used for cleaning. Contact with carbon or graphite must be avoided. The low-hydrogen flux coating on the stainless rods must be protected from water vapor in the atmosphere to reduce the risk of porosity in the weld. By the use of smaller currents and smaller rods the heat input to the joint is reduced, thus controlling such problems as grain growth in the ferritic stainless steels and excessive oxidation and loss of alloy ingredients. A short arc is used, for the longer the arc the more oxygen will be drawn into the arc to oxidize the chromium. Wherever possible, a stringer bead (electrode not oscillated across the bead) should be used to reduce the heat input to the weld.

Because the stainless steels can be austenitic, martensitic, and ferritic, they always present difficulties for inexperienced personnel. The problem is further complicated by the fact that no stainless weld deposit has a microstructure wholly martensitic, ferritic, or austenitic. Austenitic welding rods particularly are formulated to provide a few per cent of ferrite as insurance against obscure cracking tendencies. If a person could conveniently know the approximate amounts of the three metallurgical phases in a stainless deposit, he would have some inkling about probable pre- and post-weld heating arrangements.

Fortunately it is very easy to determine the approximate amounts of austenite, martensite, and ferrite in the weld. This can be done from a Schaeffler diagram. This diagram, the invention of A. L. Schaeffler of Arcos Corporation, is reproduced in Fig. 51.

The Schaeffler diagram has two scales. The vertical scale sums up the effect of the austenite promoters in any alloy mixture as the nickel equivalent, and the horizontal scale similarly sums up the effect of the ferrite promoters as the chromium equivalent. The nickel equivalent is the sum of (Ni + 0.5 Mn + 30 C), using percentages. Note that carbon is thirty times more powerful as an austenite promoter than nickel is. Similarly, the chromium equivalent is the sum of Cr + 2.5 Si + 1.8 Mo + 2 Cb. Tantalum is considered as columbium. The use of the diagram

Fig. 51 Schaeffler diagram for determining the proportions of austenite, martensite, and ferrite in deposited weld metal. (Courtesy Arcos Corp.)

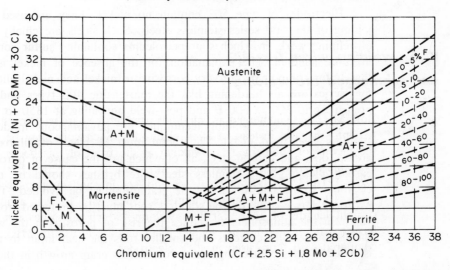

is quickly understood from an example. Consider the analysis of deposited 308 L weld metal from the previous table of stainless rod alloys. Determine the nickel and chromium equivalents. Arithmetical accuracy is not important. Assume chromium at the mid-range between maximum and minimum, say 20%, and nickel 10%.

$$\text{nickel equivalent} = \text{Ni} + 0.5\,\text{Mn} + 30\,\text{C}$$
$$= 10 + 1.25 + 1.25$$
$$= 11.57$$
$$\text{chromium equivalent} = \text{Cr} + 2.5\,\text{Si} + 1.8\,\text{Mo} + 2\,\text{Cb}$$
$$= 20 + 2.2 + 0 + 0$$
$$= 22$$

Plotting the point 11.5 and 22 on the Schaeffler diagram shows that this metal contains slightly more than 10% ferrite. The rest of the microstructure is austenite. The alloys are adjusted to provide a small amount of ferrite, as this metal has. Generally, to ensure a few per cent of ferrite in the microstructure, the chromium content must be about twice the nickel content in the analysis.

Again, if the deposited metal analysis for type 410 is plotted, the microstructure is about 20% ferrite and 80% martensite, indicating that 80% of the weld metal will be hardenable, and therefore the weld metal will harden on cooling. Type 502 weld metal plots as 100% martensite.

The Schaeffler diagram is of particular service in determining the structure of a diluted weld bead, as when stainless steel is welded to carbon or low-alloy steels. The diagram is equally applicable to steels other than the stainless group.

A mixture of two or more steel phases is the rule rather than the exception. Even carbon and tool steels have considerable retained austenite mixed with the martensite after quenching.

10.6 welding wires for MIG
and submerged arc welding

Both MIG and submerged arc methods use coils of bare wire mechanically fed into the arc, instead of stick electrodes. Such coils may be seen in the picture of submerged arc welding at the front of this book. Wire is available in a wide range of alloys, in diameters of 0.020, 0.030, 0.040, 3/64, 1/16, 3/32, 1/8, 5/32, 3/16, and 1/4 in., and in spool weights of 1, 5, 10, 25 lb and larger quantities. Such wire is also available in straight lengths of 36 in. for TIG welding, which also does not require flux-coated wire. Generally, smaller diameters are in use for MIG welding compared with those used in stick electrodes.

The small 0.030- and 0.040-in.-diameter wires are in common use. Obviously such fine wire has a large surface area per cubic inch of wire. In 0.030-in. aluminum welding wire, the surface area is more than 6 sq ft per lb of wire. This high surface-to-weight ratio has important implications for welding quality. The greater the surface area, then the greater the possibility of picking up dirt and other foreign matter on the wire, so that the possibilities of producing porosity are greatly increased. Manufacturers process such wire to reduce surface contamination to the absolute minimum, and the wire is often shipped wrapped in plastic for protection. Welding wire must be kept covered and clean at all times if good welds are to be produced, and lack of attention to this requirement has occasionally produced disappointing results. Weld porosity has resulted when wire has been stored at too low a temperature with imperfect protection against condensation of water vapor; 6 sq ft per lb can pick up a great deal of water vapor, and 1 cu in. of water vapor will produce more than 1000 cu in. of steam. Steel wire has the problem of rusting and is often given a flash coat of copper for protection and improving the pickup of electric current. Any copper retained in the weld metal does no harm.

Like covered stick electrodes, the wires with larger diameters are cheaper per pound than those with smaller diameters and the deposition rate is higher. Since the wire is continuously fed, there are no stub losses, and deposition efficiency is almost 100%. The rule that deposition rate is proportional to current holds for welding wire too. Figure 52 shows typical burn-off curves for MIG welding wire. The speeds at which the wire is fed should be noted.

Carbon steel wire is available as rimmed steel, but it is more usual to use killed steels deoxidized with manganese, silicon, or aluminum. For dirty or rusty steel, triple-deoxidized wire containing all three deoxidizers is available. The deoxidizers are needed to prevent porosity and brittle fracture and to provide good mechanical properties in the weld. If the shielding gas used with MIG welding is argon oxygen or carbon dioxide, then deoxidizers in the filler wire are essential to protect the wire from oxidation by the gas. Low-alloy wire in several grades is available for the welding of high-strength structural steels such as Cor-Ten, T-1, Stelcoloy, the low chrome-moly grades of high-temperature piping, and other low-alloy applications. The hard-facing and tool-steel alloys discussed under arc welding rods are available also as wire.

Stainless welding wire is made of the same alloys as stick electrodes of stainless steel are. Stainless 308 may be considered the general-purpose welding wire for a wide range of stainless steels, including the non-austenitic grades. Type 347 and a few other columbium alloys are available as stabilized grades. Special grades are in use for the welding of nuclear reactor components, in which the use of alloys which absorb neutrons (that is, have a high neutron capture) is not allowed. For

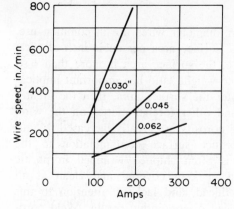

Fig. 52 Burnoff curves for steel MIG wire.

stainless cladding of low-carbon steels, the Arcos Corporation offers instead of a wire a flat strip of stainless steel 2 in. wide and 0.030 in. or more thick. This strip is deposited by a type of submerged arc welding termed the ARCSTRIP process. If dilution by the base metal is severe, a dual Arcstrip is used. A cold strip is laid down as a barrier layer under the arc from the hot strip electrode.

10.7 flux-cored wire

There are many ways of conveying flux to the weld pool. In submerged arc welding and in most brazing the flux is supplied as a bulk powder. Stick electrodes carry their flux on the outside of the wire. In recent years flux-cored wire has come into extensive use for a considerable number of welding processes, and it is estimated that by 1970 about 20% of all filler wires will be flux-cored. Flux-cored wire is an inside-out version of the stick electrode, in which the flux is packed inside the sheath of filler wire.

Some advantages of flux-cored wire come immediately to mind. First, maintaining such a protected flux in a low-hydrogen condition is not difficult. Second, the shipping and handling damage to the coatings on stick electrodes cannot happen to a flux core. Moreover, there are advantages in welding technique. Flux-cored wire is fed from coils, and in addition to its use as an a MIG wire it makes possible other welding methods such as electrogas welding, to be described later. When shielding such as carbon dioxide or argon plus carbon dioxide is used with flux-cored wire, unusually deep penetration is obtained, providing two further advantages: fewer passes are possible when welding heavier plate, and 30° V joints are possible instead of the 60° V needed with manual methods.

Flux-cored wire requires currents in the range of 500 to 750 amp usually. In most applications CO_2 shielding gas is used, but often such shielding is omitted. Ductility, penetration, and notch toughness are not quite as high in the absence of shielding, but shielding may be impossible when welding outside under windy conditions. Carbon dioxide is a source of oxygen, and when welding with this shielding gas, killed steel wire must be used, as the flux itself contains deoxidizers. The composition of the wire and the flux must be adjusted to compensate for the loss of manganese and silicon in the CO_2 arc. Alloying elements are often supplied in the flux rather than in the wire, since this is the cheapest method. The flux base is always a low-hydrogen type. Wire sizes range from 5/64 in. to about 5/32 by 1/64-in. increments.

At present only a limited number of wires are available, chiefly mild-steel, low-alloy grades for the high-strength low-alloy structural steels, low-nickel wire for low-temperature applications, and 304 and 316 stainless steel. A few hard-surfacing types of wire are available. Other types of wire, including cast iron, are under development at present and will be available shortly. A "low-flux burden" type that does not require slag cleaning between passes is also becoming available. Obviously flux-cored wire is going to make changes in future welding techniques.

10.8 aluminum welding wire

Aluminum welding wire is available in the same diameters and coil weights as those of steel wire. In general, the parent metal alloy governs the choice of filler metal, and the two correspond approximately. Use of the wrong filler wire may be the cause of weld cracking, poor color match, poor mechanical properties, and poor corrosion resistance or even galvanic corrosion.

The high-strength aluminum alloys of the 2000 series (20S to 29S) with copper and the 7000 series (70S to 79S) with zinc obtain their strength from solution heat treating and age hardening. Welding heat reduces this high strength because of the annealing effect of the weld heat, and it is not generally convenient to re-heat-treat after welding. Such aluminums therefore are rarely arc-welded.

The commonly used aluminum welding wires are the following:

Alloy Number	Alloy		Ultimate Tensile Strength of Butt Weld, psi
1100 (2S)	99%	aluminum	13,000
4043 (33S)	4.5–6%	silicon	30,000
5154 (54S)	3.1–3.9%	magnesium	33,000
5356 (59S)	4.5–5.5%	magnesium	38,000

A few other wire alloys are available from a restricted number of wire producers.

Wire 1100 is used to join the high-aluminum alloys such as 1100 and 3003. The 4043 wire is a general-purpose wire and will successfully join most of the aluminum alloys of the 1000, 2000, 3000, and 6000 series but will not necessarily provide the strength of the parent metal. Alloys 5154 and 5356 give higher weld strengths and are selected for structural aluminum work, such as trucks and semitrailers.

10.9 copper-base welding wires

Four copper-base welding wires are in common use:

Alloy	Designation	Approximate Composition
deoxidized copper	ECu	98% Cu, 1% Sn
silicon bronze	ECu–Si	94% Cu min., 3–4% Si
phosphor bronze	ECu–Sn	93% Cu min., 4–6% Sn
aluminum bronze	ECu–Al	94%, 6% Al

A number of other compositions are available, including 30% nickel copper. These wires are used to join materials of generally similar composition, although plain copper and aluminum bronze will join copper alloys to steel. Both copper and nickel are compatible with a very wide range of metals and do not form brittle intermetallic compounds with them. Copper-zinc brasses may be joined with silicon bronze or the other wire compositions listed. Copper-zinc welding wire is produced only for oxyacetylene welding and brazing. In the intense heat of the arc most of the zinc is boiled away.

10.10 nickel-base welding wires

Nickel wires and rods may be divided into two groups: those for joining nickel parent metal and those for joining metals other than nickel. Nickel resembles copper in its capacity for making ductile welds on a variety of metals.

Perhaps the commonest use of nickel for welding a different metal is in the welding of cast iron, for which pure nickel or 60% nickel, 40 (Ni-Rod) may be used. Wire of chromium-iron-nickel, with trade names such as Inconel 182, Monend 14/75, and others, will join Inconel to itself or to other materials and is also used in cryogenic vessels to join such materials as 9% nickel steel. Monel rods and wire, two-thirds nickel and one-third copper, are employed in the joining of the Monel alloys. Inco-Weld A is a general-purpose welding rod or wire for more difficult joining problems and is usable on a wide range of metals, even including zirconium. It will tolerate considerable dilution by other metals without losing ductility or strength. Inco-Weld A has a high-nickel composition with 0.15% carbon maximum and about 15% chromium.

PROBLEMS

1 Suggest why carbon arc welding is not recommended for welding stainless 316L sheet.

2 Why are flux-coated titanium rods not used?

3 In cladding a carbon steel plate with a high-nickel alloy such as Monel, why would you use a welding rod with a higher nickel content than that required by the deposited metal?

4 How does a carbon electrode provide a protective atmosphere?

5 For what reason is tungsten used as a nonconsumable electrode?

6 Decide whether silicon carbide would make a reasonably successful nonconsumable electrode and give your reasons. Consider its relative melting point, conductivity, and the elements of which it is composed.

7 Copper is a difficult metal to weld. Why is this an advantageous feature of a copper resistance welding tip?

8 What difficulties would arise if a welder attempted overhead welding with 6024 rods?

9 What is the relationship between
 (a) arc voltage and arc length
 (b) current and deposition rate
 (c) rod diameter and deposition rate
 (d) penetration and dilution
 (e) rod diameter and deposition efficiency

10 What is the difference between a 6010 and a 6011 rod?

11 What is the purpose of the following flux coatings: (a) cellulose, (c) iron powder, (c) lime.

12 Select rods for the following applications:
 (a) general pipe work
 (b) high deposition rate on horizontal fillets
 (c) butt welds in quarter-inch plate, horizontal welding

(d) butt welds in 20-gauge sheet metal

(e) high-quality tank fabrication with good impact values

(f) poor fit-up

(g) teaching a new man how to weld

(i) welding of stainless 321

(j) welding of stainless 304

(k) welding a copper conductor to a steel ground

(l) welding of a 15-y truck dump box

13 What two reasons account for the brittleness in a stainless 430 ferritic deposit?

14 Plot the following burn-off curves. The current scale is calibrated horizontally, and wire speed in inches per minute vertically. The curves are for aluminum wire MIG-welded with argon shielding and DCRP.

0.020-in. wire		0.062-in. wire	
Current, amp	ipm	Current, amp	ipm
$62\frac{1}{2}$	525	100	100
75	630	150	130
$87\frac{1}{2}$	775	200	165
100	860	250	195
		300	235
		350	265

15 Why does flux-cored wire require a protective atmosphere, whereas a rod coated with the same flux does not?

16 Explain in your own words the difference between abrasion and impact.

17 What are the differences in welding characteristics between lime- and rutile-coated stainless rods?

18 The following are the published analyses of Sandvik austenitic stainless rods. Determine their approximate percentage of ferrite.
Sandvik 3R17 0.025 C, 0.4 Si, 1.8 Mn, 20.6 Cr, 9.7 Ni
Sandvik 3R61 0.025 C, 0.4 Si, 1.4 Mn, 18.4 Cr, 10.6 Ni

19 Assume that you are depositing an overlay of 18% Cr, 8% Ni, 0% C rod on a mild-steel plate of 0.2% C and that each metal dilutes the other by 50%. Decide whether the diluted blend will tend to crack. The easiest way to solve this problem is to locate both the mild steel and the austenitic steel on the Schaeffler diagram, draw a straight line between these two points, and locate the mid-point of this line as being 50% dilution each way.

20 Name what you consider to be the most general-purpose welding wire in the following types of metals: (a) stainless steel, (b) aluminum, (c) nickel.

21 Why is copper-zinc brass wire not used for arc welding?

WELDING
METHODS

Part III

11.1 Faraday's discovery

Of all the scientific discoveries in the last 2000 years, one surpasses all others for the great range of its usefulness and its impact on technology. This outstanding discovery, which made electric welding possible, was made about 150 years ago by a modest Englishman, Michael Faraday, who was no learned scientist but an unlettered man. The most unlikely person to remake a technical civilization, he came to make his great discovery through a chain of circumstances that would be completely improbable if it were not true. Faraday had no formal schooling and was apprenticed as a bookbinder. While binding scientific books he became completely engrossed in their subject matter and determined to devote his life to scientific learning. In the course of his labors, he discovered that magnetism and electricity are related and that the one can produce the other. He never knew what this discovery would mean for the human race.

From Faraday's scientific curiosity has developed much of the basic equipment that make present-day industry and life possible—the automobile ignition coil, the electric relay, the loudspeaker, the electric generator, the electric motor, the transformer, the radio antenna, and, for welding technology, electric welding machines. All these basic devices use an electromagnetic coil to produce electric power. If welding has a patron

ELECTRICAL PRINCIPLES

OF

WELDING MACHINES

11

saint, it must be earnest, modest Michael Faraday, the apprentice book-binder, who made possible the welding machines to be described.

11.2 electric charges and particles

Perhaps the most basic fact about the universe is that there are two kinds of electric charges, positive and negative. By the word "charge" we mean some certain amount of electricity, actually the amount of electricity associated with an electron.

Further, the whole universe is composed of many types of ultimate particles, one of which is the famous *electron*. The electron always carries a unit of negative electricity and has an extremely minute weight that makes it rather mobile; hence electrons are the usual means of electric current. Being negatively charged, electrons move toward the positive end of a circuit. When welding with DCSP, the workpiece is positive. The electrons in the arc will therefore move toward the positive workpiece from the negative electrode.

The human race will probably never be able to see an electron, and the problem is compounded by the fact that this particle does not have a definite shape. In diagrams, however, it is customary to draw an electron as a little circle, sometimes with a negative sign (−) inside to signify the type of electric charge. It is a mistake, though, to allow the diagrammatic circle to signify that electrons are round.

All things in the universe are not negatively charged, however. This book is not, in fact it is probably uncharged, an indication that it has as many positive as negative charges. If the electron is a particle with a negative charge (there are other negatively charged particles, not yet important in welding), then there must be particles with a positive charge. The most important of the positively charged particles is the *proton*. This particle is about 1800 times as heavy as the electron. Its relatively heavy weight and resultant sluggishness is only one of a number of reasons why protons do not move in electric currents from positive electrodes to negative electrodes. The proton is shown in diagrams as a circle, which in reality it is not, with a positive sign (+) inside.

A number of fundamental particles without an electric charge also exist. Being uncharged, such particles cannot be moved or influenced by applied voltages or magnetic fields. One of the uncharged particles is the *neutron*, so named because it is electrically neutral. Another uncharged particle, the *photon,* will be dealt with later. The neutron weighs very slightly more than the proton and can be dissociated under certain circumstances into a proton (+), and electron (−), and a neutrino (uncharged). The uncharged neutrino has no present significance in welding.

electrical principles of welding machines
164

The fundamental particles proton, neutron, and electron are usually combined in systems to comprise atoms of the various elements, such as hydrogen, iron, and carbon.

The simplest of all atoms is the hydrogen atom. The atomic structure of hydrogen is the simple one shown in Fig. 53(a), one electron revolving around a nucleus of one proton. The atom of hydrogen is electrically neutral since the two electric charges of the two particles mutually cancel.

The next heaviest and more complicated atom is that of the inert gas helium. Here we find, as in Fig. 53(b), two electrons revolving in an orbit about the nucleus. The nucleus has four particles, two protons and two neutrons. As before, the sum of the negative charges balances the sum of the positive charges.

The next heaviest atom after helium is lithium, the lightest of all metals. Lithium has two electrons in the same orbit as helium but has in addition a third electron in an orbit farther out from the nucleus. The nucleus has four neutrons and three protons.

Fig. 53 Atomic structures of the elements.

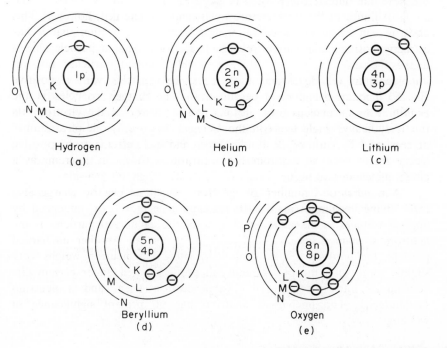

Hydrogen
(a)

Helium
(b)

Lithium
(c)

Beryllium
(d)

Oxygen
(e)

At this point we should stop and establish some principles. We have uncovered the simple patterns that govern the structures of the 100 or so elements of the universe, most of which are metals.

1. Any amount or weight of an element, such as a bar of copper, is composed of atoms. A crystal is an array of atoms in a definite pattern, such as face-centered cubic.
2. Each atom has a nucleus made up of the heavy particles, protons and neutrons. Nearly the whole weight of the atom is concentrated in the nucleus.
3. The lightweight electrons take their position in orbits around the heavy nucleus.
4. Each element has its own distinctive number of protons. An element that has two protons can be helium and only helium, for example.
5. The number of neutrons in the nucleus is somewhat irregular.

So far, we have implied that the number of electrons is the same as the number of protons. Electrons can move and produce electric currents, however, and an atom can lose or gain electrons, thus acquiring a positive or a negative charge. In general the electrons are rather loosely held to the nucleus. Also, it is better to refer to the electron orbits as "shells" or "energy levels," for reasons to be explained. Lithium has electrons in two shells or energy levels. Heavier atoms such as iron may have more than two energy levels containing electrons. Hereafter, the first energy level closest to the nucleus will be referred to as the K shell, the next one outside the K shell is the L shell, then M, N, O levels and so on. All atoms have these energy levels, and actually the single hydrogen electron can be in any shell or energy level. However, because of the attraction of opposite electric charges, electrons favor the levels closest to the nucleus.

To show the development of these atom patterns and principles, Fig. 53 includes the atom of beryllium and the heavier atom of oxygen. Beryllium has a nucleus of 4 protons and 5 neutrons and 2 electrons in the K shell and 2 electrons in the L shell. Oxygen has a nucleus of 8 protons and 8 neutrons, 2 K electrons, and 6 L electrons. Finally, to heavy metal such as uranium has 92 protons, 146 neutrons, and 92 electrons, enough to fill up the K, L, M, N, O, P, and Q levels.

The *maximum* number of electrons that can occupy any energy level follows a simple rule:

the K level will hold	$2 \times (1)^2 = 2$ electrons (maximum)
the L level will hold	$2 \times (2)^2 = 8$ electrons
the M level will hold	$2 \times (3)^2 = 18$ electrons
the N level will hold	$2 \times (4)^2 = 32$ electrons
the O level	50 electrons
and so on	

So far, we have dealt with the atom patterns of the elements as they exist at rest or under equilibrium conditions. However, if these atoms are put to work, under the heat of the oxyacetylene flame or welding arc, the atoms acquire heat energy. Heat can produce minor changes in the electron patterns.

Consider a single atom of, for example, hydrogen in the 6000 F of the inner cone of an oxyacetylene flame. The effect of this heat is that the single electron acquires energy, and if it is in the closest shell, the K shell, the electron will move out to a more remote shell. The same effect is produced on the electrons of the heavier multielectron atoms. When the heat of the flame is removed, the electrons will move back to energy levels closer to the nucleus, a clear sign that they have lost energy or cooled down.

Actually 6000 F is a remarkably high temperature and can supply enough energy to move some electrons out of reach of the nucleus altogether. If the atom has thus lost one or more electrons, then the balance of electric charge is lost. The atom then has a net positive charge. In this condition the atom is said to *ionized*, or becomes an *ion*. Ionization takes place to a considerable degree in the gases of the electric arc (about 9000 F), so that the arc is an active mixture of neutral atoms, positive ions, and negative electrons. The electrons will move rapidly to the positive side of the arc, while the heavier ions will move sluggishly to the negative side. The speed at which these charged particles move depends on the voltage across the arc. A voltage constantly accelerates such particles, and the rate of acceleration increases directly with the voltage.

Another modification of the basic atom pattern is used in the examination of welds by gamma ray photography. A small amount of a substance such as cobalt, with a total of 59 protons and neutrons, is placed in a nuclear reactor and bombarded for a considerable time with neutrons from the reactor. A substantial number of the cobalt atoms capture an extra neutron, thus converting the cobalt from Co-59 to Co-60. The number is of course the total count of particles in the nucleus of the atom. Such an element, many of whose nuclei contain extra neutrons, is called an isotope. Note, though, that the number of protons is not changed; the cobalt is still cobalt, therefore, and might with good reason be called heavy cobalt. The atom isotopes used for gamma ray photography of welds become unstable because of the presence of the extra neutron and usually break up into two or more atoms of different elements, at the same time emitting the powerful gamma rays that can penetrate metals and record the weld quality on a photographic film. Such radioactive isotopes are termed *radioisotopes*. Only two are in common use, cobalt-60 and iridium-192.

11.5 molecules and chemical compounds

The atoms of the metal elements array themselves in the crystal arrangements described earlier, almost always the cubic or hexagonal crystal structure. Thus pure iron forms crystals or "grains" with a body-centered cubic structure, whereas carbon steel has the same structure except that the small alloy carbon atoms fit into the spaces between iron atoms. Any element, such as iron, can combine with other elements to form chemical compounds such as iron oxide, ferric chloride, and iron sulfide. These chemical compounds form their own structural patterns, usually by sharing electrons in the outermost populated energy level. This unit pattern combining different atoms is called a molecule, the smallest possible unit of a chemical compound. Another method of explaining the molecule is to take it apart. Thus, for example, Fe_2O_3 represents the molecule of iron rust. It can be separated into two atoms of iron and three of oxygen. If dismantling of the pieces is then continued, they will not break down further into substances or elements but into particles such as neutrons and protons.

11.6 the capacitor

A capacitor, also called a condenser, is a device with the function of temporarily storing electrons in an electrical circuit, or in everyday language, it is simply an electron warehouse. The electrons are moved into the capacitor by the use of an applied voltage across the plates of the capacitor.

A capacitor is built of two (or sometimes more) parallel thin metal plates, which may be flat or coiled. The plates must be very close together and parallel in order to obtain a high electron storage capacity. Suppose that a 6-v battery is connected across the capacitor shown in Fig. 54. No electrical connection exists across the capacitor plates, so that the circuit is an open circuit. One of the plates is positive and is connected to the positive terminal of the battery; the other is negative.

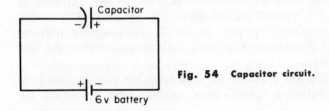

Fig. 54 Capacitor circuit.

Under the influence of the 6-v force, electrons will move from the negative plate of the capacitor, the connecting wires, and the battery to collect on the positive plate of the capacitor, gradually building up voltage on the positive plate to oppose the battery voltage. As the number of collected electrons increases on the positive plate and the opposing voltage increases, it becomes progressively more difficult to move electrons onto the positive plate against the negative charge or voltage of all these electrons. Finally, all current will stop when no more electrons can be forced over to the positive plate. When current ceases, the capacitor will be charged by the collected electrons to exactly the 6 v of the battery, but opposing the battery voltage. If the battery voltage is disconnected, the capacitor can be discharged. During discharge of the stored electrons, the capacitor acts as a momentary voltage source.

The electron storage capacity of a capacitor is rated in microfarads (millionths of a farad), and this capacity is printed on the capacitor, usually abbreviated as μf.

As a voltage source, the capacitor is capable of producing high currents, but only of short duration. These are useful characteristics, however. A spot welder, for instance, uses high currents for only a few cycles. Some spot-welding machines use the capacitor-discharge principle to provide the momentary high current for spot welding. The bank of capacitors is recharged between spots. The same method is also used to fire a laser welder, which operates intermittently like a spot welder.

11.7 vacuum and gas-filled electronic tubes

The control systems of more complex welding machines such as some resistance welders and MIG wire feeders use vacuum tubes. In control systems vacuum tubes are used as switches or relays to control small currents. Larger currents, even as large as those used in resistance welding, can be controlled by tubes, but such high-capacity tubes are gas-filled.

The simplest of the vacuum or gas-filled tubes is the *diode,* so named because it has two electrodes, a negative cathode that is heated to supply electrons and a positive anode to which the electrons are attracted by the voltage across the vacuum of the tube. The electrons traverse the vacuum in the tube from cathode to anode. The cathode may be a 6- or 12-v heated filament or a separate cathode surrounding the filament and heated by it.

A diode cannot act as a control valve or relay but only as a rectifier. The anode, often called a "plate" in a vacuum tube, is always the positive electrode, and the cathode is always negative. Therefore if alternating current is impressed on such a diode, its output will be direct current, since the tube will suppress the negative half cycles. If the tube must handle current much above 1 amp, it must be a gas-filled tube. If the currents are higher than about 1000 amp, the diode will be an *ignitron*, mercury-filled. Many of these high-power tubes must be water-cooled.

The X-ray tube is simply a vacuum tube diode with a very high voltage across the tube, 50,000 v or more, usually much more. The reason for the high voltage is simply that the X-ray tube does not control or rectify. Its purpose is the production of X rays. When an electron leaves the X-ray tube cathode, it is furiously accelerated by the high voltage, until by the time it arrives at the anode it may be traveling at half the speed of light. The impact as the electron strikes causes the anode electrons to jump wildly from one energy level to another, and

Fig. 55 X-ray photograph of a vacuum tube triode.

in doing so they produce a great deal of heat and a small amount of X radiation.

It is pertinent to note that any arc, within an electronic tube or not, which has a voltage across it exceeding about 10,000 v, will produce X rays at the anode. At present the only welding arc using such high voltages is the electron beam. The operator of electron beam welding equipment must be shielded from the X rays produced by the welding operation.

There are a very great many types of diodes. The photoelectric cell, which is used on some types of automatic flame-cutting equipment, is one type. The photocell uses for cathode a material that will emit electrons when irradiated with light. Such cathodes contain metals with a single electron in the outermost populated energy level, like lithium of Fig. 53(c).

Even the capacitor may be considered a kind of diode. The welding combination of workpiece, electrode, and arc is a kind of tubeless diode, gas-filled of course, with characteristics rather similar to those of the "arc" of electrons across a vacuum tube. A manual welding arc gives the highest voltage across the arc on open-circuit conditions of no current and draws maximum current on short circuit (zero voltage drop) when the rod contacts the work. Vacuum tubes have much the same characteristics, that is, minimum current at maximum voltage, and maximum current at lowest voltage drop, though they do not short-circuit.

A *triode* contains three electrodes: a cathode, an anode, and a grid. The grid is a fine wire-mesh screen between cathode and anode and can be used to control the flow of electrons across the tube. Suppose the grid voltage is made more positive with respect to the cathode, to be specific, say 0 v at the cathode, +10 v at the grid, and +300 v at the anode. Then the effect of the grid is to increase the flow of electrons from cathode to anode. Suppose next that the voltage at the grid is steadily lowered back to zero and then to increasingly negative values. The electron flow through the tube will be caused to decrease progressively until at a sufficiently negative grid voltage the tube current will be cut off. Thus the addition of a grid electrode to a tube converts the tube into an electronic relay for controlling the flow of current.

The disadvantage of a vacuum tube is its high resistance to the flow of current from cathode to anode. It requires a voltage in the range of 100 v to bring current across the tube. Suppose that a current of 1 amp is being used. Then 100 w of heat is developed in the tube. This would be perhaps enough to burn out the tube, and yet 1 amp is no great current.

For higher amperages the solution is to use a gas-filled tube with mercury vapor or some other inert gas. Such tubes have very low tube resistance, low enough that they are virtually short-circuiting like a welding arc. At low anode voltages, less than about 15 v, the gas-filled triode behaves like a vacuum triode. The tube current is small and can be controlled by the grid voltage as explained above. At a certain critical anode voltage, 15 v or so depending on the ionizing voltage of the gas in the tube, the electrons from the cathode acquire enough velocity to ionize the gas molecules that fill the tube. The grid then becomes surrounded and smothered by positive gas ions, and a large tube current that can no longer be controlled by the grid circuit is suddenly established. The heavy tube current is composed of both cathode electrons and gas electrons. To extinguish the tube current, the anode voltage must be dropped below the ionization voltage that caused the high current. The positive gas ions and their electrons then recombine very rapidly.

Such a gas-filled triode makes an excellent relay for the control of larger currents. The name given to such a gas-filled triode is *thyratron*. A common use for the thyratron is control of the very large ignitrons that handle the big currents of resistance welders. That is, the thyratron is used as a relay to control the ignitrons, the relays for resistance welding currents.

The ignitron is a diode capable of controlling thousands of amperes of current. It does not have a heated filament for a cathode but instead uses a pool of mercury. It is thus a mercury vapor tube. The anode is a carbon electrode. So much heat is produced by the heavy current flow even at the low voltage drop that the ignitron must be water-cooled.

11.8 direct and alternating
current

Electric energy is simply one form of energy that has a number of advantages over other forms of energy:

1. It is clean.
2. It is easy to transport over long distances, needing only the stringing of wire for this purpose.
3. It is easy to supply in small amounts of energy.
4. It is easily converted into other kinds of energy, such as heat.
5. It is economical of space.

It should be noted, however, that whereas electric energy is transported to an infinity of locations, this energy is rarely used as electric energy. In arc welding, we do not primarily weld with electricity, we weld with *heat,* using the electric form of energy for transportation along wires up to the rod and the workpiece, finally converting the energy into heat in the arc. In the same vein, a pot of coffee can be boiled over a campfire or over an electric stove, but either way is the same. Coffee is boiled with heat not with electricity.

Electric energy is produced by large mechanical prime movers such as steam turbines and waterwheels and on a smaller scale by gasoline and diesel engines by coupling the mechanical prime mover to an electric generator. The electric energy is supplied either as direct current or alternating current. With direct current, the electron movement along the conductor is in one direction only. With alternating current the electron flow reverses periodically. Whereas some types of electric generators will produce direct current directly, such as batteries, dry cells, d-c generators, and thermocouples, most direct current is developed from alternating current by rectifiers.

The waveform of an alternating current or voltage is the familiar since wave of Fig. 56(a). One complete cycle of alternating current comprises one positive and one negative wave, positive meaning electron flow in one direction and negative meaning electron flow in the opposite direction. The frequency of alternating current is the number of such com-

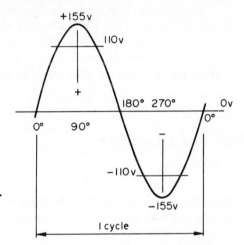

Fig. 56 (a)   Alternating current or voltage waveform.

plete cycles per second. For most power applications, 60 cycles per second is the standard frequency at present in North America, although the use of higher frequencies becomes more common and will increase in the future. Higher frequencies are necessary for arc starting in tungsten inert gas welding, for induction brazing, for ultrasonic testing of welds, and for a wide range of other uses.

One complete cycle of alternating current is considered to be 360° (one rotation of a circle). The maximum positive voltage occurs at 90°, and the maximum negative voltage at 270°. At 0 and 180° the voltage reverses and passes through zero. For welding purposes, it is often convenient to think of the one half-wave of the a-c cycle as DCSP and the other half-wave as DCRP.

Since the alternating voltage is constantly changing, the problem arises: Just what *is* the voltage? Or if we are talking about 110 v a.c., which voltage in the fluctuating wave of voltage is 110 v?

The solution to this problem takes a very practical approach. Suppose an electric resistance, such as an electric stove or an electric toaster, puts out a certain power in watts when connected to 110 v d.c. Then if this resistance is connected to an a.c. source that likewise causes the device to produce the same wattage, the a-c source is called 110 v a.c. Under this arrangement, the nominal voltage of an a-c wave is not the maximum voltage but what is called the *effective voltage*.

effective voltage or nominal a-c voltage = 0.707 × peak voltage
peak voltage = 1.414 × the effective voltage
for a 110-v a-c wave, peak positive and negative voltage = 1.41 × 110 = 155 v

Note that 110 v a.c. is 141% as dangerous as steady 110 v d.c. If a person should be electrocuted by 110 v a.c., actually 155 v pass through his body. Electrical insulation on a-c wires likewise must be able to withstand the surges of 141% of the nominal voltage.

There is one exception to the practice of rating voltage by the effective voltage. X-ray tubes are rated in terms of the peak voltage. Thus a 250 X-ray tube produces 250 kilovolts *peak*.

On most a-c–d-c welding machines, the direct current is rectified from the alternating current received by the machine. Such direct current will be 120-cycle direct current and have a wave shape as shown in Fig. 56(b). This is full-wave rectified d.c. If the negative half-waves of a.c. are suppressed by the rectifier, such d.c. is referred to as half-wave rectified d.c.

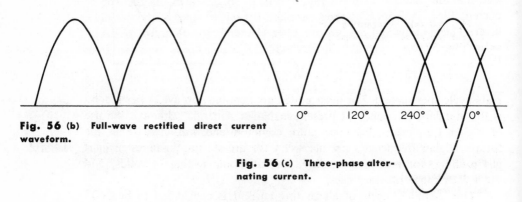

Fig. 56 (b) **Full-wave rectified direct current waveform.**

Fig. 56 (c) **Three-phase alternating current.**

Larger welders use a three-phase a-c supply. Three phase is simply three sources of power at identical voltages brought in by three wires, the three voltages or phases being separated by 120 electrical degrees (see Fig. 56c). The meaning of "phase" in electrical work is not the "phase" used in metallurgy. If voltages or currents are in phase, they are in step and pass through zero together. If they are out of phase, one passes through zero at a different time or electrical angle from the other. Figure 56(c) shows that three-phase power is smoother than single-phase, because the overlapping three phases prevent the current or voltage from falling to zero, a feature that permits better and easier welding. However three-phase welding machines are more expensive.

electrical principles of welding machines
174

An electrical rectifier is any device for converting alternating to direct current. A rectifier has the same function in an electric circuit that a check valve has in a piping circuit. Vacuum and gas-filled diodes are one type of rectifier already mentioned. If a positive wave of alternating current is applied to the anode of such a tube, an electron current will flow. When the following negative half cycle is applied to the anode, the electrons are repelled and no current flows through the tube. The tube will thus produce half-wave d.c.

Most welder operators prefer to weld with direct current rather than alternating current. Rectified d.c. for welding is a rugged service and a high-current operation. Instead of a tube, semiconductor rectifiers, sometimes called solid-state rectifiers, are used in welding machines. Some companies, such as Miller Electric, prefer a selenium rectifier, others such as Mid-States, use a silicon rectifier. The silicon rectifier has a shape and size somewhat resembling a spark plug (Fig. 57a). In the selenium rectifier, a layer of selenium about 2 to 3 thousandths of an inch thick is deposited on a support plate of steel or aluminum, which also has the function of dissipating the heat generated in the rectifier by current flow. A front electrode contacts the other side of the selenium layer. These individual modular rectifier elements are mounted in stacks, as in Fig. 57(b). Current will flow with little resistance from the front

Fig. 57 Rectifiers for welding transformers.
(a) Silicon diode.

(b) Selenium rectifier.

electrode to the selenium and its support plate, but the backward resistance from the other direction of flow is about 1000 times higher, making reverse currents very small.

Although welding generators and transformers are rated for a certain amperage, it is possible to draw a higher current than the rated current for a period not long enough to overheat and burn out the machine. This cannot be done with rectifiers. The current rating of the rectifier must be considered as the maximum current.

In connection with rectification, another similarity between an electronic tube and a welding arc must be noted. Tube diodes are used for rectification, and under certain conditions even welding arcs will rectifiy alternating current. This arc rectification is most pronounced in the welding of certain nonferrous metals with a tungsten electrode. The tungsten electrode, especially if it is thoriated tungsten, acts as a much better cathode than anode. This arc rectification problem will be mentioned again in discussion of TIG welding machines.

11.10 solenoids in welding

Having dealt with the basic information on electrons and electron flow, we shall now consider Faraday's contributions to the basic science of welding. Faraday showed that an electric current invariably produces a magnetic field. For an electric current moving along a straight wire, the magnetic field is, as in Fig. 58(a), concentric with the wire and in the direction shown if the electric current were flowing downward into the paper. The magnetic field has the same relation to the current flow that the left-hand threads have to a bolt. The arrows showing the direction of the field indicate the direction to which a north magnetic pole of a magnet would be attracted. The strength of the magnetic field is proportional to the amperes of current flowing in the wire.

To produce a stronger magnetic field, the wire is wound into a coil.

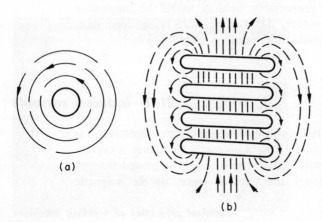

Fig. 58 Magnetic fields:
(a) Around a wire carrying electric current into the page,

(b) around a solenoid coil carrying a current upward through the coil.

(a)

(b)

Such a coil is called a *solenoid*. The simple rule for the direction of the magnetic field (direction in which a north pole is pulled) around a solenoid is this: if the thumb of the left hand points in the direction of the field inside the solenoid, the fingers will point in the direction of current flow in the wire. The relationship is shown in Fig. 58(b). In alternating current, the magnetic field will reverse when the current reverses.

The strength of the magnetic field in a solenoid is proportional to the product of the current in amperes times the number of turns of wire, or more simply, *proportional to the amp-turns*. Either winding more turns or increasing the current, or both, will increase the field strength.

Unsuspected solenoids exist in the most unexpected places, especially in welding, in which the high currents used ensure a high value for amp-turns. The two arms of a spot welder act as a one-turn solenoid. If, say, 10,000 amp are used for spot welding, this makes up a 10,000 amp-turn solenoid. As this is an extremely high field strength, a powerful magnetic field exists around the spot welder. It may be powerful enough to heat up the pieces of metal being spot-welded.

A more familiar example of an unsuspected solenoid is the following. There is a call for some emergency welding to be done on a building under construction, and not knowing how long a cable he will need, the welder takes with him a 200-ft set of cables. Arriving at the site, he finds that 40 ft of cable will serve. While he is setting up the equipment, he orders his helper to coil the excess cable. The helper is a conscientious fellow and makes a neat coil of the excess.

Such neatness may be no virtue, because the helper has made a solenoid. Suppose that the welding job requires 300 amp (rather high for casual welding perhaps) and that the helper has laid 16 loops. The amp-turns are 4800, a fairly strong magnetic field. The welding machine will have to supply the energy to reverse this magnetic field 120 times a second, and as a result the current setting on the machine will be higher than the current actually delivered to the arc. If the job required a-c high frequency TIG welding, presumably welding would be impossible with such a long cable. If, however, d-c welding were being done (d.c. is zero frequency), the coil would not interfere with the job.

11.11 induced currents

Perhaps the most useful of Faraday's discoveries in electromagnetism was that if a conducting wire is moved across a magnetic field, then a current will be induced to flow in the wire. Either the wire can be moved through the magnetic field to cut through the lines of force, or the magnetic field can be moved over the wire. Such a current is called an *induced current*, since it is induced to flow by the relative motion of field and conductor. Induction by this method is the means of creating electric power in all types of electric generator.

To be strictly correct, we ought to say that an electromotive force (a voltage) is set up across the ends of the wire and that this voltage force is what causes electron flow. The electromotive force set up in this way is proportional to the rate at which the invisible lines of force are cut through.

If a noninductive resistance is connected across a battery as shown in Fig. 59(a), when the switch is closed, the current immediately jumps to its full value. When the switch is opened, the current immediately falls to zero (Fig. 59(b)).

Figure 59(c) shows an inductive circuit. The two switches of this circuit are synchronized so that when switch A opens, switch B closes. Close switch A and open switch B. The current does not immediately rise to full current condition but takes a small interval of time to do so. Next open switch A and close switch B, grounding the coil. The current does not immediately collapse but decays somewhat slowly. The behavior of the current is indicated on the graph of Fig. 59(d).

The current does not immediately rise to full steady value because some of the electric energy from the battery is diverted to create the magnetic field in the coil. When the magnetic field is saturated, then this diversion of energy ceases and at this point full current flows: it takes energy to build up a magnetic field but no energy to maintain it unchanged. When the switch A is opened and B closed, a transient current flows to ground. The circuit is disconnected from the battery at this time, yet it requires a voltage to cause the ground current to flow. The source of this electromotive force is the magnetic field as it collapses, delivering a decaying electric current.

Comparing the induction coil with the capacitor, both can store energy and act as a momentary source of electromotive force when discharging. The coil, however, stores energy in its magnetic field, converting the magnetic energy to electric energy as the field collapses. Note that the magnetic field always opposes the desired current effect. If the current is to be built up, the magnetic field opposes this action by drawing off energy to promote the magnetic field. If the current is collapsing because the switch is opened, then the magnetic field prolongs the current by putting the energy of the magnetic field back into the circuit.

Suppose next that alternating current is applied to such a coil. The magnetic field will build up in one direction or polarity, collapse, and then build up in the reverse direction as it follows the a-c fluctuations. As always, energy is required to build up a magnetic field, and this energy is then not available for electron flow. Therefore the current is

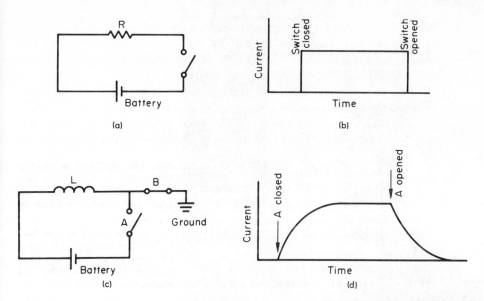

Fig. 59 (a) **Resistive circuit.** (b) **Current-time relationship for a resistive circuit.** (c) **Inductive circuit.** (d) **Current-time relationship for an inductive circuit.**

reduced as a result of the constant activity of the magnetic field. For this reason coils are often referred to as *chokes*, because they choke or restrict current in a-c circuits.

The energy supplied to the field is of course returned to the circuit when the field collapses. No energy permanently leaves the circuit as heat, as occurs with a resistance.

11.12 *the transformer*

Figure 60 is a photograph of an a-c welding transformer rated at 300 amp 60% duty cycle. The 60% duty cycle means that the transformer will deliver 300 amp for a maximum of 6 min out of every 10 if it is not to be overheated. Of the two coils wound on the transformer core, the top one is the primary coil and the bottom one the secondary, connected to the electrode and the workpiece. This particular transformer is designed to be connected to a 550-v supply. Suppose that we want to wind the coils to supply 55 v open circuit for the arc. (The number 55 is chosen simply for convenience. It is not the output voltage of the transformer.)

The input voltage is ten times the output voltage. Ideally, the manufacturer would wind ten times as many turns on the primary coil

Fig. 60 A 300-amp welding transformer. The current control method used is the adjustable coil spacing method of Fig. 69. The fixed secondary transformer coil is at the bottom of the machine. The movable primary coil has been cranked up to the 100 amp position.

as on the secondary coil. The number of turns on each coil is proportional to the voltage desired, or by formula

$$\frac{E_{\text{pri}}}{E_{\text{sec}}} = \frac{\text{turns}_{\text{pri}}}{\text{turns}_{\text{sec}}}$$

This supposes that the magnetic lines of force induced by a-c current in the primary coil are confined to the transformer iron core and that all the lines of force cut the secondary coils as the field grows and collapses. Since a magnetic field is continually moving across the secondary coils, a current and a voltage are induced in the secondary.

The magnetic field is proportional to the amp-turns, however, and vice versa. Suppose that the primary coil has 10 turns and carries 1 amp. The primary amp-turns are then 10, creating a certain strength of fluctuating magnetic field. This same field cuts the secondary coil and induces the same number of amp-turns, namely, 10. If the primary winding has 10 turns, the secondary will have only 1 turn. For 10 amp-turns the secondary current must be 10 amp.

Unfortunately, this simple theory of the transformer is subject to two qualifications. First, all the induced lines of force do *not* cut the secondary coil, especially in a welding transformer. They might perhaps do so if the two coils were wound one on top of the other. In the welding transformer shown, however, the primary is more than a foot above the secondary, and much of the magnetic field will miss the secondary coil altogether. The manufacturer will compensate by modifying the turns ratio from this theoretical 10 : 1 ratio.

The second qualification concerns the transformer's iron core. It too is a conductor with a magnetic field moving across it. There must be a current in the core too. This core current is referred to as an *eddy current*. Like all electric currents, eddy currents move at right angles to the magnetic field. In the vertical legs of the transformer of Fig. 60, they will move in horizontal planes.

It is instructive to make an estimate of the eddy current heating effect, supposing that the core is a solid block of steel instead of core laminations. The core then is a one-turn secondary. Let us take the more realistic figure of 250 for the number of primary turns and 30 amp for the primary current.

amp-turns in the primary coil then $= 30 \times 250 = 7500$

The amp-turns in the core are also 7500. The current will be 7500 amp in the core. Estimate the core resistance as 0.0001 ohm. The estimated heating effect in the core is then

$$\text{watts} = I^2R = 7500^2 \times 0.0001 = 5625 \text{ w}$$

which should be enough to burn out the transformer in a short time.

Transformers are made of neither solid blocks of steel nor ordinary welding steels. To reduce eddy currents, two modifications are made. The core is a silicon steel, which offers better resistance to flow of current. The core is also made of laminations of small-gauge steel, using for insulation only the oil, varnish, and rust between the laminations. By means of lamination the eddy currents are divided up into small currents in each lamination.

However, modern technology can make use of almost anything known, including eddy currents. Eddy currents are suited to induction heating. In induction heating, a copper coil is wound around the workpiece to be heated and alternating current passed through the coil (Fig. 104). The workpiece inside the coil acts as a one-turn secondary and is heated very rapidly. The rough calculation for eddy currents, completed above, suggests that very high currents can be developed.

An example of basic transformer calculations A welding transformer is to be connected to a 120-v supply and must have an output of 24 v and 100 amp. Two hundred turns will be wound on the primary coil. Determine (a) the number of secondary windings and (b) the primary power in watts.

$$\frac{E_p}{E_s} = \frac{\text{turns}_p}{\text{turns}_s}$$

$$\frac{120}{24} = \frac{200}{T_s}$$

Secondary turns will be 40
Secondary amp-turns $= 40 \times 100 = 4000$
Primary amp-turns $= 4000$
Primary amp $= 4000/200 = 20$ amp.
Primary power $= 20$ amp $\times 120$ v $= 2400$ w

The primary power is always equal to the secondary power by these formulas, giving the transformer an efficiency of 100%. This is almost true for a very large transformer with windings fixed in place and complete sharing of the magnetic field, but eddy current and resistance losses are significant in smaller transformers with smaller gauge wire.

11.13   resistance in a-c circuits

If an alternating current flows through a pure resistance of R ohms, then, using effective values of current and voltage, $E = IR$. Current and voltage are in phase with each other, as indicated in Fig. 61. The

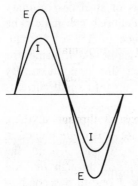

Fig. 61 Voltage-current phase relationship in a resistive circuit.

steady power loss through the resistance is the product of the effective volts times the effective amperes but varies within each half cycle from zero to a maximum of twice the effective power. This power loss is always positive, because E and I are either both positive or both negative.

11.14   inductance in a-c circuits

The unit of inductance is the *henry*(h). The inductive or magnetic effect that causes an induced electromotive force of 1 v when the current is changing at a rate of 1 amp per sec is an inductance of 1 henry. The symbol L is used for henrys.

Current and voltage are not in phase in an inductive circuit that includes coils or transformers. Recall Fig. 59(c). The current built up relatively slowly to its maximum value, and when the induction coil was disconnected from the battery, the energy in the field prolonged the current. The voltage and current are then not in phase, because when the full voltage is applied to the coil, the current delays in coming up to its steady-state value. We say that the current *lags* behind the voltage in an inductive circuit.

If alternating current is applied to an inductance of zero resistance, the current lags behind the voltage by 90°. Figure 62 shows the angular relationship.

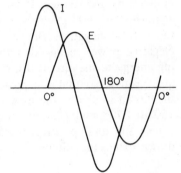

Fig. 62 Voltage-current phase relationship in an inductive cir-cuit.

The magnetic field of the coil produces an opposition voltage that opposes the change of current. To push an a-c current through the coil, a voltage from the power source equal to this opposing voltage, or back emf as it is called, must be applied. This voltage, required to cause the current to move through the coil, is given by the formula

$$E_L = 2\pi fLI$$

where $f =$ frequency in cps
$L =$ inductance in h
$I =$ current in amp

Recall the form of Ohm's law, $E = RI$. The constant $2\pi fL$ is the equivalent of R in the Ohm's law formula, although it is not a resistance. A resistance removes energy from an electric circuit in the form of heat, but a magnetic field of an inductance does not permanently remove energy from an electric circuit. The factor $2\pi fL$ is termed inductive reactance and has the symbol X_L. Reactance is measured in ohms, since it represents opposition to current flow.

$$X_L = 2\pi fL$$

and is proportional to frequency and henrys. The number of henrys must increase with the number of windings on the coil.

Example A 1-hp single-phase 60-cycle electric motor operated on 115 v draws 16 amp. If the motor is considered to have zero resistance, find the number of henrys in the windings.

$$E = 2\pi fLI$$
$$115 = 2\pi 60L \times 16$$
$$L = 0.019 \text{ h}$$

It is easy to show from Fig. 62 that no watts are consumed in a nonresistive inductance. If we multiply the voltage by the current at any angle in the 360° cycle between 0 and 90°, the voltage is positive and the current negative. Between 0 and 90° then, the power is negative. Negative power means that the magnetic field is collapsing and supplying energy to the circuit. Between 90 and 180°, both current and voltage are positive, so that the power is positive, energy being removed from the circuit to charge the magnetic field. The power is again negative from 180 to 270° and positive from 270 to 360°. The total negative power equals the total positive power, and the net result is that no power is drawn from the circuit.

11.15 capacitance in a-c circuits

If a capacitor is connected across an a-c source, first one plate of the capacitor will be charged with electrons, and then as the cycle reverses, the plate will discharge and the other plate will be charged. Even though a capacitor is an open circuit, an alternating current can flow in such a circuit. In such a purely capacitive circuit, the current *leads* the voltage by 90°, exactly the opposite of the inductive effect. No energy is withdrawn from the circuit as heat in a purely capacitive circuit. The relationship between voltage and current is then

$$E_c = \frac{1}{2\pi fC} I$$

where f = frequency, cps
C = capacitance in farads
I = current

Every welding circuit contains considerable resistance and induct-

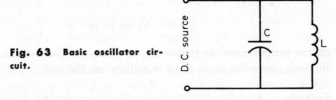

Fig. 63 Basic oscillator circuit.

ance, but capacitive effects can generally be ignored, except in certain special cases that will receive mention as they arise.

Neither a capacitor nor a choke permanently withdraw energy from an a-c circuit, but they can both serve as temporary storage of energy. By putting these two devices together in parallel, as in Fig. 63, we have an oscillator like that used to produce high-frequency alternating current for such uses as induction brazing.

Assume that the magnetic field of the oscillator coil is charged up by the external source. The field will then discharge, inducing a current that will charge the capacitor with electrons. The capacitor then discharges, recharging the magnetic field. This cyclical operation produces alternating current from a direct-current source. The frequency produced is given by the formula

$$f = \frac{1}{2\pi \sqrt{LC}}$$

where L is the number of henrys in the coil and C is the capacitance of the capacitor in farads. Hence any desired frequency can be produced by adjusting these two values.

11.16 summary of fundamental relations for alternating currents

Circuit Element	Phase Relation	Value of E/I
resistance, R ohms	I in phase with E	R ohms
inductance, L henrys	I lags E by 90°	$2\pi f L = X_L$ ohms
capacitance, C farads	I leads E by 90°	$\dfrac{1}{2\pi f C} = X_C$ ohms

11.17 saturable reactors

Saturable reactors are inductance devices used to control current.

As stated before, the magnetic field produced in any coil is proportional to the amp-turns. This is certainly true for an air-core transformer

electrical principles of welding machines

or a solenoid or for a steel-cored inductance, up to a certain point. Figure 64 shows what happens to the magnetic field of a steel core when the amp-turns are piled up without limit. At lower values of amp-turns, the number of lines of magnetic force steadily increase in proportion to the amp-turns. But at very high values of amp-turns, the magnetic field strength increases more slowly and finally does not respond to the amp-turns. The amount of magnetic field that can be packed into the core is limited, and when this limit is reached, the core is said to be saturated.

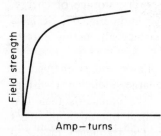

Fig. 64 Saturation of a magnetic core.

Transformer cores are not driven to saturation, but the saturable reactor may be. Figure 69(c) shows a saturable reactor as used to control the current output of the welding transformer connected to it. The reactor has two alternating current windings in series with the welding arc and a d-c winding of many turns of fine wire on the middle leg of the core. Assume that the core is driven to saturation by the d-c winding. Then no magnetic field can be set up by the main d-c coils. This is the condition for maximum welding current, since the only impedance to current flow is the resistance of the main winding. The maximum inductive reactance in the a-c coil occurs with no current in the winding, and this is the condition for minimum welding current. The welding current is thus adjusted by varying the amount of current applied to the d-c winding; the greater the d-c current, the larger the welding current.

11.18 power factor

Motors, transformers, and other coil-wound electrical devices are in common use in industry, and as a result most circuits include both resistance and inductive reactance. The voltage E_R required to drive the current through a resistance is given by $R \times I$ and is in phase with I. The voltage E_L required to drive the current through the inductance L is given by $2\pi fL$ and leads the current by 90°. In any circuit containing both resistance and inductive reactance, E_R and E_R cannot be added arithmetically to find the total voltage drop, for to do this would ignore the 90°

difference in phase angles. The total voltage drop required to supply both E_L and E^L is found by laying out the two voltages at right angles to preserve the 90° phase difference, and the total voltage drop is given by E, the hypotenuse of the triangle (see Fig. 65).

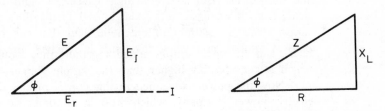

Fig. 65   **Reactance and resistance relationships.**

The resistance in ohms and the reactance are laid off similarly, the hypotenuse of the ohms triangle being given the name *impedance* and symbolized by Z. The impedance Z is the sum of all the effects that impede current flow.

$$E = \sqrt{(E_R)^2 + (E_L)^2}$$
$$= \sqrt{(RI)^2 + (2\pi fL)^2 I^2}$$
$$= I\sqrt{R^2 + X_L^2}$$
$$Z = \sqrt{R^2 + X_L^2}$$

Example   A particular coil has a resistance of 25 ohms and an inductance of 0.01 h. It is connected across 60 v at 400 cycles. Find the current through the coil and the voltage drop across R and L.

First, the resistance and the reactance are separated out as two independent factors (see Fig. 66).

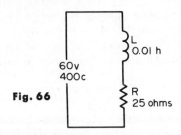

Fig. 66

$$X_L = 2\pi fL$$
$$= 6.28 \times 400 \times 0.01 = 25.12 \text{ ohms}$$

$$\text{Total impedance} = Z = \sqrt{R^2 + X_L^2}$$
$$= \sqrt{25^2 + 25.12^2}$$
$$= 35.5 \text{ ohms}$$

Then
$$E = IZ$$
$$60 = I\ 35.5$$
$$I = 1.69 \text{ amps}$$

$$E_R = IR = 1.69 \times 25 = 42.3 \text{ v}$$
$$E_L = IX_L = 1.69 \times 25.12 = 42.5 \text{ v}$$
$$E = \sqrt{E_R^2 + E_L^2} = \sqrt{42.3^2 + 42.5^2} = 60$$

If E_R and E_L were simply added together, they would sum to 84.8 v, which is considerably higher than the supply voltage—an impossibility.

Now the power consumed in this coil is presumably supplied by an electric power company, which must at all times be able to meet your demands for power.

The resistance of this coil consumes power by turning it into heat. This is the power that the power utility charges you for. This power lost to the circuit is

$$P_R = E_R I$$
$$= 42.3 \times 1.69 = 69.5 \text{ w}$$

Consider next P_L, the product of $E_L \times I$. This quantity represents the power drawn from the line used to supply your magnetic field. This power is not lost to the electric power system but is repeatedly returned to it. Therefore you are not charged for it. The power company nevertheless has to supply this reactive power free to thousands of customers and provide the facilities for it.

The total power drawn from the line, both for resistance heating and the inductive magnetic field, is

$$P = E \times I$$
$$= 60 \times 1.69 = 101.4 \text{ w}$$

You are drawing 101.4 w but paying for only 69.5 w.

Since this total power, 101.4 w, is not the true power *consumption*, it is called volt-amps (va or kva). The ratio of the actual resistive power consumed to the total volt-amp power drawn, is termed the power factor:

$$\text{power factor} = \frac{P_R}{P} = \frac{E_R I}{EI} = 69.5/101.4 = 68\frac{1}{2}\%$$

Power companies do not like low power factor loads, for obvious reasons. A power factor of $68\frac{1}{2}\%$ falls within the power factor range for welding machines, which of course have a considerable amount of reactance. But suppose you were to operate a device rated at 50 kva with a power factor of 10%. Such a device would have little resistance but a great deal of inductance. Your demand on the power utility would be 50 kva, but you would be paying for only 5 kw.

There are no such bargains in electric power. Power companies have a rate system that penalizes loads with low factor. On such a device with a 10% power factor, you will pay for the 5 kw, but in addition you will pay a power factor penalty.

A completely resistive circuit has a power factor of 100%. A completely inductive and nonresistive circuit has a power factor of 0%. The actual power factor will depend on the relative proportions of resistance and inductive reactance in the electrical machine. The disadvantages of low power factor extend to more than a power factor penalty. Compared with a high power factor machine, a low factor will call for heavier gauge wiring, larger fuses, larger disconnects, and higher installation costs, since extra amperes must be brought in to the machine beyond the actual power consumed resistively.

Low power factors can be corrected, however, by the use of capacitors. A capacitor's operation is approximately opposite to that of an inductance. Current through an inductance lags 90° behind the voltage, whereas with a capacitor the current leads the voltage by 90°. If a capacitor is connected into the same line as the inductance, the phase angle will be advanced, thus improving the power factor, and the circuit will behave as though the inductance were reduced. In fact, by suitably sizing the microfarad capacity, the circuit can be made to give a power factor of 100% or more (leading power factor).

Welding machines of the transformer type are inherently low power factor machines. This low power factor is not an important matter for light-duty welders operating below 100 amp, and such machines are not usually corrected. But power factor correction is usual for larger welders. To obtain some notion of power factor effects in a typical welder, we shall examine the published data for the Miller Electric Manufacturing a-c welder model 103, rated at 300 amp.

The power factor of any welding machine will vary with the load current to the arc. At rated load of 300 amp and without power factor correction, this machine draws an input power of 15.2 kw and 24.4 kva. Therefore its power factor at rated load is

$$15.2/24.4 = 62\frac{1}{2}\%$$

With a capacitor for power factor correction, power input is 15.2 kw and 20.2 kva for a power factor at rated load of $15.2/20.2$ or 75%. The power-factor–corrected machine always draws less current than the same machine without correction. This does *not* mean that the two machines use different amounts of electric power. Under idling conditions or low current, the power factor is higher than at rated load.

PROBLEMS

1 What is the peak voltage in every half-wave of (a) 440 v a.c. (b) 220 v a.c.

2 What is the maximum power in watts dissipated in a resistance dropping 20 v and drawing 10 amp during any half cycle of alternating current?

3 An X-ray tube is rated for 250,000 v peak. What is the effective voltage across this tube?

4 An automobile ignition system is powered by a 12-v battery, and the ignition coil must provide 15,000 v at the spark plug. The primary winding has 300 turns. The secondary current is 0.0005 amp. Find
(a) the number of secondary turns in the coil
(b) the primary current
(c) the primary power in watts, for 100% efficiency

5 The gas burners on a stress-relieving furnace are ignited by a spark plug supplying a 6000-v arc for ignition. The ignition transformer has a 120-v primary with 200 turns. How many secondary turns are required on this transformer?

6 An induction coil has a rating of 0.1 h. Find the inductive reactance of this coil at the following frequencies: (a) direct current, (b) 60 cycles, (c) 10 kc.

7 Find the current through the coil of question 6 at the same three frequencies if the coil is connected across 120 v.

8 Find the impedance Z in ohms of the following combination in series:
(a) a 6-ohm resistance and an 8-ohm inductive reactance
(b) a 10-ohm inductive reactance and a 24-ohm resistance
(c) a 1000-ohm resistance and a 10-h coil, at 120 cycles

9 Explain in your own words how a saturable reactor can control an a-c current with the use of a d-c winding.

10 Find the power factor of the circuits in question 8.

11 The following data are from *The Mid-States Welder bulletin:*

Model	Input	Input	
MAG 300	16	21	(at rated load)
MAG 200	12.2	16.1	(at rated load)

Determine the power factor of these two machines at rated load.

12.1 arc welding processes

The subject matter of this chapter is the description and operation of the machines employed for a wide range of arc welding processes. The most widely used arc processes for which these machines are suitable include the following:

1. Manual arc welding using flux-coated stick electrodes. The American Welding Society recommends the name "shielded metal arc" for this method.
2. TIG welding, using a nonconsumable electrode and a separate filler metal with an inert shielding gas. This method has a variety of names: tungsten inert gas (TIG), argon tungsten arc, argowelding, heliarc, and others, but the American Welding Society recommends the term "gas tungsten arc." The designation "TIG" is used in this book because it has a conversational informality that seems to appeal to welding personnel.
3. MIG welding, using mechanically fed filler wire for the consumable electrode with an inert shielding gas. This method also has several names: metal inert gas (MIG), shielded inert gas metal arc (SIGMA), inert metal arc, argonarc, and others, but the recommended AWS term is "gas metal arc."
4. Submerged arc welding, which is automatic welding under a blanket of powdered flux in which filler wire fed from coils as for MIG welding is used. Submerged arc welding is often simply called "subarc" in conversation.

ARC WELDING MACHINES

AND

EQUIPMENT

12

5. Carbon arc welding, usually with two carbon electrodes.

A welding machine such as a welding transformer that is suited to one of these arc welding methods is not necessarily suited to other types of arc welding.

The arc welding process can usually be recognized from the appearance of the equipment used. The frontispiece photograph shows a large subarc arrangement. There is no arc flash because the arc is invisible under the cover of granular flux that hides the welding operation. Figure 67 is a typical TIG welding setup using Liquid Air accessories. Components include a suitable welding transformer, a cylinder of argon gas,

Fig. 67 TIG welding equipment using Liquid Air torch and accessories.

and a TIG torch. Torch connections include a cable connection for current, tubing for shielding gas supply, and tubing for water-cooling the torch. The shape of the torch is characteristic, having a cap at the back end to protect the rather long tungsten electrode against accidental breakage. Finally, Fig. 68 shows a Hobart MIG welding setup. Since the filler wire is fed continuously through the torch or gun, the shape of the gun is unlike that of a TIG torch. This gun requires connection for electric

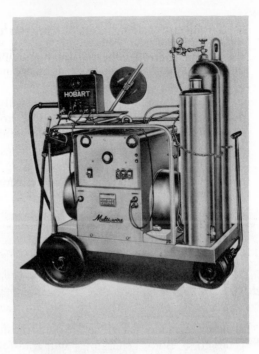

Fig. 68 (a) MIG arc-welding machine, gun, and accessories. (Courtesy Hobart Brothers Co.)

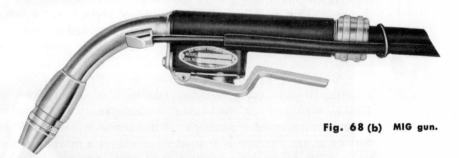

Fig. 68 (b) MIG gun.

current, water cooling in and out, shielding gas, filler wire, and control cable. The photograph shows also the cylinders of shielding gas, the welding transformer, the wire feeder mechanism above the transformer, and the reel of filler wire.

During arc welding, three variables must be controlled: (1) current, (2) voltage, and (3) speed of travel. In *manual welding* with stick electrodes or manual TIG the welder sets the desired current on the machine, and during his welding he controls two of these three variables: speed of travel and arc voltage. Arc voltage is controlled by controlling arc length, for the two are related. In *semiautomatic welding,* of which MIG welding is a typical example, the current is again preset on the machine. The arc length, and therefore the arc voltage, is automatically controlled by the wire feeder, which maintains a constant arc length.

arc welding machines and equipment
193

As a result, the operator controls only the speed of travel. Finally, in *automatic welding*, as in submerged arc welding, all three variables are preset and controlled by the welding equipment.

The following statements review arc welding principles already discussed:

1. Direct-current straight polarity means that the workpiece is connected to the positive terminal of the welding machine.
2. Arc voltage increases with arc length. If the electrode is shorted to the workpiece, the voltage drop across the arc is zero.
3. Deposition rate of filler metal increases with current.
4. Penetration is deepest for DCSP, less for a.c., and least for DCRP.
5. About two-thirds of the useful arc heat appears at the anode and one-third at the cathode.

12.2 duty cycle

Welding machines are either welding transformers or engine-driven electric generators. Both generators and transformers are rugged low-voltage high-current machines. The A. O. Smith 650E a.c. welding transformer is typical. This machine has an efficiency of about 80%, a power factor of about 80% at the rated load of 650 amp, and a power factor of 100% at half the rated output, in both cases using power factor correction.

All welding machines are rated at a certain amperage load current at a particular duty cycle. Welding machines are tested for consecutive 10-minute intervals on the basis of a certain number of minutes on and a certain number of minutes off. If a machine is rated 300 amp 60% duty cycle, the machine is guaranteed to deliver a maximum of 300 amp for a full 6 min if the machine is next allowed to idle for 4 min, after which it will again deliver 300 amp for six min. The duty cycle applies only to a 10-min interval. A 60% duty cycle does *not* mean 36 min in every hour followed by a 24-min idling time. The 60% duty rating is suitable for manual welding, for an operator doing such work can rarely put in more than 6 min of arc time in 10. He must stop the arc to replace rods, make tack welds, chip slag, align workpieces and handle other interruptions.

Other types of welding require a duty cycle higher than 60%. Pipe thawing may be a 100% duty operation. Automatic, semiautomatic, arc-air cutting, and plasma torch cutting may go on without interruption for more than 6 min in 10, or may well be uninterrupted until the bead or cut is completed. For such operations manufacturers supply machines rated for 100% duty cycle, which is continuous operation.

The maximum current that a welder can draw from the machine is limited by the temperature rise within the machines. This temperature rise increases with the square of the current, since power $= I^2R$. This power relationship is the basis for determining the maximum load current that the welding machine can deliver at a different duty cycle from the rating. By formula

$$\frac{t_r}{t_n} = \frac{(I_n)^2}{(I_r)^2}$$

where $t_r =$ rated duty cycle
$t_n =$ new duty cycle
$I_r =$ rated current
$I_n =$ current at the new duty cycle, maximum

To clarify matters, here is an example. A 300-amp 60% duty cycle welder is put to work on pipe-thawing service. What is the maximum current that can be drawn from the machine?

We make the assumption that pipe thawing will require continuous operation, or 100% duty cycle.

$$\frac{60}{100} = \frac{I_n^2}{300^2} \qquad I_n = 232 \text{ amp or, say, } 230 \text{ amp}$$

A rule of thumb is to say that a 60% duty welder will deliver 75% of rated current at 100% duty.

The following example suggests another type of problem that may arise. An emergency demands that we draw 275 amp from a 200-amp 60% duty welder. What is the limiting duty cycle?

$$\frac{60}{t_n} = \frac{275^2}{200^2}$$

The new duty cycle is 32%, or 3 min out of 10.

These two examples should indicate that a current rating for a welding machine is meaningless without specifying a duty cycle. On some machines, should the machine rating be exceeded, a thermostat cuts off the welding current while power to the cooling fan is maintained. When the machine has cooled to a safe temperature, the thermostat closes the welding circuit again, and welding can then be continued.

12.3 engine driven welders

Engine-driven welders must be employed if utility power is not available. Both diesel and gasoline engines are available as prime movers. Fire regulations in mines, on shipboard, on off-shore drilling rigs, and in other such places sometimes require the use of diesel fuels. Besides being safer, the diesel engine has other advantages over the gasoline engine. Diesel fuel is cheaper. A diesel engine is also more efficient at rated load than a gasoline engine is, and although the efficiency of a gasoline engine falls drastically at part loads or idling, the diesel engine's high efficiency (about 30%) is maintained at light load conditions. Smaller machines are usually driven by gasoline engines, which are cheaper in first cost because of lighter construction and a simpler fuel-metering system. The gasoline engine thus provides the cheaper first cost, and the diesel engine offers the lowest operating cost. As in most industrial equipment, both advantages are not available in the same item of equipment. Low first cost will be paid for later in operating costs: low operating costs will be paid for in high first cost.

A diesel-driven 300-amp 60% duty welder will weigh about 2400 lb, and a gasoline-driven machine of the same capacity will weigh about 1700 lb. Since there is a direct relationship between cost and weight in industrial goods, the weights suggest relative costs. Engine-driven welders are available in a-c and d-c outputs from 200 amp output up, at 60% and 100% duty cycles.

In one respect, the engine-driven welding machine does not compare favorably with the welding transformer. When striking an arc, the voltage output of the machine must go from open-circuit voltage (usually 60 to 70 v) to zero voltage when the rod is shorted to the work and finally to arc voltage, all in a very short interval of time. The engine-driven welder, because of the weight of its rotating parts, has too much inertia to respond promptly to these changes. For much standard welding, this inertia does not matter particularly, but for critical types of welding in which all conditions must be closely controlled, an engine-driven welder cannot be used.

12.4 welding transformers

The following table gives the standard single-phase a-c welding transformer ratings for manual welding but does not include a number of light-duty machines. Open-circuit voltages may range from 55 to 80 v, depending on the model and its purpose. Primary windings are available for connection to 208, 230, 460, or 575 v.

A-C–d-c or d-c welders use a silicon or selenium rectifier to produce direct current. Such welding machines have a polarity switch to supply straight or reverse polarity. On combination a-c–d-c machines the d-c open-circuit voltage is about 10% less than the corresponding a-c voltage.

Two welding machines are sometimes connected in parallel in order

STANDARD WELDING TRANSFORMERS

Rated Current Output, amp	Duty Cycle, %	Load, volts
200	50	30
200	60	40
295	20	30
300	60	40
400	60	40
500	60	40
750	60 min	40
1000	60 min	40
1500	60 min	40

to obtain higher current output. This may be done if both machines are connected to the same phase of a three-phase line, assuming that they are single-phase machines and that both machines have the same polarity. Polarity is determined before connecting the output leads together by determining with an a-c voltmeter whether the voltage between the two is less than about 15 v. If this output voltage is double normal voltage, then the polarities of the machines are opposite, and the primary connections of one machine must be reversed. An ordinary 110-v light bulb may be used instead of a voltmeter. If the lamp does not light, polarity is correct.

A few of the common methods for current control to the arc are diagrammed in Fig. 69. Instructions for the moveable primary coil method of Fig. 69(b) will be found on the brand-name welders manufactured by Miller Electric Manufacturing Company, such as Airco and National Cylinder Gas. This method is used in the transformer of Fig. 60, which actually shows the position of the primary for delivering 100 amp (machine rating is 300 amp 60% duty). The higher the primary coil is cranked away from the secondary, the less of the magnetic field the secondary will intercept, in effect reducing the secondary amp-turns. Figure 69(c) uses saturable reactor control of current. This method was explained in the previous chapter, but in brief, arc current is increased with increase in current on the middle direct-current winding. The required direct current for the control winding is obtained from the line a-c supply by means of a rectifier bridge circuit.

In the method of Fig. 69(d), movement of the moveable core downward will increase the inductance of the control winding and reduce the output current. Figure 69(e) uses a moveable short-circuiting core to short-circuit the magnetic flux. The greater the magnetic flux that travels the short-circuiting path, the less is available to induce current in the secondary winding. Current therefore is reduced by moving the moveable core downward.

arc welding machines and equipment
197

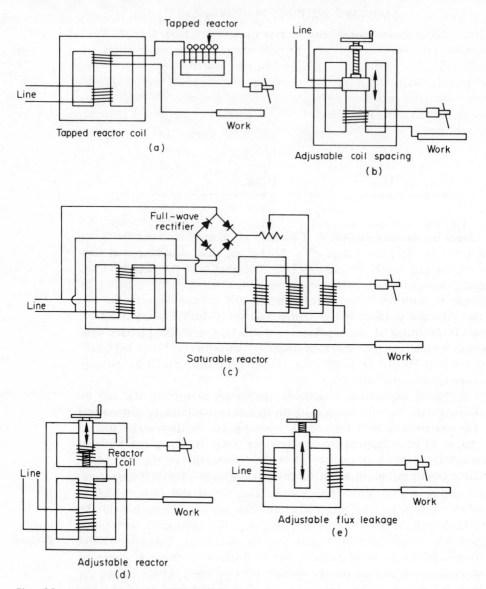

Fig. 69 Welding current control methods.

The voltage drop across the arc varies with the length of the arc. In manual welding the operator controls the voltage by controlling arc length, and in general he maintains as short an arc as possible, about ⅛ in. Generally a short arc with the proper current gives a sharp crackling noise. The operator, however, cannot hold an exactly uniform length of arc with his arm, particularly when the stick electrode is continually shortening, so that the arc voltage is continually varied. For this variable voltage and constant current, a constant-current machine must be used. Machines for automatic welding, to be discussed later, are usually constant voltage machines. The constant current machine has a drooping volt-ampere relationship as shown in Fig. 70. The volt-ampere graph droops from the open-circuit voltage, so that for any variation in arc voltage the changes in arc current will be slight. This current is not truly constant but is as constant as can be managed with a low open-circuit

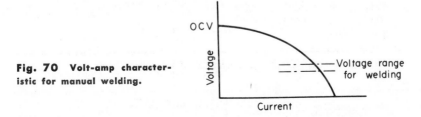

Fig. 70 Volt-amp character-istic for manual welding.

voltage. A true constant-current curve would give a vertical line for current, but its open-circuit voltage would be so high that the operator would be in danger of electrocution. With the type of output characteristic shown, however, the following features are possible:

1. Low open-circuit voltage.
2. Only small changes in current for variations in voltage.
3. Low enough currents to avoid burning out the welding machine when the rod short-circuits the arc, as when an arc is struck. The current will at all times remain reasonably close to the setting given it on the machine. Welding of course is not done at a voltage near the open-circuit voltage but at about a third or a quarter of this voltage.

12.5 voltage drops

If the machine has a voltmeter, this will indicate the total output voltage —the sum of voltage across the arc plus voltage drops in the cables, rod, electrode holder, workpiece, and ground clamp. Since welding is always a high-current operation, voltage drops are unusually high. Cables particularly can represent a considerable voltage drop owing to both resistance and reactance. To counter a-c inductive reactance (not a problem with d-c welding), the two cables should be located close together to cancel each other's magnetic field. The inductive effects of coiling cable have been noted in the previous chapter. A 4-v cable drop is the maximum recommended.

RECOMMENDED SIZE OF COPPER WELDING LEADS FOR D-C WELDING*

Distance from Welding Machine in Feet

Amp	50	75	100	150	200	250	300	400
100	2	2	2	1	0	00	000	0000
150	2	2	1	00	000	0000		
200	2	1	0	000	0000			
300	1	0	000	0000				
350	0	00	0000					
400	00	000	0000					
500	00	0000						
600	000							

*Use the next larger size for a.c. because of reactance effects.

WELDING CABLE DATA

Cable Size	Diameter, Bare Conductor, in.	Ohms/ft Copper	Ohms/ft Aluminum
4	0.275	0.000249	0.000408
2	0.335	0.000156	0.000259
1	0.400	0.000124	0.000213
0	0.440	0.000098	0.000161
00	0.490	0.000078	0.000128
000	0.545	0.000062	0.000101
0000	0.635	0.000049	0.000080

Example of a cable calculation A stick welding job is assumed to require 200 amp. Distance from machine to the work is estimated at 200 ft. Will the voltage drop through the cable exceed the recommended maximum of 4 v if a No. 4 copper cable is used?

> ohms per foot for No. 4 cable = 0.00025
> number of feet of cable = 200 ft × 2 cables = 400 ft
> total cable resistance = 400 × 0.00025 = 0.1 ohm
> voltage drop = 200 amp × 0.1 ohm = 20 v

The wattage dissipation through the cable is 4 kw. The cable is impossibly small for the job.

Other sources of voltage drop and excessive heating occur as a result of poor maintenance of cables, ground clamps, and electrode holders and include the following possibilities:

1. Broken cable strands at cable connections.
2. Loose connections.

3. Bad contact of rod in electrode holder due to dirt, corrosion, or low spring pressure, or the same conditions at the ground clamp.
4. Use of too small an electrode holder. Electrode holders are usually sized in ratings of 200, 250, 300, 350, 400, and 500 amp.
5. Ground clamp located too far away from the arc.
6. Poor ground clamp contact.
7. Use of lightly tacked steel grounds unable to carry the required current.
8. Burning of rods too short and too close to the electrode holder that may overheat the holder and raise electrical resistance.

In summary, both the high current and the low voltage of arc welding magnify the importance of any unsuspected voltage drops.

12.6 arc blow

D-C welding has one disadvantage not present in a-c welding: arc blow. When a current flows in any conductor, a magnetic field is formed around the conductor and at right angles to the current. Since there is current through the electrode, arc, workpiece, and ground clamp, magnetic fields exist around each of these components. In welding with direct current, the arc sometimes wanders and lacks control as though it were being blown to and fro by the influence of these complex magnetic fields. This is arc blow. Arc blow is more common in welding with very high or very low currents, and especially in welding in corners or other confined spaces. Usually arc blow results from the interaction of the magnetic field of the workpiece with that of the arc.

These arc blow movements may cause atmospheric gases to be pulled into the arc, resulting in porosity or other defects. To correct arc blow, the usual methods are

1. Weld away from the ground clamp.
2. Change the position of the ground clamp.
3. If working on a steel bench, alter the position of the work on the bench.

12.7 TIG welding machines

TIG welding is usually done manually, although semiautomatic and automatic methods are in use. No flux is required, since the tungsten electrode, the tip of the filler rod, and the weld puddle are protected by the flow of inert gas, usually argon. Almost all metals and alloys may be joined by the TIG method, including titanium and zirconium.

arc welding machines and equipment
201

TIG welding transformers use the drooping volt-ampere character-istic that is used for manual arc welding, with open-circuit voltage of 75 to 80, and duty cycle of 60%. Most machines designed specially for TIG welding will supply a.c., DCSP, and DCRP by means of a three-position polarity switch on the front of the machine. However, a TIG machine has certain special characteristics based on the use of the tung-sten electrode and the requirements peculiar to TIG welding.

The inert gas used in TIG welding is usually argon, helium, or mix-tures of the two. Copper may be welded with nitrogen, although this is not done in North America. To establish a conducting arc through the shielding gas, the gas atoms must be ionized by removing one or more electrons from the atom. The ionization potential for argon, that is, the applied voltage necessary to pull an electron off the atom, is 15.7. For helium it is 24.5 v. These figures indicate that a higher voltage drop occurs across a helium arc and that in general for any type of welding, the arc voltage is determined by the shielding gas as well as other variables.

Three arc starting methods are in use in TIG welding:

1. touch starting
2. high voltage
3. high frequency

The touch starting method is used if possible, but is often not allowed as it can contaminate the tungsten electrode and cause deterioration. It may also leave particles of tungsten in the weld, causing such welds to be rejected. In other welding, especially with thoriated or zirconiated electrodes, touch starting may be permissible. Touch starting is also done on a piece of copper or carbon to initiate the arc, which is then transfer-red quickly to the weld.

The second method of starting is the use of a surge of about 165 as the electrode is brought close to the workpiece. This high voltage is then cut off, and the welding machine returns to its normal open-circuit voltage for welding.

The high frequency method superimposes a high frequency current on the standard 60 cycle if a.c. is used, or on d.c. straight or reverse polarity. The high frequency current ionizes the gases in the path of the arc so that touch starting is unnecessary. A switch is provided on the machine with positions for continuous high frequency current, high frequency only for starting, or to cut out the high frequency generator. When TIG welding with d.c., high frequency current is used only to start the arc and not for welding; with a.c., high frequency current is maintained for the welding operation. When TIG welding with a.c., the arc may be extinguished when the voltage goes through zero during cycle reversal. By the use of high frequency current, the cycle reversal is so rapid that the arc does not have time to extinguish or the shielding gas to deionize. An alternative method to high frequency current for preventing extinguishing the arc is the use of square wave alternating current instead of the usual sine wave. Square wave generators, however, are not in common use, being complex and expensive.

If the TIG transformer has a high frequency voltage control, the control should be set to the minimum necessary for proper welding. The problems of inductance in the welding cables are much worse on high frequency. Chapter 11 demonstrates that inductive reactance increases with frequency. Long cables cannot be used with high frequency current, since there is considerable inductance merely in the two straight cables. If the cables are overly long or coiled, the high frequency voltage may be dissipated in the cables and almost none would appear at the arc.

Arc starting characteristics are better when zirconiated or thoriated electrodes (thorium is best) are used. Tungsten, especially alloyed tungsten, is an excellent emitter of electrons, which means that it is a good cathode. This characteristic, however, gives rise to another problem. If the electrode behaves like a cathode, then it will rectify the arc when a-c power is supplied to it, and arc current will be greater in the positive half cycle (the straight polarity part of the a-c cycle) than in the negative half. This rectification may be even more pronounced if the metal of the workpiece has a heavy oxide film. Arc reignition then becomes more difficult in the negative half of the cycle. This problem can be overcome in a standard welding transformer by connecting 6 or 12 v of battery power so that the battery voltage adds to the negative half of the cycle. One hundred amp-hours of battery capacity per 100 amp of welding current are recommended. TIG welding machines are available with built-in wave-balancing compensation for this effect.

These observations suggest that a TIG welding transformer is basically a DCSP machine, and it might appear that TIG is unsuited for welding with reverse polarity on direct current. On DCRP also, too much heat develops at the electrode, and currents must be reduced for this polarity. There is, however, one important application of TIG welding with DCRP—the welding of aluminum and magnesium. These two metals may also be welded with high frequency (HF) alternating current. Both metals develop highly refractory oxide surfaces, which TIG with DCRP can very effectively clean from the metal surface. How this cleaning is accomplished is a little uncertain and more than one explanation exists. Perhaps the best theory is that the positive ions in the arc sandblast the oxide. The appearance of the metal surface near the weld supports this explanation, as does the fact that the cleaning action is greater with the heavy argon ions than with the very light helium ions. Aluminium and magnesium are exceptional, however; other metals are TIG-welded with ACHF or DCSP.

TIG welding transformers with switches to operate the water and shielding gas control valves can be obtained. Compared with oxygen and acetylene, argon is an expensive gas, and the operator sometimes forgets to shut off the gas flow. Another useful optional device is crater control, provided by reducing current at the termination of the weld.

Standard d-c welding machines are suitable for TIG welding, but a-c machines must be provided with high frequency generators, available from any supplier of welding machines.

An interesting feature of high frequency alternating current is that if the frequency is high enough, a person cannot be electrocuted by it. High frequency currents travel toward the outside surfaces of conductors —the "skin effect." In the human body, therefore, the current cannot reach the nervous system and produce the heart and respiratory upsets (ventricular fibrillation) that cause death. Nevertheless, a high frequency burn heals more slowly than a d-c or 60-cycle burn.

12.8 TIG accessories

The argon gas system requires an argon regulator to reduce argon cylinder pressure to about 20 psi. A flowmeter is also used since different welding conditions call for different argon flow rate and because consumption of the gas should be controlled owing to its high cost.

The TIG torch with its tungsten electrode supplies both current and argon to the arc. Like stick electrode holders, torches are rated for the maximum current that can be passed through them. Below a 200-amp capacity such torches are air-cooled, but at higher ratings they are water-cooled.

Figure 71 is an exploded view of the Linde HW-17 Heliarc torch, typical of TIG torches. The tungsten electrodes are held in the torch by means of collets and collet bodies made in sizes to fit standard tungsten electrode diameters. Shielding gas flow is shaped by a gas cup or nozzle on the end of the torch body. These gas nozzles are made of either metallic or ceramic material. Although ceramic nozzles are subject to accidental breakage, they are used at currents below 300 amp and in confined areas where arcing to a metal nozzle could occur. The metal gas nozzles are a little easier to keep clean and can be water-cooled for heavy currents. To reduce gas turbulence, which is a cause of inspiration of atmospheric gases into the arc, gas lens accessories may be used with the nozzle. The gas lens passes the argon gas through fine wire screens.

Spot welds by the TIG method can be produced with an arc spot pistol grip gun. This method of spot welding is called "gas tungsten arc

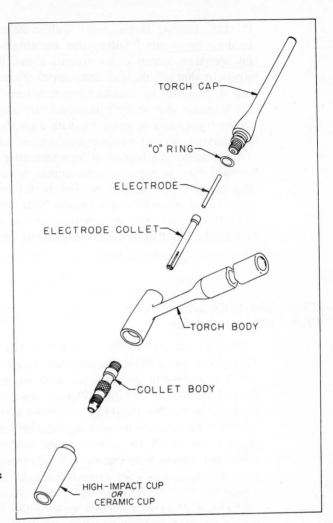

TORCH CAP

"O" RING

ELECTRODE

ELECTRODE COLLET

TORCH BODY

COLLET BODY

HIGH-IMPACT CUP
OR
CERAMIC CUP

Fig. 71 Linde HW-17 Heliarc torch for TIG welding.

spot welding," or arc spot welding. It has these advantages over standard resistance welders:

1. Use of an inert gas for shielding
2. Portability
3. Ability to produce a spot weld using one side of the joint only
4. Use of a standard TIG welding machine for power supply instead of a resistance welding transformer

The spot gun is held against the workpiece, and a short-duration current produces the spot weld. This method produces a slight hollow or low spot, which may be located on the rear side of the weld, if appearance is a factor. Filler metal may have to be added for appearance or to prevent cracking at the hollow, although the addition of filler metal is hardly convenient. If alternating current is used to produce spot welds, the tungsten electrode is retracted above the workpiece and the arc is struck by means of high frequency. With direct current, the electrode usually contacts the workpiece and is then retracted to produce the arc. Since direct current produces greater penetration, it is preferred for heavier gauges. Arc spot welding can be applied to a wide range of metals, such as carbon, alloy, and stainless steels and most nonferrous metals including titanium and zirconium, but the method is not recommended for aluminum or galvanized metals. Thicknesses greater than about 0.100 in. cannot be welded by this method.

TIG welding need not be a manual method. Various accessories are available for semiautomatic and automatic TIG welding using filler wire fed to the arc from coils as in MIG welding.

12.9   the MIG arc

Of all the common welding methods, MIG welding probably produces the least dilution in transferring metal across the arc. The most common are semiautomatic methods, usually requiring a 100% duty machine. Direct current reverse polarity is almost always used. With alternating current the arc is extinguished when the voltage goes through zero, if the standard 60-cycle sine wave is employed. DCSP has the problems of spatter and erratic arc. These problems arise largely from the arc of the MIG shielding gases—argon, carbon dioxide, or mixtures of these.

The electric arc in MIG welding has other interesting features. A fine wire is used, with a high amperage, perhaps 0.030 in. ($\frac{1}{30}$ in.) and 200 amp. As a comparison, 200 amp would be about the limit for a $\frac{3}{16}$ in. stick electrode, which is $\frac{1}{5}$ in. diameter. The use of such high currents with fine wire gives a rapid burn-off rate in inches per minute, 100 in. per min minimum. At such rates, the wire cannot be fed manually.

The method of transfer of filler wire across the arc in MIG welding depends on the current range. At very low currents, the filler metal is transferred in large globules or drops. As the welding current increases, the drops of filler metal become progressively smaller, until at a certain transition current, which depends on wire diameter and material, the metal transfer changes from droplets to a spray. If the current is further increased, it is possible actually to boil off the filler wire, though the boiling method is not used for metal deposition.

The large-globule method of transferring metal is used with low currents for welding thin-gauge materials. This welding process goes by such names as Short Arc and Dipmatic. The large globules of filler metal may transfer at a rate of 100 or more per second. Each one contacts the weld puddle and short-circuits the arc before separating from the filler wire. The globule is pinched off from the wire by the constricting effect of the magnetic field of the high-current arc. Figure 72 illustrates the sequence of metal transfer. The short arc method uses low currents of

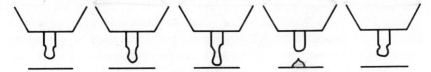

Fig. 72 The short-circuiting method of metal transfer from MIG wire.

50 to perhaps 200 amp, reverse polarity, and maximum wire diameter of 0.045 in. Arc voltages are low, 12 to 22 v. Because of the constant short circuiting of the arc, the conventional welding machine with its drooping voltage characteristic cannot be used. Constant-voltage machines better suited to such welding demands are employed.

12.10 current density

Current density means the amperes per square inch of electrode cross-sectional area. All electrodes must operate within a certain range of current density. Too low a current density produces a lumpy type of metal transfer and a rough weld; too high a current density produces burned metal and a variety of other unsatisfactory effects. In general, however, a welding method that can produce a high current density over a narrow weld area, as the MIG and electron beam processes do, will generally produce a better weld than a lower current density over a greater weld area will. If the heat of the weld can be concentrated in a narrow area, the welding will be faster, the distortion will be less, the heat-affected zone will be smaller, and the heat-treating complications in the heat-affected zone will possibly be fewer.

If welding with a $\frac{5}{32}$ in. stick electrode and with 0.045 in. MIG wire are compared, both being burned off with the same current, these differences will be noted:

1. A greater weight of stick electrode must be deposited per inch of weld, even without considering stub losses.
2. The weld is wider with the stick electrode.
3. The penetration is less with the stick electrode, if the same polarity is used in both methods.

WIRE DATA FOR CURRENT DENSITY

Wire Diameter, in.	Decimal Equivalent	Wire Area, sq in.
0.020	0.020	0.00031
0.025	0.025	0.00051
0.030	0.030	0.00071
0.035	0.035	0.00096
0.045	0.045	0.00160
0.062	0.062	0.00307
5/64	0.078	0.0048
3/32	0.094	0.0069
7/64	0.109	0.0093
1/8	0.125	0.0123
5/32	0.15625	0.0192
3/16	0.1875	0.0276

To compare current densities of flux-coated electrodes, tungsten electrodes, and filler wire, we shall take a $5/32$-in. rod at 150 amp, a $5/32$ pure tungsten electrode at 150 amp, and a 0.035-in. MIG filler wire at 150 amp. Both filler metals are mild steel.

Current density for the tungsten electrode and the rod are the same.

$$\text{current density for the } 5/32\text{-in. rod} = \frac{\text{current}}{\text{area}} = \frac{150}{0.0192}$$
$$= 7800 \text{ amp/sq in.}$$

$$\text{current density for the 0.035-in. wire} = \frac{150}{0.00096}$$
$$= 156,000 \text{ amp/sq in.}$$

The difference in current density is 20 to 1.

12.11 MIG welding machines

MIG welding may be done by either the spray method of transferring metal across the arc, in material $3/32$ in. or thicker, or the short-circuiting method, for thin-gauge material. In the spray transfer method, arc voltages range from 25 to 32 v, whereas the short-circuiting method uses arc voltages of 15 to 22 v.

The conventional welding machine with the drooping volt-ampere characteristic is used for much MIG welding but cannot be used for the short-circuiting arc. Generally, the constant potential (constant voltage) welding machine is preferred for MIG welding and is also used for submerged arc welding. Such machines make possible a wider range of applications of the MIG process. A constant potential machine has a lower open-circuit voltage than a welding machine suited to shielded metal arc or TIG welding does, and a constant or nearly constant voltage for changes in current, as shown in Fig. 73. Thus welding voltage and open-circuit voltage are almost identical. With a constant potential welder, the arc

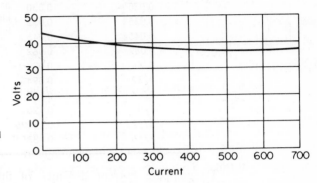

Fig. 73 Constant potential welding characteristic.

is usually initiated by a run-in start, that is, by feeding the wire into the work.

Both the run-in start and the short-circuiting arc require control of the short-circuiting characteristics of the machine. Short-circuiting current is adjustable by means of *slope control*. Figure 73 is essentially a flat curve and has no slope. If the welding machine has slope control, it will have several reactance turns and a slope control handle to cut reactance into the circuit to give adjustable slope as shown in Fig. 74. The more reactance turns cut into the circuit, the greater the reactance, the steeper the slope, and the smaller the short-circuiting current. Slope therefore means the use of reactance to control the shape of the volt-ampere curve of the welding machine output. The open-circuit voltage is not changed by slope control.

Steel filler wire requires a flatter slope for a higher arc ignition current on short circuit, or about 3500 amp for $\frac{3}{32}$-in. wire. Smaller steel wire and soft wire such as aluminum require a steeper slope to prevent spatter, burning out of the wire, and freezing of the wire to the work during short-circuiting. Too much slope may give insufficient current to start the arc. Increasing the slope tends to produce a flatter or less convex bead when steel is welded.

Slope may be expressed as the number of volts slope per 100 amp. Figure 74 shows two slopes, 1 v per 100 amp and 10 v per 100 amp. For an open-circuit voltage of 30, these slopes give short-circuiting currents of 3000 amp and 300 amp respectively. These two slopes correspond approximately to the available minimum and maximum slope control in commercial constant-voltage welding machines. The conventional drooping voltage machine has a volt-ampere relationship, which,

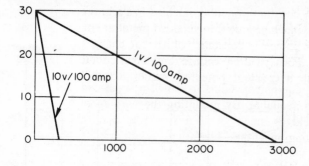

if it is considered as slope, is usually about 20-v per 100 amp, this higher slope requirement being due to the higher open-circuit voltage used on the conventional welding machine.

The word "slope" may have meanings in welding that do not apply to the voltage-current characteristic of the welding generator or transformer. Sometimes machines that reduce the current at the end of a weld are required, for crater filling, heat treating, or other purposes. This current action may be referred to as *downslope*. Similarly, at the start of a weld the current may be gradually increased from zero to its operating value. This current-starting characteristic may be called *upslope*. The rate of upslope and downslope are usually controllable over several cycles of alternating current or even several seconds. The upslope type of current control is also sometimes applied to resistance welding and is referred to as "slope control."

12.12 MIG welding accessories

For semiautomatic MIG welding a water- or air-cooled gun feeds the filler wire into the arc through a guide tube, which also conducts the welding current into the wire. The guide tube must of course be changed if the wire size is changed. For current pickup, the contact between the guide tube and the wire must be good, for welding voltages are too low to overcome considerable contact resistance. The gas nozzle on the end of the MIG gun is always metal. Conversion parts are sometimes available for converting TIG guns into MIG guns.

Many of the MIG hand guns have a pistol grip and a trigger switch. Some are equipped with an inching or jogging control for the wire feed. When the trigger is squeezed, shielding gas, welding current, cooling water, and wire feed are all initiated. On releasing the trigger, the wire feed and current both stop, but shielding gas continues to flow for a short period while the weld puddle cools.

The wire-feed method may be either push gun or pull gun. In the pull gun, which is necessary for feeding finer and softer wires or for feeding wire through long cables, the wire drive rolls are in the gun itself. In the push gun, the drive rolls are in the wire feeder instead of the gun. The push gun will not feed wire through more than 12 ft of cable, a feature that restricts the extent to which the welding operation can be removed from the welding equipment. Guns to which a small coil of filler wire can be attached also available. By mounting the wire spool on the gun, the operator can weld as much as 50 ft from the control panel and 200 ft from the welding machine. The total weight of the gun is much heavier, however.

Spot welding is possible with the MIG method. This spot-welding technique is commonly termed "arc-spot." The method requires high currents ranging from 300 to 500 amp, a constant-potential power source, suitable nozzles for the gun, and control panel equipped with timer controls. The arc-spot operation does not demand a high degree of operator skill. The gun is placed against the work and an arc drawn with the filler wire. Current duration, wire feed, water flow, and gas flow are all timed in the control box with electronic control circuitry (pneumatic time delays may also be used). Arc-spot welding is possible on sheet thicknesses from about 0.020 to 0.375 in., using either plug, fillet, corner, or butt spot welds in steels, stainless steels, or aluminums. Unlike ordinary spot or resistance welding, contact is necessary only with one side of the work instead of both sides. It is possible even to make arc-spot plug welds without first drilling or punching a hole in the top sheet—the arc melts through the top sheet to reach the bottom sheet. If the voltage is too high, the arc will melt through both sheets.

The shielding gases used for arc-spot welding are either CO_2, 1 to 2% oxygen-argon, or argon. Carbon dioxide is used only for mild and low-alloy steels. The arc-spot method is especially useful for very large or heavy items that cannot be brought between the arms of the usual resistance welder.

ARC-SPOT PLUG WELDS IN MILD STEEL USING CARBON DIOXIDE

Thickness Each sheet, in.	Arc Time Cycles	Amp	Volts	Wire Diameter, in.
0.022	36	100	28	0.062
0.064	50	300	30	0.062
0.125	65	420	34	0.062
0.250	42	675	40	0.062

For all MIG welding methods, the wire feeder contains sequence controls for flow of current, shielding gas, and water, and the motor speed control for the wire drive rolls. Control of arc length is managed by two methods. In the method used with constant potential welding machines, the wire feed is preset and fixed. Any change in arc length produces a change in welding current, which alters the burn-off rate to re-establish the correct arc length. If the power supply is of the constant current drooping type, the speed of the wire feed motor is varied. If the arc lengthens, the arc voltage rises. This arc voltage is applied across the wire drive motor, and the increased voltage speeds up the feed motor, thus increasing the rate of wire feed. Contrariwise, if the arc shortens, the rate of wire feed is reduced.

Automatic MIG welding requires the use of automatic welding heads with capacities of 600 amp or more in order to develop maximum burn-off rates. By means of automatic methods, MIG welding beads may be laid down at rates of 100 in. per min or even faster. Carbon dioxide is the most frequently used gas for automatic MIG welding. There is some spatter around the workplace with CO_2 shielding, though the workpiece itself will be clean.

The automatic welding head may be carried on a wheeled tractor, on an I beam, or on a boom. Two handwheel adjustments are usually required to position the torch in exact relationship to the work. (See the automatic welding head in the frontispiece photograph.) The automatic control panel must include circuitry for such operations as driving the welding head or the work positioner, plus required time delay circuits to synchronize all movements. Although little operator technique is demanded for automatic welding, a degree of competence is necessary in making the initial adjustments to the equipment so that all components synchronize properly. In the language of the production trades, the equipment must be "debugged."

The automobile and farm equipment industries are heavily converted to automatic MIG welding using carbon dioxide. Indeed, the modern automobile is an outstanding example of the use of automatic MIG and resistance welding, other welding methods being rather insignificant in the production of automobiles and trucks.

12.13 equipment for flux-cored wire

Bare solid steel filler wire can be used in the MIG process with carbon dioxide as shielding gas, using spray transfer across the arc. Usually constant-potential welding machines with a slight amount of slope are used. If welding conditions are not quite properly adjusted, CO_2 shielding with solid wire may produce much spatter.

The use of flux-cored wire instead of solid wire with CO_2 shielding generally produces better results, including better weld appearance, less convexity of the weld, and less spatter. Flux-cored wire is also superior on dirty or corroded steel parent metal.

The welding power sources specially adapted to flux-cored MIG wire requirements have capacities from 500 to 750 amp at 100% duty cycle DCRP, low open-circuit voltage, and a constant potential characteristic with a slight slope, although some machines have a slightly rising voltage characteristic. The open-circuit voltage may be adjustable. If the machine is a welding transformer, it will usually have a three-phase input connection. The MIG gun for feeding flux-cored wire into the arc is usually cooled by the flow of carbon dioxide through the gun.

Still another of the carbon dioxide shielded MIG processes is the use of solid wire with magnetic granular flux. In this method of welding the filler wire, together with a suspension of magnetic flux in the shielding gas, is fed to the welding gun. The magnetic field around the wire attracts the flux to the surface of the wire, producing in effect a flux-coated wire. Again, a constant-potential welding machine is usually employed with reverse polarity.

12.14   electrogas welding equipment

All things considered, probably the best method of automatic welding of steel plate in the flat position is the submerged arc method, discussed in the next section. Subarc welding, however, is restricted to the flat position. The companion method to submerged arc welding for vertical seams in plate is the electrogas method, an automatic method that uses carbon dioxide shielding gas and flux-cored wire. Electrogas, like submerged arc welding, is capable of high deposition rates. At present, deposition rates for electrogas run to 30 lb of metal per hr or more, more than ten times the rate of manual welding. Plate from about ⅜ to 2 in. thick can be welded by this method in one pass and without the usual edge preparation, except that plate edges should be square and parallel.

The plates for a butt weld to be filled by electrogas welding are separated by a gap of about ¾ in. The gap requirements are set by the fact that the filler-wire guide tube must pass between the plates and must not arc to them. A water-cooled copper shoe bridges the gap between the plates on each side and acts as a dam to hold the molten pool of metal in the gap. The copper shoes move up the joint with the molten pool at a speed controlled by the operator. No welding gun is used. Both filler wire and shielding gas are fed into the weld area from the back, as shown in Fig. 75. All this equipment, including the operator's control panel and the spool of filler wire, ride up the welding gap on an elevator mechanism supported by two vertical tracks. Setup time is about half an hour, after which welding proceeds at a rate of ½ to 3 in. per min. The filler wire must be oscillated across the gap to ensure uniform distribution of both filler metal and heat.

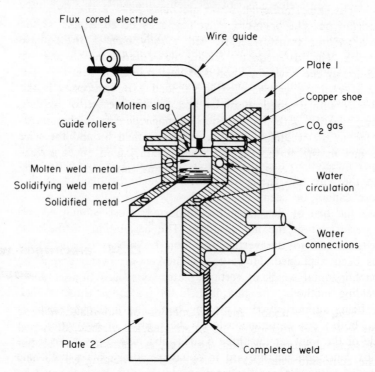

Fig. 75 Electrogas welding. (Courtesy Arcos Corporation)

Electrogas welding is virtually a foundry technique for producing a continuous casting. The method results in good strength and ductility in the weld metal, however, despite some tendency toward grain growth. The slag freezes against the water-cooled shoes as an easily removed coating over the weld surface. The depositing of weld metal on top of weld metal is a favorable feature of the process, and the water-cooled shoes restrict the extent of the heat-affected zone. Obviously only single-pass welding is possible, but additional passes are not needed.

Electrogas welding requires a generator or transformer with a rating of 600 to 700 amp 100% duty cycle using direct current reverse polarity and a conventional drooping volt-ampere power supply.

Instead of the flux-cored wire and shielding gas of the electrogas process, solid wire and granular flux used for a cover and a slag may be substituted. This method is called *electroslag welding*. Developed and used in Europe, electroslag welding is not yet well established in the United States. Perhaps a dozen electroslag installations operated in the United States in 1965. The electroslag weld freezes with a coarse grain structure, a structure which is viewed with some reservations. The electroslag method uses alternating current (in contrast to DCRP used in electrogas welding). It is not recommended for metal less than ½ in. thick, whereas the electrogas method is used to join plates thinner than 1 in. Electroslag welding is actually a vertical submerged arc method.

Submerged arc welding, like MIG welding, uses coils of bare filler wire. The welding zone is covered with a blanket of granular flux from a flux hopper metered to the welding zone ahead of the filler wire. The arc between the wire and the work passes through the blanket of flux and therefore cannot be seen.

Because the bed of flux must be supported, most submerged arc welding is performed in the flat position. The adaptation of the submerged arc principle to the vertical position by means of electroslag welding has been explained. However, submerged arc welding may be executed on horizontal welds in vertical plates by means of the "three o'clock" welding method. The flux is held in place for three o'clock welding by being supported on a moving belt. The horizontal joint is welded from both sides simultaneously by the feeding of two wires, one on each side of the joint, at the three o'clock and nine o'clock positions.

The flux must conduct the arc in subarc welding. When cold, the ceramic flux is of course an electrical insulator. But its resistance to current flow decreases as its temperature increases, and in the molten state it becomes conductive. Starting the arc, however, is not difficult, and several methods are in use:

1. If alternating current is used, high frequency current may be used to initiate the arc, as is done in TIG welding.
2. A small, tightly rolled ball of steel wool is placed on the work, the welding wire is inched down to compress the ball, flux is applied, and current is drawn.
3. A carbon rod is used as a jumper between the welding wire and the workpiece.
4. Wire-retract start is used as in MIG welding.
5. Scratch start is used. The wire is inched down to the work, the flux is applied, the carriage is started, and welding current is applied.

The steel wool method is most frequently employed. The scratch start does not give control over the starting point of the weld but can be used on girth welds on tanks and pipe.

Submerged arc welding, with its flux blanket over the weld zone, provides the conditions for high currents, large heat inputs, and high deposition rates. This method gives very deep penetration, but techniques are available for shallower penetration where needed, as in cladding applications. In subarc welding massive deposition rates have been attained, occasionally as high as 300 lb per hr, feeding more than one filler wire into the arc and using currents as high as 4000 amp, 100% duty cycle. DCRP produces the deepest penetration and the best weld bead contours, whereas DCSP produces the highest deposition rates. Since very large welding currents may be used, arc blow effects can be pronounced when using direct current. Arc blow may even limit the magnitude of the welding current. Alternating current minimizes the effects of arc blow. Aside from arc blow considerations, a.c. is generally preferred for welding steels, and d.c. for nonferrous metals.

Since the power requirements for subarc welding are large, three-phase welding transformers should generally be used. The required high current is often obtained by the use of two welding machines in parallel. Subarc welding, like MIG welding, requires a low open-circuit voltage of 40 to 50 v. Both constant-current and constant-potential welding machines are in use. Wire feed controls use the same operating principles as those used in MIG welding. If the welding machine is constant current, the wire feed motor is connected across the arc voltage and the speed of the motor controls arc length. If the power supply is constant voltage, the wire feed motor runs at a constant speed and variations in arc length are corrected by variations in current and burn-off rate.

The submerged arc process is capable of a variety of multiarc techniques feeding more than one filler wire. The use of multiple arcs increases deposition rates and may also be used to control arc blow. The frontispiece photograph illustrates the use of automatic tandem arc welding by the submerged arc process.

1. Two-wire series arc welding In series arc welding each filler wire has its own wire feed motor. The power-supply cable from the welding machine, which may be either a.c. or d.c., is connected to one welding head. The return cable is connected to the second welding head, not to a ground clamp. Thus the two electrodes are in series across the power supply, and the workpiece is not a part of the welding circuit. The two electrodes are mounted at 45° to each other. The welding current passes through the first filler wire, the arc, the weld puddle, and the arc, to the second filler wire. This arrangement of series arc welding is sketched in Fig. 76(a).

The two conducting filler wires are of opposite polarity. Fig. 76(b)

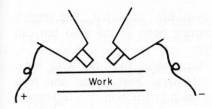

Fig. 76 (a)   Series arc arrangement.

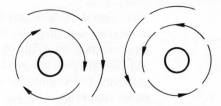

Fig. 76 (b)   Magnetic fields about two series arc wires.

shows the magnetic fields about the two conducting wires. The two fields repel one another. This condition produces an arc blow that widens the arc. This effect results in low penetration.

2. Two-wire parallel arc welding   In this arrangement two filler wires are supplied in parallel from a single power source. Here the two wires have the same polarity, and the two interacting magnetic fields will attract one another to pull the two arcs together. The two arcs may be aligned in the direction of travel. There is therefore back blow on the front arc and forward blow on the rear arc, across the direction of travel or at any angle to the direction of travel. Deposition rate is about 50% more than for a single filler wire under similar welding conditions.

3. Multiwire multipower arc welding   In this method two or more electrodes are used, each with its own independent power supply. Because of arc blow problems, usually at least one arc uses alternating current. Setting up for welding becomes complicated and time consuming with this method and can only be justified for long welding runs on mass production work.

4. Spreadarc welding   Spreadarc is Lincoln Electric's name for a method of depositing an unusually wide bead for cladding by using one or two filler wires. The welding head is oscillated at right angles to the direction of travel. With a single wire a bead width of 2 in. is possible; with two wires, 4 in. The Arcstrip method of depositing a wide cladding bead using a strip electrode instead of a filler wire was briefly described in Chapter 10. Both Spreadarc and Arcstrip are similar in purpose.

Most of the components required for automatic submerged arc welding are visible in the frontispiece photograph of Linde Unionmelt equipment. Either a self-propelled carriage moves the equipment along the joint, or the workpiece must be traversed beneath the welding equipment. The filler wire unreels, passes through a wire straightener and then through the motorized wire drive rolls, and picks up welding current before entering the weld zone. Granular flux is metered to the weld zone from a flux hopper through the flux tube at the front of the filler wire.

The control cabinet may control a considerable range of functions, such as starting sequence, timers, high-speed carriage return, control of multiple arcs, oscillation of the arc, and limit switches. The control panel itself will be fitted with voltmeter, ammeter, switches, knobs, and fuses, and pushbuttons for such operations as WELD START, WELD STOP, and WIRE INCH. Handwheels permit vertical and horizontal adjustment of the welding head during setup. Steering attachments, which ride the joint to ensure accurate alignment of the electrode, are often used.

For semiautomatic submerged arc welding the flux hopper may be mounted on the hand gun itself.

12.16 stud welding

Not all stick electrodes for manual welding become filler metal. Sometimes the operator shorts a stick electrode to the work to serve as a hook to hang a trouble lamp on, to attach insulation to, or for other such purposes.

Welding specifications do not usually allow this sort of casual and makeshift treatment, however. If studs are needed, specifications will call for proper stud welding. Welded studs are used for the attachment of block and blanket insulation to welded tanks, refractory concrete to the doors of open-hearth furnaces, or concrete to steel beams, and for a wide range of other purposes. The studs used are specially manufactured for stud welding and contain a cavity into which granular welding flux is packed. The available types are threaded, unthreaded, and flat studs; bent studs such as hooks and eyebolts; and special types, in various lengths, in diameters from $\frac{3}{16}$ to 1 in., and in various ferrous materials including stainless steels.

The studs must be attached with a special stud gun. The stud is inserted into the chuck of the welding gun, a ferrule is slipped over the stud, and the gun is placed against the work. The trigger is pressed to start the welding sequence. The stud is first retracted from the work surface by a solenoid coil in order to draw out an arc. The arc fuses the end of the stud and the immediate area of the work. When the arc is timed out by the control unit the welding current is shut off, the solenoid coil de-energizes, and the main spring of the gun drives the stud into the molten workpiece. The fused metal is pushed out to form a fillet around the perimeter of the stud.

Stud welding requires a direct current machine that can provide large currents at a duty cycle of about 20% and an open-circuit voltage of at least 75 v. Arc voltages range from 32 to 37 v. The following are typical figures for stud welding:

¼-in.-diameter stud	425 amp for 10 cycles
⅜-in.-diameter stud	550 amp for 20 cycles
½-in.-diameter stud	800 amp for 30 cyyles

PROBLEMS

1 What is the current density if 300 amp is conducted by a #00 cable?

2 For a ⅛-in. thoriated tungsten electrode using argon gas and ACHF, 300 amp is about the maximum possible current. What is the corresponding current density?

3 What is the current density if a ⅜-in. diameter resistance welding tip is carrying 24,000 amp in spot-welding magnesium?

4 Maximum and minimum amperages recommended for a ¼-in.-diameter EutecTrode 680 rod (Eutectic Welding Alloys) are 275 and 175. What are the corresponding current densities?

5 Assuming that stud welding is a 30% duty cycle operation, can a 300-amp 60% duty cycle welder be used for welding studs that require 425 amp?

6 If a welding machine will deliver 750 amp at 30% duty, what is its rating at 100% duty?

7 What is the cable drop when welding with 200 amp using 200-ft long cables made of #000 copper?

8 What is the cable drop when welding with 300 amp using 100-ft long aluminum #000 cables?

9 The voltmeter on the welding machine reads 35 v. What is the arc voltage if 300 amp must be carried through 100-ft cables of #00 copper?

10 What is the short-circuit current delivered by a welding machine with 52 v open circuit using a slope of 5 per 100 amp?

11 What is the short-circuit current from a welder with an open-circuit voltage of 80 and a slope of 18 v per 100 amp?

12 Sales of subarc equipment are not expanding as fast as other types of welding equipment. What are the disadvantages of subarc? What are its advantages?

13 Make an approximate calculation for the amount of deposited metal per foot of weld for both electrogas and submerged arc welding of butt joints, in both 1- and 2-in.-thick plate. Make the convenient assumption that the gap between the plates is ¾-in. for electrogas welding and that for submerged arc welding the joint preparation is a double 90° V. Which method of welding uses least metal in each case?

arc welding machines and equipment

14 MIG welding is being done using a transformer with an open-circuit voltage of 51 v and a slope of 3 v per 100 amp. Welding current is 200 amp.

(a) If the welding power is proportional to the square of the current, how many times more power is drawn when short-circuiting?

(b) The steel being welded is an air-hardening steel, and one of the specifications governing the welding operation states that no accidental arc strikes may be made on the steel. In the light of the calculation for the first part of this question, is this specification justified?

15 How could electrogas welding equipment be set up for butt-welding the girth seams of 72-in. diameter pipe?

16 One-in.-thick tank plates are to be electrogas-welded with a gap of ¾ in. between the plates. Deposition rate is 30 lb of weld metal per hr. If mild steel weighs 0.28 lb per cu in., find the welding speed in inches per minute.

Many of the arc welding methods use shielding gases, and operators like to think of such welding methods as combination arc and gas welding. Certainly many arc characteristics are set by the particular gas used. But gas welding itself includes those fusion welding processes that use for welding the heat energy of a flame, without electricity. In addition much brazing and soldering are done by the gas flame.

13.1 industrial gases

The wide range of industrial gases used for welding and cutting may be classified into three groups according to their functions:

combustible gases — acetylene, propane, etc
oxidants — oxygen and air
inert shielding gases — carbon dioxide, nitrogen, argon, helium

Although carbon dioxide is used as a shielding gas, it is not truly inert since it can carburize or decarburize a steel and breaks down in the arc to carbon monoxide and oxygen.

In addition to these main functions, a few gases, such as helium and krypton, are used for the leak testing of welded tanks.

First in importance of the industrial gases are air and its components.

WELDING GASES

AND

GAS WELDING

13

Atmospheric air contains water vapor (actually superheated steam), but the amount of this water vapor in air varies with the temperature and relative humidity and since it is always less than 1%, is therefore not usually reported. The analysis of atmospheric air is therefore normally reported as dry air. The analysis by volume of dry air at sea level is

78.03%	nitrogen
20.99%	oxygen
0.94%	argon
0.03%	carbon dioxide
0.01%	hydrogen
0.00123%	neon
0.0004%	helium
0.00005%	krypton
0.000006%	xenon

On a weight basis, air is composed of 75.5% nitrogen, 23.2% oxygen, and 1.33% argon.

On the basis of either weight or volume, air is largely *nitrogen*. Nitrogen has few uses in welding at present. It can be used as a shielding gas in inert gas welding of copper and is also frequently employed as a purging or filling gas to remove oxygen or other reactive gases from piping, tubing, and furnaces. Cylinders of nitrogen have left-hand threads.

Oxygen, one-fifth of air by volume, derives its importance from oxidation or combustion, which provides most of industry's heat and power. Atmospheric air, which is nitrogen-diluted oxygen, is used chiefly for this purpose because of the cheapness of air and the vast amounts of oxygen needed. For most combustion processes more than ten times as much air as fuel is required. However, flame temperatures are limited to about 3000 F or slightly more when atmospheric nitrogen is present, since the nitrogen dilutes and cools the flame. Industry therefore has shown a trend toward the use of pure oxygen since World War II. The first uses of these oxy-fuel reactions were in oxyacetylene and oxyhydrogen welding, but usage has extended to tonnage oxygen in rocketry, oxygen converters for melting steel, oxygen lancing of blast furnaces and melting furnaces, and flame drilling of hard rock using oxygen and kerosene. Tonnage oxygen is stored in liquid form at about −320 F in specially constructed welded tanks. Oxygen boils at −297 F at an atmospheric pressure of 14.7 psi.

Oxygen cylinders and regulators have right-hand threads, and oxygen hoses are green. Because of the explosion hazard in bringing any combustible material into contact with oxygen, no grease or oil may be used with oxygen systems. The standard oxygen cylinder is 51 in. high at the neck, 8½ in. in diameter, and has a wall thickness of about ¼ in. A full cylinder contains 244 cu ft of oxygen compressed to 2200 psi.

Carbon dioxide is supplied either as solid "dry ice" or as gas in cylinders with right-hand threads. Carbon dioxide has no liquid phase at atmospheric pressure, but at −109 F the solid "sublimes" to the gas. The specific gravity of carbon dioxide referred to air as 1.0 is 1.53. Carbon dioxide is principally used as a shielding gas in the MIG welding of carbon and low-alloy steels, either alone or in mixtures with argon.

Other than for atomic hydrogen and oxyhydrogen welding, *hydrogen* has few uses in welding. It is the lightest of all gases, yet has the highest specific heat of any material, 3.4.

The "inert" gases argon, helium, krypton, xenon, and neon are truly inert, since under welding conditions they do not react with, or dissolve in, any metals. All have eight electrons in the outermost filled energy level. The inert gases are remarkable elements; for instance, one of them, helium, was discovered on the surface of the sun before it was discovered on our own planet, by a relatively simple method of analyzing the sun's radiation.

Except for argon, and perhaps helium, the inert gases have rather minor uses in welding. Neon, the filler gas for neon tubes, is also used as a fill gas with bromine or chlorine in Geiger-Muller tubes for detecting X or gamma rays during radiographic inspection of welds. Xenon is the fill gas for the high-power tubes that fire lasers. Krypton-85, a radioisotope of krypton, is used for leak detection in piping and similar weldments.

Argon and *helium* are the only two of the inert gases used as shielding gases for welding. They are more expensive than buyers would like them to be, but their high cost is explained by the necessity for a high degree of purity for welding purposes, 99.75% or better. Usually an even higher degree of purity than this is supplied. Argon is separated from liquid air and has a boiling point of −302 F at atmospheric pressure. Helium is obtained from helium-rich natural-gas wells in the western United States and Canada, as well as from air. Helium boils at −452 F, only 7° above absolute zero, and has no solid phase.

Neither argon nor helium will dissolve in metals or react with them. Both gases ionize readily at the low voltages used in welding arcs. The ionization voltage of helium, and therefore the voltage of a helium-shielded arc, is higher than that of argon. Thus a helium-shielded arc produces more arc energy, and for this reason helium is sometimes selected for welding thicker materials or metals with high thermal conductivities such as copper. On the other hand, helium is less suitable for welding thin-gauge metals, for they may be burned through. Other welding considerations stem from the difference in density of the two gases, helium being about one-tenth as heavy as argon. Helium is more easily blown away from the area of the arc by cross-drafts and is not as dependable as a shield as argon is. The low density of helium makes it considerably less effective in sandblasting the oxides of aluminum and magnesium during TIG welding of these metals, as discussed in Chapter 12.

13.2 fuel gases

The most frequently used fuel gases for welding, brazing, and flame cutting are acetylene, hydrogen, natural gas, propane, and butane. The acetylene-oxygen mixture gives the highest of all flame temperatures used in gas welding, 6300 F at the inner cone. An oxyhydrogen flame can provide a maximum temperature of about 4000 F, and the other fuel gases have still lower flame temperatures. The wide range of operations in the gas welding, brazing, and soldering of the many metals requires a range of flame temperatures, and much brazing, soldering, and lead burning do not require the maximum heat of the oxyacetylene flame. For still lower temperatures, these fuel gases can be burned with air instead of oxygen.

Natural gas, propane, and butane burn more slowly than acetylene and therefore are not nearly so easy to use for welding. Because they are cheaper than acetylene, many shops use oxyacetylene for welding and propane for cutting. However, the same torch or torch tip cannot be used if the fuel gas is changed. The chemical formulas of the fuel gases are as follows:

acetylene	C_2H_2
natural gas	CH_4 (methane)
propane	C_3H_8
butane	C_4H_{10}

All these gases burn to carbon dioxide and water vapor and cannot be used for the welding or cutting of metals sensitive to these gases or to oxygen. Many of the metals, steel included, can pick up oxygen from carbon dioxide and hydrogen from water vapor, and this consideration sometimes imposes restrictions on the type of work that can be done with the oxy-fuel gas flame.

The heating values of the fuel gases compare as follows:

Btu/cu ft at 14.7 psi and 70 F

acetylene	1475
natural gas	1000
propane	2520
butane	3200

The gas with the highest heating value does not necessarily have the hottest flame, because flame temperature is influenced by other factors besides heating value, such as the proportion of oxygen required for combustion.

Acetylene cylinders are of various sizes, though the standard seems to be 12 in. in diameter and 40½ in. at the neck. Acetylene is unstable and explosive when compressed to very high pressures, and for this reason is dissolved in acetone in bottles or tanks. The acetone is held in an asbestos filler in the cylinder. The acetylene pressure is usually about 250 psi. Because the acetylene is in a dissolved condition, the amount left in the partially emptied cylinder cannot be determined from a pressure gauge reading. Because of the method of filling the acetylene cylinder, such cylinders should stand upright and should not be laid on their sides. Acetylene equipment has left-hand threads.

13.3 temperature, pressure, volume relationship in gases

All gases fall into two groups: ideal (or perfect) gases and imperfect gases. This classification is by no means scientific, but it is convenient for industrial and engineering purposes. Briefly, the difference between these two groups of gases is simply this:

1. The temperature, pressure, and volume of an ideal gas can be calculated from a reasonably simple formula.
2. The same properties of an imperfect gas are not easily calculated but are obtained from gas tables.

The ideal gases include oxygen, nitrogen, air, hydrogen, water vapor in the air, and the rare or inert gases. All these gases have boiling points of about 400 F below room temperature (except water vapor in the air, which usually has a boiling point of 40 to 60 F). The so-called "imperfect" gases include steam (in steam systems), the freons and other refrigerants, carbon dioxide, acetylene, natural gas, propane, and butane. These imperfect gases have boiling points not too far from room temperature. Unless gases are heated well above their boiling points, they do not in general behave "ideally," which simply means that they do not follow the simple formulas that one naturally prefers to more complicated mathematics.

Before the ideal gas formula is discussed, the Rankine temperature scale must first be explained. Industry generally uses the Fahrenheit scale for temperatures, though the electrical and chemical industries prefer the Centigrade scale. The Fahrenheit scale was the first temperature scale to be invented, so that it should be no surprise that it was a rather crude effort. It was developed about 300 years ago by Fahrenheit, who took as zero the lowest temperature that he could obtain with a mixture of salt and water and made 100 degrees the temperature of the human body. Some day this temperature scale will be obsolete, for it should be no surprise that such a scale is not well suited to the industrial gases. In making computations for the industrial gases, complications are avoided by the use of the Rankine scale. The Rankine temperature is simply the Fahrenheit number plus 460 and is based on absolute zero, which is –460 F. Thus 32 F = (32 + 460) = 492 R.

The ideal gas formula, used for calculating the pressure, temperature, volume, or weight in pounds of any ideal gas (but not of any imperfect gas) is

$$PV = wRT$$

Here P = gas pressure in pounds per square *foot* (psf)
  = psi × 144
V = volume of the gas in cubic feet
w = weight of the gas in pounds
T = temperature of the gas in degrees Rankine
R = is called the gas constant and is different for each gas:

Gas	R
hydrogen	772
air	53.3
nitrogen	55.2
oxygen	48.4
argon	38.6
helium	386

The gas constant is also calculated from $R = 1544/\text{molecular weight}$.

For an example of the use of the ideal gas equation, we shall find the weight of 244 cu ft of oxygen compressed in a cylinder at 2200 psi.

First, note that the 244 cu ft is measured at atmospheric pressure, 14.7 psi or 14.7 × 144 lb per sq ft, and at 70 F, which is 530 R.

$P = 14.7 × 144$ lb/ sy ft
$V = 244$ cu ft
$T = 530$ R
$R = 48.4$
$PV = wRT$
$14.7 × 144 × 244 = w × 48.4 × 530$
$w = 20.1$ lb of oxygen in the cylinder

We cannot undertake such cumbersome calculations without a slide rule or a desk calculator. In the absence of these calculating aids, we must try for a "ball-park" answer by rounding off numbers. Often ball-park approximations are sufficient for industrial purposes, and accuracy is of no virtue whatever. If this computation is approximated, we obtain the following solution:

$14.7 × 144 × 244 = w × 48.4 × 530$

Substitute the following numbers:

$$15 \times 150 \times 240 = w \times 50 \times 520$$
$$w = 108000/520 = 20 \text{ lb of oxygen}$$

The rough solution is thus as good as the exact solution.

If this 244 cu ft of oxygen is pumped into an oxygen cylinder at 2200 psi, what will be its volume in the cylinder?

In the cylinder the volume will be much less than 200 cu ft, but the weight of the oxygen does not change.

$$P = 2200 \times 144$$
$$V = ?$$
$$w = 20 \text{ lb}$$
$$R = 48.4, \text{ and } T = 530 \text{ as before}$$

The volume is 1.6 cu ft at 2200 psi.

Rearranging the ideal gas formula, $w = PV/RT$. In terms of common sense, this formula says that more pressure or more volume mean a greater weight of gas and that gases are lighter at higher temperatures.

13.4 flames

Two types of flames are used in industry: premix and nozzle-mix. In the premix flame, the fuel gas and the air or oxygen are mixed together before they leave the burner. This type of flame is blue and often is nearly invisible. The premix flame provides the maximum possible flame temperature and is used for welding operations. The nozzle-mix flame is produced by having separate passages for the air or oxygen and the fuel gas, the fuel gas meeting its combustion oxygen only at the outlet of the burner. A nozzle-mix flame is very long and yellow. The bright color indicates that this flame is radiating heat, and heat lost by radiation cannot be used to promote a high flame temperature. Hence the nozzle-mix flame cannot quite produce the high temperature of the less radiating premix flame. Nozzle-mix burners are found in industrial furnaces, because the long bushy flame radiates heat throughout the volume of the furnace to ensure uniform temperature without hot or cold spots. Such a flame does not concentrate the heat in the small zone required for welding and brazing. However, the long lazy yellow flame obtained when an oxyacetylene torch is first ignited is a nozzle-mix flame.

Any flame must necessarily burn its way backward toward the source of fuel. Every flame mixture has a certain flame propagation velocity, as it is called, which means the burning speed of the flame front in feet per second. To make a flame hold a stationary position, the

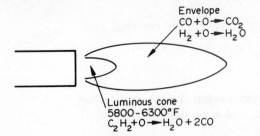

Envelope
$CO + O \rightarrow CO_2$
$H_2 + O \rightarrow H_2O$

Luminous cone
5800-6300°F
$C_2H_2 + O \rightarrow H_2O + 2CO$

Fig. 77 Oxyacetylene flame.

reacting gases generally must leave the burner in the forward direction at the same speed at which the flame burns backward in the opposite direction. When a flame is "turned down" by reducing the gas supply, it becomes more difficult to hold the flame at the front of the burner or torch. Should the gas outlet velocity be too slow, the flame then enters the burner and extinguishes with a "pop" sound. This is blowback or flashback, familiar in gas welding, especially when the gases are shut off. Flashback in a welding torch usually indicates that the pressure is insufficient for the nozzle being used. Flashback is not usual in industrial furnaces because the heat of the furnace can constantly reignite the burner. Burners with a high "turn-down ratio," the ratio of maximum to minimum gas flow from the burner, are less likely to flashback.

Figure 77 shows the characteristic oxyacetylene flame with its temperatures, flame cones, and chemical reactions. The inner cone is a premix cone; the outer cone may draw air from the atmosphere and become a nozzle-mix cone. The most suitable combustion mixture for oxyacetylene welding is given by approximately equal proportions by volume of acetylene and oxygen through the torch. Such a mixture gives a "neutral" flame, meaning that the flame will neither oxidize the weld metal, nor at the other extreme carburize it. The use of more oxygen or less acetylene gives an oxidizing flame, and the use of less oxygen than acetylene produces a carburizing or reducing flame. Actually oxyacetylene flames change their characteristics from moment to moment, and one cannot be sure that a carburizing flame, for example, does not occasionally momentarily change to an oxidizing flame. This erratic flame characteristic means oxyacetylene welding is not very well suited for the very best quality welds on such materials as the stainless steels. The following tabulation summarizes oxyacetylene flame characteristics:

Ratio O_2 to C_2H_2	Type of Flame	Max Flame Temp, °F
0.8 to 1.0	carburizing	5550
0.9 to 1.0	carburizing	5700
1 to 1	neutral	5850
1.5 to 1	oxidizing	6200
2.0 to 1	oxidizing	6100
2.5 to 1	oxidizing	6000

With equal proportions of oxygen and acetylene, the chemical reaction producing the hot inner cone is

$$C_2H_2 + O_2 = 2CO + H_2$$

In the outer flame envelope atmospheric oxygen burns the carbon monoxide and hydrogen to carbon dioxide and water vapor:

$$2CO + O_2 = 2CO_2$$
$$2H_2 + O_2 = 2H_2O$$

The neutral flame is indicated by the clearly seen white inner cone at the tip of the torch. An oxidizing flame shows as a shortening of the inner cone and a less luminous inner cone. The carburizing flame has a middle luminous zone between the inner cone and the outer envelope. The oxidizing flame is used for preheating operations in welding or cutting.

13.5 welding torches

The oxyacetylene torch mixes oxygen and acetylene in the required volume ratio and burns the mixture at the torch tip. Both high- and low-pressure torches are available. A range of tips is available for any torch model to provide the required combustion heat. The high-pressure torch is used most and is simply a mixing device to supply approximately equal volumes of both gases to the torch tip. Regulating valves and handles for each gas, oxygen and acetylene, control the pressure of the gases to the tip. Low-pressure torches, also called injector torches, are required if the fuel gas is supplied at low pressures instead of the usual cylinder or regulator range of pressures. An injector nozzle inside the torch or the torch tip uses the high-pressure oxygen supply to pull in the low-pressure fuel gas.

A range of torch tips must be available for every torch in order to weld all gauges of metal. The small tips have lower tip numbers. Some suppliers of torches, such as Linde, use tip numbers that indicate the flow of each gas in cubic feet per hour at 5 lb pressure, that is, a no. 12 tip would use 12 cu ft of gas every hour. This system, however, is not universal. The table on the next page compares tip size numbers for two torch manufacturers, Linde and Smith Welding Equipment (of Minneapolis). The proper tip size must always be used because of the limitations of flame velocity of the fuel gases. If a tip is too large and the supply of gas is reduced at the hand valves to the proper level, flashbacks will occur. If on the other hand a tip is too small, gas pressures will have to be so high that the flame will be blown off the torch tip.

Metal Thickness	Linde Tip No.	Linde Drill size	Smith Tip No.	Smith Drill Size
32–28 gauge	2	74	0	76
25 ga.–$\frac{1}{32}$''	4	64	1	71
$\frac{1}{32}$–$\frac{1}{16}$''	6	58	2	69
$\frac{1}{16}$–$\frac{3}{32}$''	9	55	4	63
$\frac{3}{32}$–$\frac{1}{8}$''	12	54	5	57
$\frac{1}{8}$–$\frac{3}{16}$''	15	53	7	54
$\frac{3}{16}$–$\frac{1}{4}$''	20	50	8	52
$\frac{1}{4}$–$\frac{3}{8}$''	30	45	9	49
$\frac{3}{8}$–$\frac{1}{2}$''	40	40	10	44
$\frac{1}{2}$–$\frac{5}{8}$''	55	33	11	40
$\frac{3}{4}$–1''	70	30	12	34
1''	85	28	13	30
over 1''	100	24	14	26

A wide range of special-purpose tips are available. These include multiflame heating tips, twin-flame tips, instrument tips, lead-burning tips, soldering iron tips, bendable tips, and tip extension pieces.

Regulators are necessary to reduce the high cylinder pressure to a more usable pressure and to maintain constant delivery pressure and steady gas flow. Regulators require two pressure gauges, one to indicate cylinder pressure and the other to show the pressure supplied to the torch. The working pressure is adjusted to the desired value by a hand valve that also shuts off the gas supply. The gas pressure is held constant by a spring-loaded diaphragm in the regulator. Regulators are available as single-stage or two-stage regulators, the two-stage regulator being used when a more constant delivery pressure is required instead of wide variations in cylinder pressure. If gases are supplied from a piping system instead of from cylinders, then a so-called station regulator, not suited to cylinder operation, must be used. Regulators are supplied for oxygen, acetylene, nitrogen, argon, hydrogen, and carbon dioxide, but each must be used to regulate the flow of the gas for which it is designed.

13.6 operation of oxyacetylene equipment

Certain safety practices must at all times be adhered to in the operation of oxygas equipment, since such gases are potentially dangerous in the hands of irresponsible personnel.

Cylinders should be stored in a ventilated and fireproof room, where both smoking and exposed flames are forbidden. Fuel gases should not be stored with oxygen, and empty cylinders should be so marked and separated from full cylinders. All cylinders for any type of bottled gas should be protected from dangerous pressure rises due to direct radiation from the sun or other sources of heat, since cylinder pressure increases with temperature.

Oil and grease, cleaning solvents, and a wide range of other organic materials may ignite spontaneously or even explode in the presence of pure oxygen. If air is one-fifth oxygen, then the fire and explosion hazard of pure oxygen must be at least five times as great as with air. Electric arcs should be well removed from bottled gases. Leaky lines are especially dangerous. Soapy water should be used when testing for leaks.

An oxygen and an acetylene cylinder are usually combined at the workplace on a two-wheeled truck as shown in Fig. 3. The two cylinders should be chained to the truck or otherwise fastened so that they cannot be overturned accidentally.

When setting up cylinders for gas welding, the cylinder valve on each cylinder is first "cracked" to blow any dirt out of the nozzles, that is, the valve is opened slightly for an instant and then closed. When valves or hose are blown out, no one should be in the path of the gas blast. An oxygen regulator is then attached to the oxygen cylinder and an acetylene regulator to the acetylene cylinder.

The pressure-adjusting screw of each regulator is turned counter-clockwise until it is loose. Then the cylinder valve is opened slowly all the way, or if on an acetylene cylinder, $1\frac{1}{2}$ turns. The gas hose is next attached to the regulator and blown out at no more than 5 to 10 lb pressure. The two gas hoses are attached to the torch and the torch tip mounted in the torch. Oxygen pressure is set at the desired value, and acetylene pressure at 5 psi.

To light the torch, the torch oxygen valve is cracked until the oxygen flow can be heard. The torch acetylene valve is then opened about a half-turn and the torch lighter is used to ignite the mixture. A long yellow nozzle-mix flame results. The acetylene pressure is reset back to 5 psi. (This was the original setting, but opening the acetylene valve on the torch caused a drop in pressure.) The oxygen valve and the acetylene valve on the torch are adjusted to give the desired flame characteristics.

To shut off the oxyacetylene torch, the torch acetylene valve is first closed, then the oxygen valve (fuel valve first).

13.7 gas welding

Two general methods of oxyacetylene welding are used: forehand and backhand. In forehand welding, the filler rod precedes the torch tip in the direction of welding, while in backhand welding the relative positions of torch and rod are reversed. Forehand welding is used for most joining of ferrous and nonferrous materials, but backhand welding is employed with pipe welding and position welding. On vertical welds using the backhand method welding upward, the weld metal that has just solidified is used as a step to hold up the molten pool.

Although a wide range of metals can be oxygas-welded, this method has some serious disadvantages, the chief of these being the wide heat-affected zone, much distortion, and the slow production rate. The influence of the welding gases on the metallurgy of the weld has already been discussed.

For the welding of *mild steel*, a neutral flame is used. Although either the forehand or backhand technique is possible, the backhand method produces a little less distortion.

Gray cast iron may be gas-welded using a backhand technique with a cast iron or nickel filler rod and a neutral flame. The casting must be clean before welding; such articles as engine blocks are thoroughly oil-soaked and good welds are impossible until such foreign matter is removed. The casting must be grooved for welding. Preheating avoids temperature stresses that may cause cracking, but usually preheating of the whole casting is necessary, otherwise the preheating itself may be the cause of cracks. Flux can be used sparingly, and helps to improve wetting of the deposited metal. After welding, the casting should be insulated with asbestos, vermiculite, or other material to prevent chilling of the deposit or the development of severe temperature changes. However, cast iron techniques and rods have greatly improved, and it is no longer uncommon to weld without preheating or slow cooling. To prevent dangerous temperature differences in the casting, the welder may control the heat input and complete the weld a portion at a time, allowing the casting to cool between stages.

In the gas welding of *copper-zinc brasses*, the chief problem is the loss of zinc through fuming and the consequent porosity. Zinc boils at a relatively low temperature and oxidizes in the heat of the torch. This fuming can be prevented by the use of an oxidizing flame, which forms a layer of zinc oxide on the surface of the molten metal to protect against further fuming. At least 25% excess oxygen is required. Low fuming rods are available for gas welding of brass; these contain less than 0.15% silicon to control the oxidation of the zinc. Flux is necessary and is added by dipping the filler rod periodically into it. Brasses have a high thermal conductivity and particularly in thicker sections may require preheating. Position welding of many of the bronzes is either difficult or impossible.

Before gas-welding *copper*, preheating to at least 800 F is required, otherwise, because of its high thermal conductivity, the copper will drain heat from the weld. The difficulties of welding copper increases with its thickness in accord with the theory of the thermal severity number used with steel. When welding copper over a quarter inch thick, two operators may be needed to obtain the required heat input. One of the operators preheats the seam ahead of the operator who deposits the bead. A larger torch tip is required for copper than for the same thickness of steel because of thermal conductivity. The flame for copper welding should be neutral or carburizing, because an oxidizing flame will form too much copper oxide and produce a brittle weld. Deoxidized filler rod should be used. Both forehand and backhand methods are used with copper. Since overhead welding of copper is extremely difficult, it is almost never done.

The gas welding of *aluminum* requires the use of special fluxes to remove the refractory aluminum oxide that forms so readily on aluminum. Such fluxes usually contain chlorides or fluorides. These compounds are chemically very reactive, and if left on the metal after welding, will pick up moisture and corrode the aluminum. The least possible flux should therefore be used and all flux removed after welding. The purpose of the flux is the removal of oxide film; such fluxes will not remove the dirt, oil, or grease that cause porosity in aluminum welds.

Because of its high thermal conductivity, aluminum requires preheating to about 400 F, if sections are heavy. A slightly carburizing flame is used, and a forehand technique is preferred. Aluminum has a melting point only slightly above 1000 F, and to prevent burning through the metal, the operator puts more heat into the filler rod by holding the torch at a rather flat angle to the work. A soft flame is used to reduce turbulence, the cause of increased oxidation of the parent metal. For this purpose torch tips should be used at the lower limits of their capacity.

The gas welding of *stainless steels* is not to be recommended if corrosion resistance is demanded of the weldment. Gas welding produces an extensive heat-affected zone, and carbide precipitation can be expected throughout this area, although subsequent annealing at 1750 F will remove carbide precipitation, provided the weldment is cooled quickly through the precipitation range of 800 to 1600 F. A neutral flame must be used in the welding of austenitic stainless steels. If the flame is oxidizing, such alloying elements as chromium will be lost. On the other hand, if the flame is carburizing, the steel will pick up carbon from the flame. For highest corrosion resistance these stainless steels should have the least possible carbon. A supposedly neutral flame cannot be expected to remain consistently neutral throughout the welding operation, however. To assist in ensuring a neutral flame, two-stage regulators should be used on gas cylinders, since the single-stage regulator does not hold sufficient control over gas pressures, slight changes of which can upset the flame characteristics.

All stainless steels have a low thermal conductivity compared with the other common metals, actually about one-third that of carbon steel. Heat from the torch therefore tends to remain in the region of the weld.

This makes possible the use of a torch tip one size or sometimes two sizes smaller than would be used on the same thickness of carbon steel. In any case the best weld metallurgy is produced if the least amount of heat is used to make the weld.

Filler rod for any stainless steels should have a chromium content 1 to $1\frac{1}{2}\%$ higher than the base metal to compensate for oxidation losses. This means that shearings from sheets will not make a suitable filler rod unless corrosion resistance is of minor importance. To reduce oxidation losses, the filler rod should not be used to puddle the weld metal pool, and the end of the weld should be protected by the flame until it solidifies.

The most commonly used method for joining *lead* is gas welding using lead-burning tips with either oxyacetylene, oxypropane, oxy-natural gas, or oxyhydrogen. A neutral flame with low gas pressures is used. A reducing flame deposits soot, whereas an oxidizing flame coats the lead with an oxide film that interferes with the welding operation. No flux is needed. Lead filler rods are available in all the required lead alloys. Lap joints are preferred in the burning of lead, except in the heavy lead sheet used in radioactive shielding.

13.8 surfacing

Surfacing is commonly applied by gas welding techniques, especially in the building up of small areas, as in the repair of dies and tools. In addition to surfacing using filler rods, other methods of gas surfacing exist. Three of these methods, ranging from the simplest to one of the most complex, are as follows:

1. the powder feeding of an oxyacetylene torch
2. the metallizing process
3. flame plating with the D–gun

The first method, that of feeding fine metal powders into a small oxyacetylene torch, is offered by Eutectic Welding Alloys (the Eutalloy torch) and Wall Colmonoy (the Fusewelder torch). The torch may also be used for standard gas welding and brazing without the use of powders. Figure 78 shows the Eutalloy torch with its plastic powder container and the long lever for controlling the powder feed. The metal powder is drawn into the torch by a slight vacuum. A wide range of overlay powders is available, including brazing powders. Little skill is required to produce overlays by this method. The surface of the work is heated with the torch until it takes on the characteristic "sweating" appearance; the powder feed lever is then depressed, the torch is advanced to "sweat" the next

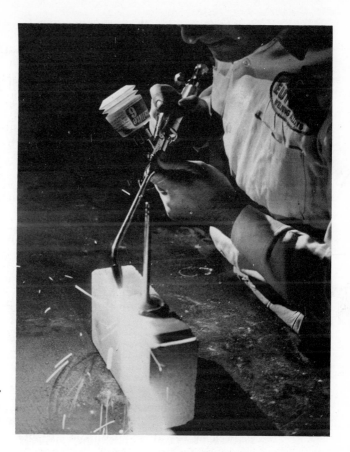

Fig. 78 Eutalloy torch building up a burned engine valve.

area, and the operation is continued with alternating sweating and feeding. If necessary, an overlay only a few thousandths of an inch thick is easy to produce. The equipment is economical in first cost, though the powders are more expensive. Operators like to use this method, but it is not suited to other than small repairs, being too slow and costly for major items of work.

A great many production processes go by the name *metallizing*, including the evaporation and deposit of metal films under vacuum conditions. In the welding industry the process usually implies the atomizing and spraying of a metal wire or powder onto a surface from a suitable gas torch. Metallizing requires heavier and more expensive equipment with higher deposition rates than the small powder-feeding torches just discussed and includes automatic methods. Problems of dilution do not arise with this method, for the base metal is not fused as it must be with the powder-feeding torch. Deposits, however, are somewhat porous and therefore less corrosion resistant. Such sprayed deposits also contract after deposit, setting up residual stresses.

For more rigorous requirements, minimum porosity, or close dimensional control of the plating thickness, flame-plating with the use of the D-gun has recently been introduced by Linde Gases. This method is one of the few welding techniques that may be applied to ceramic materials. Among the plating materials that have been applied by the D-gun are tungsten, tantalum, molybdenum, nickel, aluminum, tungsten carbide, zirconia, alumina, and chromium oxide. Only thin coatings of several thousandths of an inch are normally plated by this method, nevertheless this type of flame plating has been used to salvage tools and dies that have presented difficult surfacing problems. Since the porosity of the coating is in the range of 1%, the coatings have much improved wear resistance over metallized coatings.

The D-gun looks like a small artillery weapon with a long barrel, turret-mounted. The gas used by the gun is an oxyacetylene mixture, fired by a rapid detonation method that gives the overlay particles supersonic velocities of about Mach 2, or twice the speed of sound. This is roughly ten times the velocity that conventional metal-spray guns can deliver. The D-gun must be operated from a remote panel in a soundproof room, since the detonation noise is well beyond what the human ear can tolerate.

PROBLEMS

1 What would you say is the most important problem or consideration in the gas welding of (a) gray cast iron, (b) brass, (c) copper, (d) aluminum, (e) austenitic stainless steel?

2 If a fan exhausts 500 cu ft per min of air at 70 F and atmospheric pressure from a small welding booth, how many pounds of air does the fan handle in an hour's operation?

3 What is the weight of 200 cu ft of (a) argon, (b) helium at 2000 psi and 70 F?

4 A welder takes 90 min to flame-cut 100 lineal ft of ¼-in. steel plate, using oxygen at the rate of 44 cu ft per hr, measured at 70 F and atmospheric pressure. How many pounds of oxygen are consumed?

14.1 quality welding joints
by the shielded metal arc

The metallurgical aspects of producing quality welds have been sufficiently discussed in preceding chapters, including such important matters as dilution, heat treatment of the weld and the heat-affected zone as a result of welding, and low-hydrogen requirements. But welding techniques too are involved in weld quality, and these are the chief preoccupation of this chapter.

Welding passes made with stick electrodes may be laid down either as stringer beads or as weave passes. In the weave method, the rod is oscillated from side to side across the joint; for a stringer bead, the only movement of the rod is steadily along the path of the joint. The first pass in a V joint must be a stringer bead since there is no space for a weave motion; the last pass on the surface of the work is usually a weave pass to finish off the weld in a neat and smooth contour. A weaving pass is common in surfacing, since this method covers the maximum possible area in a single pass. Weave passes are possible in automatic welding by the use of an oscillating mechanism on the welding head. Generally a stringer pass, if it is possible, produces the better weld metallurgy, since less heat is supplied to the workpiece per inch of weld and less atmospheric gas drawn into the arc.

Oxidation and porosity are usually reduced by using a short arc,

ARC

WELDING

PRACTICES

14

for the longer the arc, the greater the possibility of drawing atmospheric gases into the arc. Spatter losses too tend to increase with a longer arc. The removal of surface rust from the work removes a source of oxide that can contribute even more to porosity.

Welding quality is especially dependent on the angle of the rod to the work. The wrong angle may produce a wide range of defects, such as slag inclusion, undercutting, imperfect fusion, or poor weld contour. The two angles between the rod and the workpiece are termed the *lead angle* and the *work angle* (Fig. 79). The lead angle is the angle toward

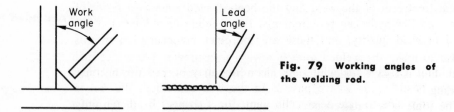

Fig. 79 Working angles of the welding rod.

the direction of welding. For a butt weld, the work angle must almost always be 90°, and the lead angle 15 to 20°. The approximate angles for other types of welds are indicated in the following table:

ELECTRODE ANGLES
(Degrees)

Operation	Work Angle	Lead Angle
butt weld, flat	90	15–20
fillet weld	45	20
butt weld, horizontal, downhand	20	5
vertical up butt weld	90	0
vertical down butt weld	90	30
overhead butt weld	90	5–10

When the arc must be broken to change rods, a crater will form at the end of the weld. In crack-sensitive steels or highly restrained joints, the crater is an area of weakness and may develop cracks. The crater may be filled by holding the electrode stationary before slowly withdrawing it and breaking the arc. The crater may also be filled with the next rod, which strikes the arc at the front end of the crater, traverses back into the crater to fill it, and then continues the weld.

Speed of welding, in inches per minute, influences the quality and characteristics of the bead. If the speed is too slow, a wide and highly reinforced bead that overlaps the base metal is produced. A proper weld bead is about $1\frac{1}{2}$ times the width of the electrode. An increase in travel speed, without changing the other welding conditions, will reduce the width of the bead and increase the penetration. However, too fast a welding speed will reduce the penetration. Generally, proper speed is judged from the surface appearance of the weld; it is generally assumed that the best appearance is given by the proper welding speed. Speed also has an influence on heat input to the weld; a higher speed produces a weld bead with less heat per inch, and it is always true that the less the welding heat, the better the metallurgical results.

14.2 welding heat

The heat to make the welded joint is always measured in joules per inch of weld. This is easy to calculate and has universal application to all types of welding.

The joule is a watt-second. The watts are taken to be the product of arc voltage times arc current. The method of calculating welding heat may best be shown by an example.

A butt joint is being made with an arc voltage of 25 and a 170-amp current. We shall calculate the joules per inch for a welding speed of 3 in. per min (ipm).

$$\text{watts} = 25 \times 170 = 4250$$

The joule being a watt-second, convert the welding speed from minutes to seconds by dividing the welding speed by 60, or what is the same thing, multiply the watts by 60:

$$\text{joules per inch at 3 ipm} = \frac{4250 \times 60}{3 \text{ ipm}} = 85{,}000$$

Now suppose that the weld can be made, using another rod or welding method, at 35 arc volts, 300 amp, and 8 ipm.

$$\text{joules per inch at 8 ipm} = \frac{35 \times 300 \times 60}{8} = 78{,}750$$

The second method of welding should then be superior, by reason of the reduced heat input.

To reduce the heat input to the welded joint further, the amount of deposited metal should be the minimum needed to make a satisfactory and sufficient joint. Many welded joints are overwelded. The exact amount of weld metal required is a problem in stress analysis, to be discussed in a later chapter; here the point must be stressed that overwelding is no virtue but a fault.

The electron beam welder is considered an outstanding welding machine because it can make a welded joint with far less heat than any competitive welder can.

14.3 edge preparation for manual shielded arc welding

Edge preparation is required in order to provide access to the root of the weld and space for manipulation of the tip of the rod. Sheet steel in gauges as thick as 10 may be sheared square, and welded with full penetration from one side only. Butt joints in material thicker than 10 gauge welded from one side only can fail through fatigue or brittle fracture at low temperatures. For plate up to ¼ in. thick, full penetration in a close-butt weld may be obtained by welding from both sides, although it is preferable to leave a small gap between the plates. Complete fusion in unprepared butt joints more than ¼ in. thick cannot be carried out consistently and dependably, and in these larger thicknesses it is hardly possible to remove all the slag at the bottom of the first pass unless the seam is back-chipped or gouged. Therefore in greater thicknesses some type of edge preparation becomes necessary.

Edge preparation for single-V joints can take any of the forms shown in Fig. 80. The feather-edge type of preparation is rarely used. The feather edges, having very little mass, are easily burned through. By the use of the backing bar shown, full penetration, extending to the bar, is obtainable. The backing bar itself may be fused, though a copper backing bar is not fused. The root gap is about ¼ in., and the included angle of the V may be as little as 45°, but is more usually 60°. The third sketch of Fig. 80(c) shows a root face, which reduces penetration, just as in an opposite way the feather edge produces too much penetration as a result of burn-through.

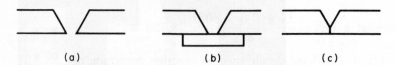

(a)   (b)   (c)

Fig. 80 Single vee edge preparation. (a) Feather edge, (b) backing bar, (c) root face.

The single-V butt weld produces considerable distortion. Both parts of the work pull toward the weld, so that the work will not be flat after welding. Such distortion can be greatly reduced by the use of a double-V joint, though distortion will not be entirely eliminated unless both sides of the plate are welded at the same time. The double V also has the economic advantage of using half as much filler metal, since the cross section to be filled is only half as large for a double V as for a single V. Against this must be balanced the extra cost of preparing two V's. An important disadvantage of the double-V joint is the ease with which slag is trapped at the centerline, and because of this double V's may not be allowed for important joints such as those on pressure vessels.

When plates to be welded are very thick, the V edge preparation produces a very large cross section to be filled with weld metal, and the opening of the V is excessively large and beyond the needs of the welder. For such large plates, the V is replaced by such edge preparation as the J and U edge (see Fig. 9). Such joints are commonly used on pressure vessels, the sides of the U edge sloping about 15° and of the J about 30°.

In these types of edge preparation, the first pass is most likely to crack. With only one pass in place, the cross section of the weld is very small, and sometimes this small cross section is not large enough to resist the restraining effect of the heavy mass of the plate on either side of the weld and must crack to relieve its stresses.

14.4 distortion

Figure 81 is a photograph of the distortion produced in a heavy plate as a result of two large fillet welds. The distortion is always toward the weld, as shown in the photograph, and indicates shrinkage in the weld metal.

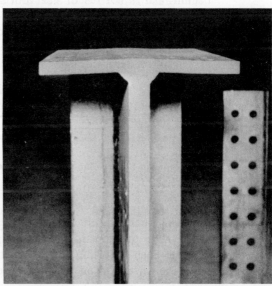

Fig. 81 Distortion due to two fillet welds.

When the area being welded heats up, it must expand. This expansion, however, is to a considerable degree prevented by the restraining effect of the mas of metal around the weld pool. These restraints give an upsetting effect (increase in cross section) instead of an expansion. Then when the weld cools, the area shrinks, producing the characteristic distortion toward the weld, as in the photograph.

Many factors influence this distortion.

1. Such distortion should be proportional to the coefficient of expansion of the metal. Thus aluminum, with a coefficient of 0.000012, should show about twice as much distortion as carbon steel (0.000006), and austenitic stainless steels about a third more than carbon steel.

2. The amount of distortion will increase with heat input, expressed as joules per inch of weld.

3. A stringer bead produces less distortion than a weave bead, as does a smaller number of passes. Both produce less heat input.

4. A thin sheet such as 14 gauge shows much more distortion than a 10-gauge sheet. Very often thin sheet may be riveted instead of welded if distortion is a serious factor.

5. Incomplete penetration causes more distortion than full penetration because of the difference in heat absorption across the thickness of the plate. Welding from both sides greatly reduces distortion; welding from both sides simultaneously may eliminate distortion.

6. Overwelding will result in increased distortion.

7. A smaller electrode may reduce distortion under some circumstances, but often a higher current or a larger electrode may provide a more uniform distribution of heat through the metal, with the same effect of reducing distortion.

8. The use of clamps and fixtures will control distortion. Tack welds have the same effect.

9. The sequence in which the weld seam is completed is an important factor under the operator's control. Skip welding, back stepping, and intermittent welding are all employed to keep distortion under control. The most restrained section of a plate is usually welded first, which means that the middle of the plate will usually be welded before the ends.

10. Even the welding process can influence distortion. Gas welding produces much distortion; electron beam welding generally none.

In the fillet welds such as in Fig. 81, the angular distortion can be assumed to be directly proportional to the welding heat in joules per inch of weld and inversely proportional to the thickness of the plate. Distortion also increases approximately in proportion to the number of beads in a multipass weld.

Thicker sections of mild steels, 1½ in. or thicker, with their higher thermal severity numbers, generally require welding procedures that control the rate of cooling. The low-alloy steels include lean amounts of alloy metals for increased yield strength and ultimate strength, and for such steels controlled cooling rates may be required for even lesser thicknesses than 1½ in. Thus T-1, low-alloy steel welded with stick electrodes will require preheating to 150 F if plate thickness is 1 to 2 in., or to 200 F for greater thicknesses than 2 in. The heat input in joules per inch must be controlled in most low-alloy structural steels. Thus for T-1 steel, the manufacturer's instructions recommend a maximum of 36,000 joules per in. when welding ¼-in. plate at shop temperature without preheat. The higher thermal severity numbers of thicker plates permit greater heat inputs per inch: the allowable maximum heat input is roughly proportional to the thermal severity number, though the manufacturer's recommendations must be consulted on these matters.

The low-alloy steels range in ultimate tensile strength from about 65,000 to more than 200,000 psi in the case of SAE 4340, compared with about 60,000 psi for unalloyed mild steel. Strength of T-1 is 100,000 psi, of Cor-Ten 70,000, and of Stelcoloy 70,000 psi. The use of standard E60xx welding rods will therefore not provide strength in the weld equal to that of the plate itself. Of the low-alloy rods the E7018 rods are used more than any other, but rods of even higher strength may be necessary, depending on the strength of the low-alloy material. Any of these steels is susceptible to underbead cracking owing to hydrogen in the heat-affected zone, so that only low-hydrogen rods are employed in welding these steels.

None of the higher-strength, low-hydrogen rods, E7018 included, have the deep penetration of 6010 or 6011 rods with hydrogen in the coating. The shallower penetration makes it more difficult to obtain complete fusion at the root of such joints as the double V. Fabricators therefore adopt special procedures to overcome this problem. One such procedure is the following: The plate edges are sheared square, butted together, and held with a bead on one side of the joint. The other side, unwelded, is gouged halfway through the thickness of the plate with an arc-air torch. (See Chapter 17 for a description of the arc-air method.) Several layers of weld metal are then deposited on this gouged groove. The reason for several initial passes was previously mentioned: a single pass will not lay down enough weld metal of adequate strength to resist distortion stresses and cracking. Another reason is that part of the weld metal from the first pass will be subsequently gouged out. After these passes lay down weld metal on one side of the plate, the other side is

Fig. 82 Starter tab on a submerged arc weld.

similarly arc-air-gouged, removing all the unwelded metal down to the first weld pass and all slag. Weld beads are then laid down on this second side and the joint completed.

Stringer beads are preferred for most high-strength steels. On vertical welds, where weaving is a necessary technique to hold the molten pool in place, the weave motion is as small as possible.

Porosity is often experienced in the first couple of inches of the weld bead when high-strength, low-hydrogen rods are used. This porosity can be overcome by two methods. In one method, the arc is struck about an inch along the joint, and the electrode is then back-stepped quickly to the starting point of the weld as it deposits a small stringer bead. When the rod is at the actual starting point of the joint, travel is reversed and the regular bead laid down. The short starter bead must be remelted, because it is likely to contain some porosity. This method is also employed when changing to a new rod. The other method is the use of a starter tab, which is knocked off the work when welding is finished. A starter tab is shown in Fig. 82, although the bead shown in this photograph is not a manual bead but was made by automatic submerged arc.

It is often supposed that this initial porosity is due to moisture in the flux coating of the rod. This is not always true, however, because the same problem of porosity can occur in thoroughly baked and dried rods. The explanation for initial porosity appears to be the lack of killing (deoxidation) of the weld deposit when the arc is initiated. A certain amount of the flux coating must be melted to release sufficient silicon in the flux to deoxidize the filler metal. The problem of initial porosity is by no means confined to the manual shielded arc welding of low-alloy steels, though it may be taken more seriously in these high-strength steels.

It should be obvious that a high standard of welding will be demanded for joining these high-strength steels, otherwise there would be little reason for using them. The full strength of such materials can be obtained only in the absence of defects such as undercut and porosity. X-ray examination is likely to be more complete with such steels than with lower-strength steels.

14.6 fabrication of high strength steels

In fabrication of low-alloy, high-strength steels, inexperienced personnel will discover that they do not behave like mild steel. The higher strengths of these steels mean that more severe demands are made on forming equipment. A mechanical shear with a capacity rated at ¼ in. of mild steel plate may be damaged if it is forced to shear ¼ in. of T-1, stainless steel, or other high-strength material. The low-alloy steels have higher yield strengths also, and this indicates greater elasticity. As a result, in forming operations on power brakes, there is more springback. Springback may be considered to increase proportionally with the yield strength of the material. The bending characteristics of some of these high-strength materials between the direction of rolling and transverse to the direction of rolling may also differ, bending being easier across the direction of rolling than parallel to it. Therefore such steels cannot be formed until the direction of rolling is known. The direction of rolling is immediately apparent in fabricating full sheets but can be perplexing in smaller pieces sheared out of the full plate.

Preheating is a common requirement for low- and high-alloy steels, cast iron, and the highly conductive nonferrous metals. If the metal must be preheated to a certain temperature, say 400 F for aluminum, there must be some method of knowing when the required temperature has been reached. Temperature-indicating crayons, available from welding supply houses, are one method. Such crayons, such as the Tempilstik brand, are formulated to melt at definite temperature. Temperature indicating pyrometers may also be used. These have a contact probe, which contains a thermocouple that is laid against the work. A pointer indicates the temperature on a dial.

14.7 manual shielded arc welding of stainless steels

The austenitic stainless steels such as 304, in wrought form such as sheet, have a fully austenitic structure. For casting purposes, including the casting process known as fusion welding, such stainless steels are formulated to include a small percentage, usually less than 10%, of ferrite with the basic austenite structure, since there is a tendency toward hot cracking in cast austenite without this ferrite.

To produce sound welds in austenitic stainless steels, such steels must first be cleaned. Cleaning entails removal of all mild steel particles and carbon, sulfur, zinc, scale, marking inks, and oil. Stainless steel brushes used for cleaning stainless steels should not be used for cleaning other types of steel.

The metallurgical problem of deposit of chromium carbides in the temperature range of 800 to 1600 F, which produces loss of the stainless characteristic, has been discussed. Little control over carbide precipitation is possible during welding, but the following measures are helpful:

1. Low welding heat in joules per inch.
2. Stringer beads.
3. Use of chill plates close to the welding zone, preferably made of copper. Do not weld on such semi-insulating materials as firebrick.

Carbide precipitation of course may be a serious matter in some types of service but not in others. Corrosion-resistance requirements of such industries as paper and pulp mills will not permit carbide precipitation. On the other hand, carbide precipitation is unimportant for stainless steel used simply for appearance on a store front or building entrance.

Carbide precipitation will be more pronounced in the heat-affected zone than in the weld metal. Unfortunately it is a very rapid metallurgical process. This precipitated carbide can be removed by a postweld anneal at 1850 to 2050 F for 4 hr per in. thickness of material, followed by rapid cooling in the temperature range of 800 to 1600 F. This sounds like a simple procedure if an annealing furnace is available, but it requires either experience or advice. The actual annealing temperature and time must be carefully controlled, and the high annealing temperature is likely to produce oxidation and distortion.

To reduce distortion, operators often use skip welding and step-back welding. These procedures are shown in Fig. 83. The seam is first tacked, the number of tacks being greater for thinner gauges. In skip welding, short stretches of weld of about equal length are laid down in a sequence such as that in Fig. 83(a). In step-back welding, the short sections are

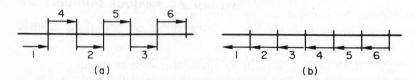

Fig. 83 Skip welding and step-back welding.

not skipped but welded in sequence down the seam, the welding being backward into the cooled end of the section just completed.

Weldments made for food or hospital service are required to be free of all cracks or crevices that may serve as sites for bacterial growth and highly polished for ease of cleaning. All welds must therefore be ground down to the level of the parent metal.

Manual shielded metal arc welding can be used on austenitic stainless steels down to thicknesses of about 18 gauge. Typical welding conditions for butt, fillet, corner, or edge welds in stainless types 302, 304, and 316 are as follows:

Metal Gauge	Electrode Size, in.	Amp
18	5/64	45
14	3/32	60
11 (1/8")	1/8	90
3/16	5/32	125

Any moisture in the flux coating may produce porosity. Porosity and oxidation are both reduced by the use of the shortest possible arc. The hardenable martensitic stainless steels such as 410 will develop underbead cracking like other hardenable steels if there is moisture in the flux. If stainless steel weldments are to be placed in service as-welded, that is, without subsequent heat treating, the following selection of rods is recommended:

Base Metal	Rod
403, 410 (martensitic)	308, 309
405, 430 (ferritic)	308, 309, 310
201, 202, 301, 302, 304, 305	308
304L	308L, 347
316	316
316L	316L 316Cb
321, 347	347

14.8 manual welding of stainless clad steels

Stainless clad steels may be cut with the oxyacetylene torch, the heavier thicknesses being easier to cut than lighter $3/16$- or $1/4$-in. plates. Cutting is done from the backing plate side. Such cutting may add carbon to the cladding, but this diluted metal can be removed with light grinding of the cut edge. Carbon pickup has not proved to be too serious a problem. Shearing is done with the clad side up, in order to keep the burrs on the backing side.

The chief consideration in welding these steels is of course dilution. The backing plate is a carbon steel, and the stainless cladding is a minimum carbon steel. If the clad plate is relatively thin, the whole joint may be welded with austenitic stainless electrodes, though this is too

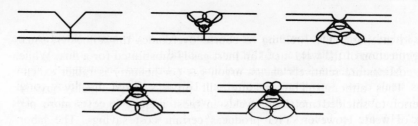

Fig. 84 Welding stainless clad mild steel.

expensive for heavier plate. The procedure adopted with standard mild steel welding rods is either that shown in Fig. 84 or some similar procedure. The edge preparation provides a nose that extends into the mild steel backing plate and protects the cladding from carbon dilution. The backing plate is then welded with standard mild steel rods, avoiding penetration into the cladding. The plate is then back-chipped or gouged on the cladding side, taking care to gouge into the backing metal. Stainless electrodes on the clad side complete the joint. The method of arc-air gouging and welding of double-V joints described in Sec. 14.5, or some variant of this method, may also be used on stainless clad plate.

14.9 metal arc welding of aluminum

The welding of aluminum with flux-coated electrodes is not recommended. It is not allowed in many specifications and cannot be used for critical structures such as aircraft or aluminum truck bodies. Very thin aluminum cannot be joined by the shielded metal arc method.

DCRP, using the shortest possible arc, is used for welding aluminum. The flux coating must be dry. A back-step procedure is often used in in order to reduce distortion. Weaving is not generally used. In position welding, the vertical downward procedure is preferred for vertical joints. Overhead welding is only rarely done.

As usual in welding aluminum, any surface oxide or contamination will produce porosity. The aluminum flux is corrosive and must be removed after the weld is completed.

14.10 TIG welding practices

The welding of lap and fillet welds in aluminum using flux-coated electrodes is not recommended because of the possibility of trapping corrosive flux in the joint. TIG welding of course overcomes this difficulty, since for protection of the weld metal an inert gas is substituted for a flux. While flux coatings are relatively cheap, argon gas (or helium) is rather expensive. Thus although TIG welding will produce weld quality greatly superior to shielded metal arc welds in most metals, it costs more per foot of weld. However, TIG produces certain cost savings. The labor cost of cleaning slag from the seam is not negligible and is avoided with TIG welding. Thin sheets may often be TIG-welded without the use of filler metal, thus saving the cost of rods.

Argon is more commonly used than helium and offers the following advantages over helium:

1. Lower arc voltage due to its lower ionizing potential
2. Less required for adequate shielding
3. Somewhat easier arc starting
4. Better cleaning action of refractory oxides, again due to its greater density
5. Lower cost

Higher arc voltage and heat input may be required for welding thick materials of high thermal conductivity, however, helium is sometimes used for such conditions and is generally superior to argon for welding thicker plates. Helium too gives greater penetration than argon. Occasionally the two inert gases are blended to obtain a suitable balance of their characteristics. For still higher arc power requirements, hydrogen may be added to argon or helium in small amounts. Since hydrogen is too reactive to be used with most metals, such hydrogen-inert gas mixtures are used only on austenitic stainless steels and some nickel alloys.

The flow of shielding gas must be adequate to protect the weld puddle from atmospheric contamination but not excessive. The required amount of gas depends on many factors. In general, TIG welding is not at all suitable for welding out of doors or in drafty areas. Metals, such as aluminum or titanium, that are more reactive with atmospheric gases require more shielding than a less reactive metal such as stainless steel does. The very reactive metals, such as zirconium or titanium, must be shielded with inert gas on both sides of the weld, top and bottom. Gas flow also increases with welding current, since a larger torch with a larger gas orifice will be required to handle greater currents. Finally the joint design also governs gas flow. A lower flow rate is possible for a fillet weld, in which the gas is confined by the right-angle fillet corner, than is suitable for an outside corner joint or even a butt weld. The shielding gas flow must not be stopped until the tungsten electrode and the weld pool have cooled to a safe temperature.

TIG welding is equally suited to any welding position, including overhead welding. The method has been used on material as thin as 0.005 in., but manual welding is limited to thicknesses of about $\frac{1}{32}$ in.

The thin sheet used and the quality requirements for aircraft make TIG welding pre-eminently suited for this industry.

The TIG method may use a.c., DCSP, or DCRP. Alternating current has the problems of arc starting, rectification, and extinguishment of the arc when the voltage goes through zero. These problems and the equipment for dealing with them have been discussed. Reverse polarity is not often used, for only low currents are possible if the tungsten electrode is not to be overheated, and penetration is shallow. Reverse polarity, however, is used for welding those metals that form very refractory oxides, chiefly magnesium and aluminum, though in heavier sections alternating current is preferred for these metals. With reverse polarity, positive argon ions can sandblast and remove the oxide coating on the metal surface.

POWER SUPPLY CONDITIONS FOR TIG WELDING

Metal	ACHF	DCSP	DCRP
magnesium up to 1/8″	lst choice		2nd choice
heavy magnesium	suitable		
aluminum up to 3/32″	lst choice		2nd choice
heavy aluminum	suitable		
stainless steel	2nd choice	lst choice	
brass	2nd choice	lst choice	
hard facing	suitable	suitable	
cast iron	2nd choice	lst choice	
copper		suitable	
all carbon steels	2nd choice	lst choice	

Penetration is deepest for DCSP, intermediate for a.c. (alternating straight and reverse polarity), and least for DCRP. The current-carrying capacity of the tungsten electrode is greatest for DCSP, is considerably reduced with a.c., and is still less with DCRP. The current capacity for

TUNGSTEN ELECTRODE CURRENT CAPACITIES

Electrode Diameter, in.	Pure Tungsten, DCSP, amp	Thorium=DCSP Tungsten, DCSP, amp	Thorium=ACHF Tungsten, ACHF, amp
0.020	up to 16	up to 25	up to 20
0.040	up to 65	up to 100	up to 60
1/16	60–150	20–180	60–120
3/32	140–275	40–300	100–180
1/4	250–375	50–475	170–250
5/32	300–480	60–600	200–320
3/16	350–500		300–400

any electrode size is also slightly less when helium is used, compared with its capacity when argon is used. The best arc characteristics are obtained by using currents at the high end of the current range.

The electrode should project as little as possible from the gas nozzle. This projection is set at 1/16 to 1/4 in., depending on welding conditions, a greater projection being required for fillet welds. A greater projection of the electrode makes it easier for the operator to observe welding conditions, but a short projection produces better shielding.

If the two parts of a butt joint are true and square and can be jigged together, no filler metal is needed except for thicker sheet. If filler metal is to be added, the butt joint is gapped, and for greater thicknesses a single or double V joint with a small root face and 60° opening is used.

14.11 TIG welding of various metals

TIG welding produces excellent joints in *aluminum* in the thickness range from 0.020 to perhaps 3/8 in. Zirconium-tungsten is the preferred type of electrode because it is least susceptible to contamination, using ACHF or DCRP for lighter-gauge material.

The following table is for ACHF on butt welds without backing, in the flat position. Two passes are required for thicknesses 1/8 to 1/4 in.

TIG BUTT-WELDING OF ALUMINUM AND ITS ALLOYS

Material Thickness, in.	Electrode Diameter, in.	Current, amp	Argon, cu ft/hr	Filler, Rod, in.	Speed, ipm	Gas Cup I.D., in.
0.032	1/16–3/32	80	12	1/16–3/32	14	1/4
0.064	3/32–1/18	105	16	3/32	13	3/8
0.081	1/8	115	16	1/8	12	3/8
0.125	1/8	160	16	1/8	14	3/8
3/16	3/16	270	20	3/16	11	3/8
1/4	3/16	270	20	3/16	11	3/8

In TIG-welding of *stainless steels*, either thorium or zirconium alloyed tungsten electrodes are preferred. Although either argon or helium may be used, helium shielding is sometimes preferred for automatic TIG welding; changes in arc length with helium produce larger variations in arc voltage, a feature that makes automatic control of the arc gap easier. Helium also produces more heat, allows faster welding speeds, and provides a slightly better bead contour.

The following table is for butt welds in the flat position using DCSP:

TIG BUTT-WELDING OF STAINLESS STEELS

Material Thickness, in.	Electrode Diameter, in.	Current, amp	Argon, cu ft/hr	Filler Rod, in.	Speed, imp	Gas Cup I.D., in.
1/32	0.040	30– 45	14	1/16	10	3/8
1/16	1/16	80–100	14	1/16	12	3/8
3/32	1/16	100–120	14	1/16–3/32	12	3/8
1/8	1/16	120–140	14	3/32	12	3/8
3/16	3/32	200–250	14	1/8	10	1/2

Thoriated tungsten electrodes are preferred for TIG-welding *copper*, using DCSP. The preferred filler wire is deoxidized tin-bearing copper. Helium or helium 75%/argon 25% is preferred to argon for the welding of copper, because the greater arc heat of helium reduces preheat requirements.

The following table assumes that DCSP is used with butt welds in the flat position.

TIG BUTT-WELDING OF COPPER AND ITS ALLOYS

Material Thickness, in.	Electrode Diameter, in.	Current, amp	Argon, cu ft/hr	Filler Rod, in.	Speed, ipm	Gas Cup I.D., in,.
1/32	0.040	90–105	15	3/64	13	1/4
1/16	1/16	110–150	15	3/64	12	3/8
3/32	1/16	145–190	15	1/16	12	3/8
1/8	3/32	175–225	15	3/32	11	3/8

Joint preparation for TIG welding of *titanium* is similar to that used for stainless steel or aluminum, except that more care must be used. Thorough cleaning is absolutely necessary. All burrs are removed. Careful fit-up promotes good welds, and where possible, filler metal is not used.

Many special procedures, jigs, and purge chambers are used for the welding of titanium. Both sides of the weld are always shielded with argon. DCSP is the usual power supply. Generally, weld color is a good general indication of quality and the effectiveness of the shielding of the back side of the seam. A good weld will be silver-colored. Traces of oxidation will give a straw color, which may sometimes be acceptable. Blue and purple indicate a poor weld. In multipass welding any color must be removed by grinding or brushing. Gas shielding must be maintained until the electrode, the filler rod, and the seam are all cooled well below a red heat.

The TIG welding of *rimmed steels* may give difficulties because of porosity. Butt joints in carbon or low-alloy steels may be close-butted up to ⅛-in. thick, as in the shielded metal arc welding of these materials. Square butt joints without edge preparation may be possible up to ⅜-in. thickness, using DCSP.

TIG BUTT-WELDING OF CARBON AND LOW ALLOY STEELS, FLAT POSITION

Material Thickness, in.	Electrode Diameter, in.	Current, amp	Argon, cu ft/hr	Filler Rod, in.	Speed, ipm	Gas Cup I.D., in.
1/32	1/16	80–100	11	3/64	14	1/4
1/16	3/32	100–130	11	1/16	12	1/4
3/32	3/32	100–150	13	1/16	12	3/8

Larger thicknesses than those in this table are not normally TIG-welded.

TIG welding of *gray and ductile cast iron* may be done with cast iron filler rods without flux. Loss of carbon or silicon in this method of welding is negligible. If the metal is to be preheated, the whole casting should be heated to at least 500 F. After welding, the rate of cooling should be controlled.

TIG BUTT-WELDING OF CAST IRONS, ALL POSITIONS

Material Thickness, in.	Electrode Diameter, in.	Current, amp	Argon, cu ft/hr	Filler Rod, in.	Speed, imp	Gas Cup I.D., in.	Power
1/4	3/32	150	16	3/16	8	1/4	ACHE
1	1/8	325	24	1/4	13	1/2	DCSP

14.12 a comparison of MIG and TIG

There are current density limitations to TIG welding. When the current carried by the tungsten electrode exceeds about 300 amp, tungsten inclusions may appear in the weld. The field of application of TIG welding is generally the quality welding of thin-gauge materials, ⅛-in. or less thick, although the method is by no means confined to this range. MIG welding does not have the current density restrictions of TIG, but on the other hand is not well suited to the welding of very thin gauges.

TIG VERSUS MIG

	TIG	MIG
power supply	ACHF, DCSP	DCRP
material thickness, in.	up to $\frac{1}{4}$, approx.	0.040 up
method	manual, two hands	semiautomatic, one hand
welding speed	half that of MIG	twice as fast as TIG
operator skill	high	less demanding
weld quality	excellent	excellent
maintenance of equipment	minor	more maintenance

14.13 gases for MIG welding

The selection of a shielding gas for MIG welding is not relatively as simple as that for TIG welding. A much greater range of gases and blends of gases is used for MIG welding. Both short-circuiting and spray transfer of metal are employed, and they do not in general use the same shielding gas.

Helium and argon are the only satisfactory shielding gases for use with the reactive metals magnesium, aluminum, titanium, zirconium, beryllium, and columbium. The characteristics of these two gases have already been discussed. Helium is better suited to the TIG or MIG welding of thick sections of metal because of its higher arc voltage, whereas argon is preferred for light gauges. Helium is also better used with highly conductive metals such as copper. Argon produces a narrower bead than helium does, and may provide a somewhat deeper penetration.

When carbon and low-alloy steels are welded with argon and MIG reverse polarity, however, the tendency toward unevenness and undercut in the weld is strong, and the arc seems to be drawn toward any oxide patches on the steel. These oxide areas act as better cathodes than the base metal in the reverse polarity of the MIG arc. In high-alloy or stainless steels under the same welding conditions, the spatter is considerable. For the welding of all types of steel, a small amount of oxygen or carbon dioxide is added to the inert gas. The addition of these reactive gases to the inert gas stabilizes the arc, reduces the spatter, improves metal transfer, and reduces undercutting. Greater amounts of carbon dioxide are used for short-circuiting metal transfer than for spray transfer. To prevent porosity when such reactive gases are used, the welding wire is deoxidized. Some chromium, manganese, silicon, and aluminum will be lost from the filler wire, but the wire composition can be formulated to take account of these losses.

Pure carbon dioxide is also used for MIG welding, especially with flux-cored wire. Again, porosity is not a problem if deoxidizers are supplied in the wire or the flux core. One of the principal effects of the flux is the reduction in spatter that occurs with CO_2 welding. The high density of carbon dioxide, about 10% greater than argon, makes it an effective shielding gas, although the flow rates for carbon dioxide are approximately the same as those used with argon. In the arc, the carbon dioxide dissociates into CO and O_2.

Since carbon dioxide is a cheap gas and premixed argon and carbon dioxide costs as much as pure argon, most users blend their own mixtures. This requires only flowmeters and a Y connection to each cylinder. The gases can be blended in any proportion desired.

The mixture of 90% helium, $7\frac{1}{2}$% argon, and $2\frac{1}{2}$% carbon dioxide is the best mixture for welding austenitic stainless steels. It has the unique characteristic of providing a weld bead with very little reinforcement

SHIELDING GASES FOR MIG WELDING

Material	Shielding Gas	Gas Flow, cu ft/hr	Arc Voltage	Remarks
1. Spray Transfer				
carbon steel	100% CO_2	30	30	possibity of spatter
	95% A, 5% O_2	30	28	
low-alloy steel	95% A, 5% O_2	30	28	
stainless steel	95% A, 5% O_2	30	26	
	98% A, 2% O_2	30	26	
	90 He, $7\frac{1}{2}$ A $2\frac{1}{2}$ CO_2	30	29	excellent weld profile
aluminum	100% A	40	25	
	50% A, 50% He	60	29	higher heat input
magnesium	100% A	40	27	
copper	100% A	40	30	
monel	100% A	40	26	
	50% A, 50% He	60	28	for heavier gauges
titanium	100% A	various	27	
2. Flux-cored Steel Wire				
carbon & low-alloy steel	100% CO_2	30	26	
3. Short-circuiting Metal Transfer				
carbon steel	75% A, 25% CO_2	20	18	
low-alloy steel	75% A, 25% CO_2	20	18	
stainless steel	75% A, 25% CO_2	25	20	
aluminum	100% A	30	20	

(buildup), a characteristic required for food and hospital equipment and other such stainless weldments. Such a mixture is not available from welding gas suppliers. How it is blended is left to problem 8 at the end of this chapter.

14.14 edge preparation for MIG welding of steels

MIG welding uses a finer filler wire than that used in shielded arc welding, and therefore the MIG weld bead is narrower and has greater penetration. This makes possible smaller root openings and narrower grooves in the edge preparation. Less deposited metal is thus required for completing joints by the MIG process. These savings in the amount of deposited metal may more than compensate for the higher cost per pound of MIG wire, which being wire-drawn to small diameters, is necessarily more expensive than the coarser flux-coated wire.

The angle of the V in a single or double V for butt welding by the manual shielded arc process is about 60°. If the joint is to be made by the MIG process, the V is usually made with an angle of 30 to 45°. Bevel cuts for MIG butt welding may be as narrow as 22°. By and large, bevel and V angles for MIG are about two-thirds to one-half those used with flux-coated rods, producing savings in deposited metal of a third to a half or more. The actual savings, however, depend on the thickness of the joint.

A butt weld in $\frac{3}{16}$-in. plate, whether made by stick electrodes or MIG wire, will be an open butt joint with a gap between the plates of about $\frac{1}{16}$ in. The amount of deposited metal must be the same by either method and is about 0.2 lb per lineal foot of weld. The only savings produced by the MIG method in this example are stub-loss savings and other factors not associated with joint design.

Next consider a single-V butt weld in $\frac{5}{8}$-in. plate. For manual welding the V must have an included angle of 60°, but for MIG welding this may be reduced to 30° for flux-cored wire (see Fig. 85). Stick electrodes must provide 1.1 lb of deposited metal per lineal foot of weld; MIG wire must supply only 0.5 lb. The saving is then about 50%. Thus the narrower openings possible in MIG welded joints will provide savings in deposited metal from zero in thin material to 50% or more in heavy plate.

The reduced edge preparation required for the MIG process is developed still further when CO_2-shielded, flux-cored wire is used. With flux core it is possible to butt-weld $\frac{1}{2}$-in.-thick plate using an open butt without edge preparation.

When the MIG process is used in fillet welds, it is common practice

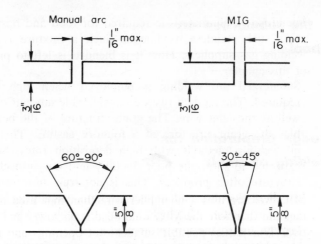

Fig. 85 Edge preparation, shielded metal arc and MIG. (a) 3/16 in. thick, (b) 5/8 in. thick.

to deposit smaller welds to obtain required strength. This practice is justified by the deeper penetration of the MIG process, which in effect increases the fillet cross section by means of penetration rather than buildup of deposited metal.

14.15 MIG techniques

For control of porosity at the start of the weld, the back-step start already mentioned is often employed. The arc is struck ½ to 1 in. ahead and moved back to the beginning of the joint, and the proper weld commerced. The short length of back-step weld may contain porosity and is therefore remelted as the joint proceeds. A forehand torch angle of 5 to 15° is generally employed when welding is done in the flat position. At higher welding speeds, the forehand angle may have to be increased. Work angle is 90° on butt welds, unless plates of different thickness are joined. Torch angle will be found to control bead contour, undercutting, and depth of penetration, although undercutting is also influenced by welding speed. Because of the deep penetration of the MIG arc, backing plates are often used to prevent burning through the metal. In vertical welding the weld should be made upward.

The short-circuiting method of metal transfer must be used for the joining of thin sheet. In this method, currents and penetration are lower than with spray transfer. The short arc method is also easier to use in position welding, even though the metal sections are heavy. Finally, distortion is less with short-circuiting metal transfer.

14.16   the submerged arc
weld pool

Submerged arc welding is employed when high deposition rates are required. The method fuses a considerable amount of the parent metal as well as the filler wire. The grain structure of the bead very much resembles the grain structure of a foundry casting. This is generally true of all welding methods with high deposition rates. Such welds would be expected to show the poor ductility and low impact strength that a cast structure often produces. This is not true, however. Subarc welds have excellent ductility and impact strength, usually at least of the quality of the base metal. The high quality of such welds is explained as being largely due to the flux protection.

Although not restricted to automatic operation, most submerged arc welding is done in automatic setups, in which positioners and fixtures hold and position the work and control distortion and arc conditions are under fully automatic control. Welding is always done in the flat or nearly flat position. Some inclination from the flat position is necessary when girth welds are produced on pipe and pressure vessels, cylindrical surfaces are built up, and certain ship plates are welded. Girth welds on plates are always made "downhill."

The high melting rates of subarc welding produce such a large molten pool that the metal will flow if inclined more than a few degrees from the flat position. This flow can be used to control weld contour. A high bead contour can be produced by uphill welding, as shown in Fig. 86. The pull of gravity makes the molten metal fall back behind the welding wire to freeze in the heaped position shown. The maximum possible angle of inclination must of course decrease if the welding current is

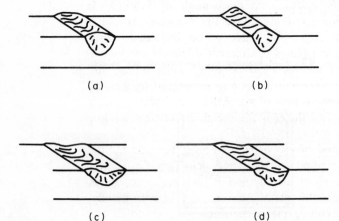

(a)

(b)

(c)

(d)

Fig. 86 Inclining the subarc weld pool. (a) Flat weld, (b) uphill weld, (c) downhill weld, (d) welding on a slope to the left.

increased. Downhill welding has the opposite effect. The molten metal drains toward the welding wire, producing a concave shape. The concave depression will increase with the angle of inclination. If a longitudinal weld is made at a small angle of inclination, the weld contour is an S curve as seen in the last sketch of Fig. 86.

These considerations govern setting-up conditions for girth welding, which is always done downhill when welding is done on the outside of the cylinder. Figure 87 shows the arrangement for such welding. The outside electrode points to the center of the cylinder with a small angle

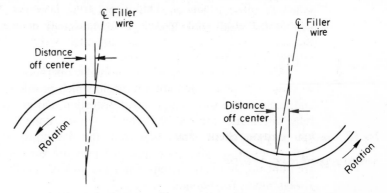

Fig. 87 Positioning for subarc welding of girth welds.

of inclination and is displaced about two to three inches from the top of the cylinder. The greater the angle of inclination, the smaller the penetration. The current must not be so high that the molten metal will run from the weld groove before it can freeze. Since a large-diameter cylinder is flatter than a small-diameter cylinder, the maximum possible current increases with diameter. Up to about 750 amp may be used on a 10-in. O.D. (outside diameter) cylinder, and 300 amp more for every 10 in. of diameter above the first 10 in.

Fig. 88 Flux backing for submerged arc joints.

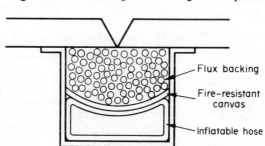

When butt-welding from one side with complete penetration, the massive weld pool must be supported on the back side of the weld. The backing support may be a steel or copper backing bar; a flux backing along the length of the weld; or less commonly glass tape, refractories, or other materials. The fluxes used for backing are usually specially formulated. Sometimes instead of a backing support, the rear side of the joint will be welded, manually or otherwise, this weld serving as support for the molten weld metal. Figure 88 shows one method of supporting backing flux with an inflatable hose.

Approximately two pounds of parent metal are melted for every pound of subarc filler wire. Dilution of the filler metal is therefore very high in the weld pool. The weld chemistry is determined primarily by the parent metal rather than by the filler metal.

14.17 edge preparation for submerged arc welding

The use of closed square butt welds may be extended to thicknesses as great as 5/8 in. if submerged arc welding is used. No backing is required if the plates fit closely. Full penetration is obtained simply by a single pass on each side of the joint. Such welds may trap slag, however, and may not pass radiographic inspection. For best weld quality, edge preparation is used for thicknesses of 3/8 in. and up. V's as narrow as 30 and 45° are possible, but if the welds are subject to X-ray inspection, wider angles of 70 to 90° are often used. For best quality, the double V with angles of 60 to 90°, is preferred for plates 3/8 in. and thicker. Narrower angles are possible on thicker plate, or are used with lower current values. Large root faces are needed at the base of a V to prevent burning through of the nose, and reasonably good fit-up is necessary.

FIRST-QUALITY BUTT WELDS WITH COPPER BACKING, SQUARE EDGES

Material Gauge, in.	Root Opening, in.	Wire Diameter, in.	Arc Current, amp	Arc Volts	Speed, ipm
14	0	3/32	325–375	25	100–150
12	0	1/8	350–400	25	75–100
10	0–1/16	1/8	400–475	26	50– 80
3/16	0–1/16	5/32	600–650	26	35– 50
1/4	0–3/32	3/16	750–850	28	25– 35
5/16	0–3/32	3/16–7/32	800–900	30	25– 30

FIRST-QUALITY DOUBLE-V BUTT WELDS

Material, in.	Depth of V, in.	V Angle	Amp (Min.)	Wire, in.	imp	Root Face, in.	Depth of V, in.	V Angle	Amp (Min.)	Wire, in.	imp
		Front Pass						Back Pass			
3/8	1/8	back gouge	600	3/16	20	3/8			550	3/16	22
1/2	1/8	back gouge	900	3/16	16	3/8	1/8	90	650	3/16	18
3/4	1/4	90	1100	1/4	13	5/16	3/16	90	850	1/4	16
1	3/8	90	1200	1/4	11	5/16	5/16	90	1000	1/4	15
1 1/2	5/8	70	1600	5/16	9	7/16	7/16	60	1300	1/4	10
2	3/4	80	1900	5/16	6	1/2	3/4	70	1500	5/16	7
2 1/2	1	80	2000	5/16	5	5/8	7/8	70	1700	5/16	5

14.18 submerged arc operation

1. Wire point   The welding wire may be forward pointing (in the direction in which the weld is being advanced), backward pointing, or at right angles to the weld. The backward-pointing position produces greater penetration. A forward-pointing wire will produce less penetration and a wider, flatter weld reinforcement. A backward-pointing wire is preferred for fillet welds in thin material in the range of 14 gauge. For flat fillet welding, the welding wire usually bisects the 90° fillet angle, but penetration may be increased by pointing the wire into the joint at a flatter angle.

2. Voltage   The shape of the fusion zone and its reinforcement are influenced by the arc voltage. A low voltage gives more reinforcement than a high arc voltage. Highter voltages widen the fusion zone and reduce the penetration.

3. Current   Higher currents produce greater penetration and more weld reinforcement.

4. Welding speed   Excessive welding speeds will promote undercutting in many welding methods, including submerged arc welding. Reinforcement is increased by reducing the welding speed.

5. Depth of flux   Submerged arc welding requires a uniform depth of flux covering. Too much flux may result in a rough weld owing to generation of excessive amounts of gas. The weld may even be porous. Too little flux may result in spatter. No difficulties arise from too wide a deposit of flux.

The appearance of a properly made submerged arc bead is similar to the bead shown in Fig. 82, which is a subarc butt weld in 1-in. plate. The use of a starter tab should be noted.

14.18 fusion welding methods

Shielded metal arc and TIG welding have already been discussed. These are manual methods, requiring a considerable degree of operator skill. MIG welding, using a shielding gas or flux-cored wire without a shielding gas, is semiautomatic. Submerged arc welding is usually an automatic method. The discussion of fusion welding by means of the electric arc is concluded in this chapter, but the chapters to follow discuss other fusion methods. These are resistance welding (Chapter 15) and induction welding (Chapter 16), both of which use the electrical resistance of the workpiece to develop the heat of fusion, and electron beam welding (Chapter 19), the last of the significant fusion welding methods using electrical equipment. This makes a total of seven electric fusion welding methods, if such methods as electroslag and electrogas and others are taken to be variants of these basic seven.

PROBLEMS

1 Find the welding heat in joules per inch for electron beam welding using 30 kv, 0.050 amp at a welding speed of 50 in. per min.

2 Determine the joules per inch in subarc welding with 600 amp at 26 v and 40 in. per min.

3 Determine the joules per inch for TIG welding at 100 amp, 30 v, and 12 in. per min.

4 Prove that the cross section to be filled with weld metal is only half as much for a double-V as for a single-V joint.

5 Prove that if the leg of a fillet weld is doubled in length, about four times as much filler metal is required.

6 Give two reasons why a double-V joint will produce less distortion than a single-V joint.

7 Why does deep penetration result in less distortion than shallow penetration.

8 The best inert gas mixture for the welding of stainless steel is 90% helium, 7½% argon, and 2½% carbon dioxide. Welding gas suppliers do not stock

such a mixture, however. Decide how to blend this mixture from the following available gas supplies:

(a) pure helium
(b) 75% A, 25% CO_2

9 In the table for First-Quality Double-V Butt Welds, Sec. 14.17, the depth of the V is one-third the thickness of the plate for thin plates such as ⅜ in. Why is it more than one-third for the thicker plates in the table?

10 (a) In edge preparation for welding, what requirements determine the gap between the plates and the V angle for a butt weld?
(b) For a welding method that uses neither filler rod, electrode, nor flux and that has unlimited penetration (this is electron beam welding), what edge preparation would be suitable?

11 Under what circumstances would a backing bar be used in butt welding?

12 What advantage and what disadvantage does the U-groove edge preparation offer?

13 The first manual pass in a butt weld in heavy plate sometimes cracks. Why?

14 Outline a back-gouging and welding procedure that will eliminate the entrapment of slag in butt welds in heavy plate.

15 What is the purpose of a starter tab?

16 How do the following job factors influence distortion?

(a) plate thickness
(b) coefficient of expansion of the metal
(c) welding heat
(d) stringer bead versus weave bead
(e) edge preparation
(f) penetration
(g) overwelding
(h) welding jigs

17 Outline a method of butt-welding Monel-clad plate that will reduce the possibility of dilution to a minimum.

18 (a) What advantages does argon offer over helium for shielding?
(b) When would helium be preferred to argon?

15.1 welding methods using electric current and pressure

The welding methods discussed in this chapter require both an electric current and a forging pressure to complete the weld and thus may be considered a technical extension of the forge-welding method used by blacksmiths. The current requirements of these welding processes exceed those of arc welding. The resistance that develops the heat for welding is the resistance of the workpiece. This is much smaller than that of an electric arc, and to compensate, much higher currents have to be used. The resistance welding machines producing such current are both large and rather costly and are not as portable as most arc welding machines. The work therefore must be brought to the machine. There are, however, small portable spot-welders, some of which can be operated from a standard arc welding machine, but the range of work that these can accommodate is limited, and many models have a limited duty cycle rating that is often a disappointment to the buyer. Such small spot welders are used only for casual spot welding, not for continuous and uninterrupted work on the production line.

One method of current-plus-forging-pressure welding, or stud welding has already been discussed in Chapter 12. Stud guns, however, can be operated as accessories for arc welding machines and do not usually require a resistance-welding transformer.

RESISTANCE
WELDING

15

Spot welding is the commonest and simplest of the resistance-welding methods and is done in four stages, each occupying only a small fraction of a second:

1. SQUEEZE time. In this period the electrodes build up the required pressure on the sheets to be welded.
2. WELD time. Welding current flows, fusing a nugget at the interface between the sheets. Electrode pressure is maintained.
3. HOLD time. Current is interrupted while the fused nugget freezes under electrode pressure.
4. OFF time. The electrodes release the work, and no current can flow during this period.

In the simplest type of spot-welding transformer, the secondary winding supplies a voltage at the welding tips between 1 and 10 v and a very large current. The welding of metals of differing electrical resistance, or different thicknesses of the same metal, requires control of the amount of heat supplied to the joint. In the very simplest type of welding control, this heat is controlled by a fixed current and a variation of the number of cycles during which current flows during WELD time. Many methods of resistance welding, such as aircraft welding, cannot use this simple method of heat control but must control both the number or cycles of weld time and the magnitude of the current.

The heat generated across the electrodes is given by the formula

$$Q(\text{in watt-hours}) = I^2Rt \qquad \text{where } t = \text{hours}$$

Since 3412 Btu = 1 kwh,

$$Q(\text{in Btu}) = 3.412 I^2Rt \quad (t \text{ in hours})$$

$$= \frac{3.412}{60 \times 60} I^2Rt \qquad \text{where } t = \text{seconds}$$

$$= 0.00095 I^2Rt \qquad \text{where } t = \text{seconds, or appox.}$$

$$= 0.001 I^2Rt$$

$$= 0.00016 I^2Rt \qquad \text{where } t = \text{cycles of 60-cycle current}$$

Suppose $R = 0.0001$, $I = 10,000$ amp, and $t = 6$ cycles.

Then Q in Btu $= 0.000016 I^2Rt$

$$= 1 \text{ Btu}$$

This is a minute amount of heat, but it is delivered to the workpieces in only 0.1 sec. There cannot be much wasted heat and therefore only an extremely narrow heat-affected zone. This small amount of heat is roughly what is required to spot-weld two sheets of stainless steel 0.050 in. thick with a single spot weld.

The amount of heat evolved is proportional to the square of the current, to the resistance of the materials between the electrodes, and to the number of cycles of weld time. The resistance of the materials is next in importance to welding current. Obviously the forging pressure of the electrodes can influence this electrical resistance by forcing the two sheets to be joined into closer contact, thus reducing the contact resistance. Actually contact resistance, more than metal resistance, constitutes the electrical resistance between the electrodes. Of the five distinguishable resistances in series with the electrodes, three are contact resistances:

1. contact resistance between upper electrode and top sheet
2. resistance of top sheet
3. contact resistance between top and bottom sheet
4. resistance of bottom sheet
5. contact resistance between bottom sheet and lower electrode

The heat generated is proportional to the magnitudes of these resistances, the largest being the electrical resistance between the two sheets. This is the region of the weld nugget.

Uniform welds are possible only on clean sheet. The welding of metal with surface oxides produces welds of variable size and strength. This is especially true of aluminum. The presence of oxides or dirt may increase the total resistance between the electrode tips by a factor of ten or more.

For spot welds of high quality and consistent strength, control of contact resistance may be necessary. The low resistance of the work will have to be measured and is done in the following manner:

The two sheets are clamped together in a small hydraulic press under a force of the magnitude employed in spot welding. This force can be determined from a pressure gauge that reads hydraulic pressure and from the area of the hydraulic piston. A small current is passed through the sheets and read on an ammeter. A millivolt meter reads the voltage drop across the sheets. The resistance is calculated from Ohm's law. The arrangement is shown in Fig. 89.

It is easier to spot-weld metals of high electrical resistance, such as carbon or stainless steels. Such metals require lower currents than do metals of low electrical resistance such as copper, which is difficult to spot-weld. More heat is generated in a high-resistance metal. In addition, high thermal conductivity always accompanies low electrical resistance, so that heat cannot be concentrated in the immediate region of the weld in such metals as copper and aluminum. Currents must then be higher for welding conductive metals to compensate for the heat drained away from the weld. For similar reasons, thicker sheets require higher currents because of the greater "thermal severity" as the thick-

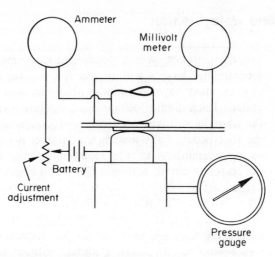

Fig. 89 Measuring contact resistance for spot welding.

ness increases. For a comparison, the spot welding of four metals of different thermal conductivity will be compared. It will be assumed that two sheets 0.032 in. thick of each of the following are to be spot-welded: stainless steel 304, mild low-carbon steel, Monel, and aluminum. The specific electrical resistances of these metals at 70 F are as follows:

stainless steel 304	29×10^{-6} ohms/cu in.
Monel	17×10^{-6}
low-carbon steel sheet	5×10^{-6}
2S aluminum	1.1×10^{-6}

COMPARATIVE SPOT-WELDING DATA
Two 0.032 in. Sheets

Material	Electrode Force	Current, amp	Cycles to Weld
stainless 304	650#	5,500	5
Monel	300#	7,000	4
Low-carbon sheet	400#	8,000	8
aluminum 2S	700#	28,000	2

The values for electrode force, current, and cycles are typical only. Currents increase as the electrical conductivities of the metals increase, though not in proportion. The weld cycle time for aluminum is reduced to 2 cycles so that the weld can be completed before the heat input is dissipated into the sheets.

15.3 time delay action

For the SQUEEZE, WELD, HOLD, and OFF times of the spot-welding cycle, four timing devices will be needed to operate four relays. The timing devices must be adjustable so that the time of each operation may be varied. Each timing device must operate the next timing device, since the four times follow each other in sequence. When the operator presses the foot pedal of the machine, a contact is closed in the SQUEEZE circuit of the machine. After the required number of cycles of SQUEEZE time, the SQUEEZE circuit activates the WELD contact. Again, after the required number of WELD cycles, the WELD circuit closes a contact to activate the HOLD contact. The HOLD circuit then closes the OFF contact, which itself closes the SQUEEZE contact. The cycle can be repeated indefinitely as each relay fires the next one in the sequence.

Figure 90 (a) shows a contact without time delay. When the switch S is closed (S could be the foot-pedal switch in the spot-welding machine), current flows in the solenoid of the relay to close the relay contacts and operate the circuit. The operating circuit could be the SQUEEZE sequence, in which the upper electrode forces together the two sheets to be welded.

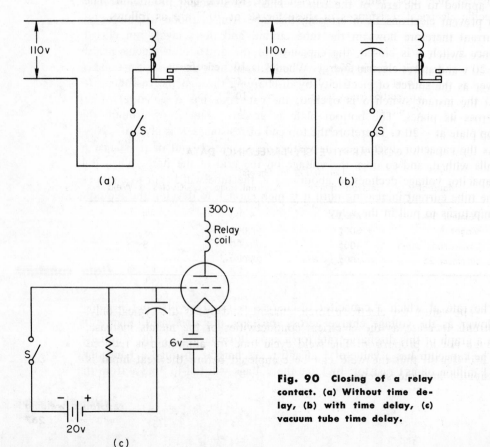

Fig. 90 Closing of a relay contact. (a) Without time delay, (b) with time delay, (c) vacuum tube time delay.

Suppose instead that the foot switch puts 110-v current on the SQUEEZE relay and that a time delay is required before the WELD sequence begins. A time delay must then be included in the circuit. Figure 90(b) shows a basic time-delay relay. A capacitor is now connected across the relay. An induction coil could be used instead of a capacitor, but capacitors are cheaper and more compact.

If the explanation of the circuit of Fig. 59(c) is recalled, it should be apparent that Fig. 59(c) is a time-delay circuit, for in this circuit what is intended to happen happens *after* the switch is opened or closed. Figure 90(b) is the most usual arrangement. When the switch S is closed, the contact to the next circuit in the sequence is closed, but at the same time the capacitor C is charged up to 110 v. When the switch is opened, the capacitor discharges electrons into the coil of the relay and holds the relay closed for a short time, thus providing time delay action. To obtain a long time delay, it is necessary to use a large capacitor with a high value in microfarads (μf), which is a high storage capacity for electrons. Also, the higher the resistance of the relay coil, the less current will flow, and the longer the capacitor will hold its charge.

Figure 90(c) is a time delay circuit which includes a vacuum tube triode as a relay. Here the purpose is to close the relay a short time after switch S is opened. When switch S is closed, a voltage of about -20 v is applied to the grid of the triode. This is a sufficient negative voltage to prevent electrons from crossing the tube from cathode to anode. No current therefore flows in the tube circuit, and the relay is not closed. Since switch S is closed, the capacitor in the grid circuit is charged to -20 v and stores electric energy. When S is opened, the capacitor C takes over as the source of electricity by discharging through the resistance R. At the instant switch S is opened, the capacitor has a potential of 20 across its plates. The bottom plate is at zero voltage, or ground, the top plate at -20 v. Therefore the top end of resistance R is also at -20 v. As the capacitor discharges, its voltage falls, the top end of resistance R falls with it, and so does the voltage on the grid of the tube. When this capacitor voltage declines to about -5 v, the tube will begin to conduct, the tube current increasing until it is high enough to develop the required amp-turns to pull in the relay.

15.4 *time constant*

The rate at which a capacitor discharges is rapid at first but becomes slower as the voltage charge across the capacitor decreases. Figure 91 is a graph of this discharge rate for a capacitor charged to 100 v initially. The capacitor has a value of 1 μf and is discharging through a 1-megohm (1 million ohms) resistor. In 1 sec the voltage will fall to 36.8 v from the initial 100 v, or 36.8% of the initial charge, about one-third. In 2 sec, the voltage has dropped to 13.5, 13½% of initial voltage, actually 36.8% of 36.8%. In 3 sec the voltage remaining is 36.8% of 36.8% of 36.8%, and so on.

This decay rate is characteristic of a great many technical processes in industry and science, and will be mentioned again in this book. The decay of current in the circuit of Fig. 59(c) follows such a decay curve. The same type of decay is found in the radioactivity of isotopes for the gamma ray inspection of welds. In electrical work the rate of decay is taken as the time required for decay to reach 36.8% of the initial value. In radioisotopes, the amount of radiation given off decays in the same mathematical way, but the rate of decay is taken instead as the time required for the amount of radiation to drop to 50% of the initial amount, or as it is called, the half-life. Thus iridium-192 after 74 days will produce only half the radiation it provided at 0 days, in 148 days (2 × 74 days) one-quarter, in 3 × 74 days one-eighth, in 4 × 74 days one-sixteenth, and so on. It is easier to understand the mathematics by thinking in terms of half-life or 50% time, as is done in radiation work, than in terms of a 36.8% time, as is done in electrical theory.

This 36.8% time period is called the *time constant* of the delay circuit. It is not necessarily the time delay—that depends on the resistance in the circuit and the exact amount of amp-turns required to pull in the relay. Some relays will not pull in before three or four time constants.

In the circuit of Fig. 91 the time constant was taken as 1 sec. This time constant can be found from any circuit by multiplying the resistance of the circuit in megohms by the capacitance of the circuit in microfarads, that is,

$$R \times C = \text{time constant in seconds}$$

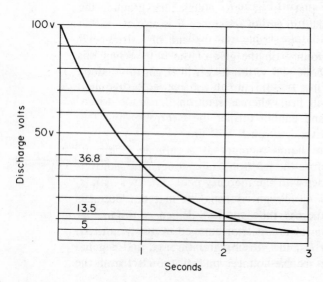

Fig. 91 **Rate of capacitor discharge for a time constant of 1 second.**

In Fig. 91, 1 megohm $\times$ 1 μf $= 1$ sec time constant. The mathematical expression for this delay curve is

$$E = \frac{E_1}{e^{t/RC}}$$

where $E =$ the voltage at time t seconds after discharge begins
$E_1 =$ the initial voltage
$RC =$ time constant
$t =$ time in seconds
$e = 2.718$

15.5 the ignitron contactor

In the brief weld time of only a few cycles, usually less than 20 or one-third of a second, the ignitron tube must switch the large welding current on and off. The ignitron, like the arc welding machine supplying power for manual shielded arc welding, does not operate on continuous duty. Its duty cycle is always less than 30%, and for this short duty cycle it can pass extremely high currents without burning itself out.

An ignitron, however, like the other electron tubes, is a d-c device and can only use one polarity. The welding power for spot welding is almost always 60-cycle a.c. supplied by the transformer in the welding machine. In order to use both polarities of a.c., two ignitrons are used in what is called a "back-to-back" circuit. Figure 92 shows this circuit. Such a pair of ignitrons is called an *ignitron contactor*.

The symbol for a gas-filled tube is a circle with a spot in it. An ignitron is a mercury gas tube and uses this symbol. The two back-to-back ignitrons are shown with their anodes marked A_1 and A_2 and their cathodes marked K_1 and K_2. When point 1 of the a-c line is positive and point 2 negative, ignitron 1 will fire, whereas ignitron 2 cannot do so because its anode is negative and cannot attract the electrons from the cathode. When point 2 is positive, ignitron 2 will fire.

Ignitrons contain a pool of liquid mercury as a cathode. Some of this mercury must be ionized before the ignitron can conduct. The ignitron therefore has an ignitor in contact with the mercury pool. The two ignitor contacts are designated I_{G1} and I_{G2}. When contact C is closed, 20 to 40 amp flow to the ignitor to make the tube conduct. When contact C is closed, suppose point 1 is positive. Current then flows from point 2 to the cathode K_1, ignitor I_{G1}, ignitor I_{G2}, the welding transformer, and out to point 1. As soon as ionization is established, the path of the electron flow is from 2 to K_1, anode A_1, welding transformer, and point 1. On the next half cycle, electrons flow from point 1 to the transformer, K_2, A_2, and to point 2.

In this arrangement, electrons flow from cathode to ignitor in the one ignitron, and they flow in the reverse direction, from ignitor to cathode, in the other ignitron. The latter flow is the wrong way and has the effect of damaging the ignitor and reducing tube life—electrons should not flow toward cathodes. To prevent this reverse current, solid-state rectifiers are added to the circuit as shown in Fig. 92(b). The rectifier symbols indicate that electrons can flow into the arrow symbol of the rectifier but not in the direction that the arrow symbol points. By means of the rectifiers, current can flow only from cathode to ignitor.

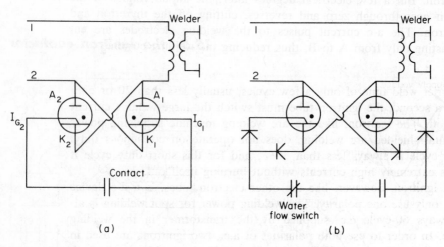

Fig. 92 **Ignitron contactor.** **(a) Basic circuit, (b) with rectifier protection.**

In very high-current resistance welders, thyratrons may be used to switch the ignitrons. The basic circuit is shown in Fig. 93(c). A water flow switch is included in the circuit to prevent operation if the flow of cooling water to the ignitrons should fail. By putting a negative voltage on V_1 and V_2, the grid connections to the thyratrons, the thyratrons are prevented from conducting. The ignitrons then cannot pass current to the welding transformer. The ignitrons will conduct if a positive voltage is applied to V_1 and V_2. This may seem an unusually complicated way to switch current on and off, but as always there are good reasons. The currents handled by resistance welders are thousands of amperes, and a simple toggle or knife switch cannot be used to interrupt such high currents. Worse still, the high current may have to be switched several times every second. This is the severest kind of switching duty.

Thyratron grid control, in addition to switching, can be used for heat control, that is, current control, for the welding electrodes. This is arranged by using a time delay device to control the voltage applied to the grid circuits of V_1 and V_2. If there is no time delay in applying a positive voltage to the grid of the thyratron, the thyratron current is a maximum, as shown in Fig. 93(a). The current lags the voltage, because a resistance welder, like an arc welder, is an inductive load. In Fig. 93(b), the grid of the thyratron is held negative until late in the half cycle. At point A in the half cycle, the grid goes positive, firing the thyratron and its ignitron. But a few electrical degrees later, the anode voltage of the thyratron goes through zero and reverses, cutting off the thyratron and its ignitron. The a-c current pulses to the welding electrodes are cut short, lasting only from A to B, thus reducing the welding current.

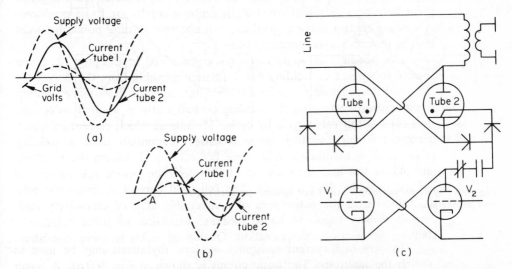

Fig. 93 **Thyratron switching of ignitrons. (a) Without time delay circuit in thyratron grid control, (b) with time delay circuit in thyratron grid control, (c) switching circuit.**

Previously a typical example of the spot welding of two 0.032-in.-thick aluminum sheets, using 28,000 amp for 2 cycles, was cited. For such a short weld time, the flow of welding current must be started always at the same point in the half-wave of 60-cycle voltage. This calls for every precise timing, but if this is not done, the same amount of heat will not be produced in each spot weld, and welding results then become unpredictable.

Because of the lagging power-factor load current, the welding machine will draw current that starts at point 1 in the cycle of Fig. 94. At this point the wave shape remains the same in each cycle and the same heat is produced per cycle. Now if the welding contact closes the circuit at point 2 in the cycle and the previously mentioned 2 cycles of weld are used, more heat will be put into the weld. If the contact closes at point 3 to make the next spot weld, this spot weld will receive much

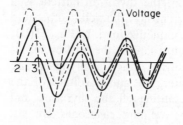

Fig. 94 Effect of random starting point for welding current.

less heat than the first weld will. Therefore all spot welds must begin at point 1 in the a-c cycle if consistently uniform results are to be produced. A welding control that can provide such accurate starting points for weld heat is termed a *synchronous control*.

The principle of *slope control* was discussed in Chapter 12. Slope control for resistance welding has a different meaning from the slope control used on constant-potential arc welding machines. Resistance welding slope control means that the welding current starts at a small value and then rises to full value cycle by cycle. The rate at which current increases per cycle is slope control. Slope control is commonly used in welding metals such as aluminum. With slope control, the aluminum sheet softens and allows full and firm seating of the electrode before full current is applied to make the spot weld. The full weld current is thus uniformly distributed over the entire area of contact. No area of excessively high current density exists to cause flashing, expulsion of metal, electrode sticking, or electrode deterioration. Quality of welds is more consistent also.

The combination of imperfect seating of the electrode tip and the high welding currents used with aluminum (e.g., 28,000 amp) will almost certainly be damaging. Consider welding aluminum sheets with 28,000 amp, and assume that all the current is confined to the fused zone of the nugget—a somewhat erroneous assumption. The fused area will be approximately $\frac{1}{6}$ in. in diameter, or roughly $\frac{1}{50}$ sq in. Even with full seating of the electrode tip, the current density is a huge figure.

Slope control can be provided in any welding machine that has phase-shifting heat control. Taper control or downslope may also be necessary when welding aluminum. Such taper control allows the use of lower forging pressures during HOLD time without the risk of cracks developing in the nugget.

Except for very large machines, most spot-welding machines are single phase. The power rating of the resistance-welding transformer is based on a 50% duty cycle. Transformer output voltage is between 1 and 10 v, lower than the voltages used for arc welding, and currents are higher. The load current is inductive, and if power factor is a problem, capacitors may be used to reduce the phase lag angle. The inductive effects of the one-turn loop made by the arms and electrodes of the welding machine are powerful, and the larger the dimensions of this loop, the worse the power factor is.

High frequency resistance welders are sometimes used. A high frequency current breaks through oxide films more readily than a 60-cycle current does. The operating frequency exceeds 100 kc and is produced by an electronic oscillator in the machine. Low frequency resistance welders, less than 60 cycle, are also used. These machines draw current from a three-phase supply, rectify it to direct current, and reconvert it to a single-phase frequency of 25 cycles or less. Since current is drawn from all three phases of the supply instead of one phase, such a machine puts a more balanced load on the system.

Occasionally the electrical demands of a resistance welder are too severe for the electrical supply. A stored-energy machine may therefore be used, drawing three-phase power during the HOLD and OFF periods to charge a bank of capacitors. The capacitors discharge to the electrodes during the WELD period. Welding energy may also be stored in the magnetic field of a welding transformer in the type of machine known as an electromagnetic resistance welder. The stored-energy welder thus delivers energy at a high rate to the electrodes but accumulates the energy from the electrical supply at a slow rate. Such machines are often used to supply the large currents required to spot-weld aluminum.

TYPICAL SPOT WELDER CAPACITIES FOR TWO THICKNESSES OF CLEAN MILD STEEL*

Kva	Steel Gauge	Short Circuit, amp	Machine Weight (Approx. lb)
20	14	14,000	2000
30	12	17,000	2100
50	$\frac{1}{8}''$	22,000	2300
75	$\frac{3}{16}''$	27,000	2600

*The kva kilovolt-ampere rating is based on a 50% duty cycle. The short-circuit currents given are for small throat openings. Available current decreases for larger openings owing to inductive effect.

For extremely small work, such as the welding of electronic components, microwelders must be used. A very small microwelder may have a maximum welding current of a few hundred amperes and electrode pressure of only a few pounds. In these microsizes, the welding machine electrical supply may be the nearest 110-v wall outlet. A microscope or stereomicroscope may be mounted on the welding machine for examination of the work. Such a spot-welding machine is about the size of a typewriter.

Two general types of mechanism are used for bringing the pressure of the movable upper electrode onto the work. The electrode may be mounted on a pivoting arm, or it may move vertically in a straight line. Machines using the first method are called *rocker-arm machines* (Fig. 95); if the second method is used, the machine is a *press type* (Fig. 96). Best-quality spot welds are produced on the press-type machine, which must also be used for projection welding, to be discussed presently. Very high electrode pressures require the use of the press-type machine, the pressure being applied by means of an air cylinder, using shop air at about 80 psi, or by means of a hydraulic cylinder. Rocker-arm machines may be operated either by mechanical linkage or by pressure cylinders. Maximum electrode pressure is decreased on a rocker arm if the throat

Fig. 95 Small rocker arm spot welding machine. (Courtesy Miller Electric Manufacturing Co.)

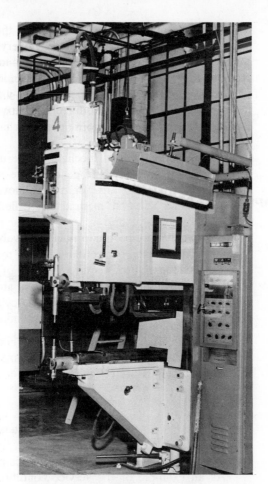

Fig. 96 Press type resistance welding machine. (Courtesy Taylor Winfield)

depth is increased, since then less leverage is available with the longer arm.

Multiple-spot welding machines are built for a specific application in large-quantity production work, such as the body work of automobiles. As a general rule, it is not possible to make simultaneous multiple spot welds using two or more electrodes in parallel because of the undependable current distribution among the electrodes. Three methods of producing multiple spots are in use:

1. One common welding transformer and a separate hydraulic cylinder for each electrode. The electrodes contact the work one at a time.
2. Commutator system. In the common SQUEEZE time all electrodes are brought into contact with the work simultaneously. Current from a common transformer secondary winding is commutated to one electrode at a time.

resistance welding
277

3. Separate transformer and controls for each electrode set. The third method is preferred at present. It allows more than one weld at a time. It is also easier to put together a special multiple-spot machine by this method, since the machine is simply an assembly of separate spot welders and standard components. Such special machines may produce a hundred or more spots in a single operation.

15.8 spot welding practices

The spot weld must be made in a relatively few cycles of current for a number of reasons:

1. Time must not be allowed for the heat to dissipate from the area of the weld.
2. The metal is softened and the electrode may be forced through the sheet, given sufficient time.
3. The electrical resistance is constantly changing as the work heats.
4. Heat-treating effects must be minimized. Thus a fast weld in an austenitic stainless steel will result in a minimum of carbide precipitation.

The current density in the work is controlled by the size of the spot welding tip. Standard tip diameters are $\frac{3}{16}$, $\frac{1}{4}$, $\frac{3}{8}$, $\frac{1}{2}$, $\frac{5}{8}$, $\frac{3}{4}$, and $\frac{7}{8}$ in. The current density in the tip itself is not usually greater than 70,000 amp per sq in., to prevent damage to the tip.

As an example of the service conditions that the electrode and its tip must meet, consider welding 16-gauge mild steel with a $\frac{1}{2}$-in.-diameter tip using 10,000 amp and an electrode force of 650 lb. Current density in the tip = amp per sq in. = $\frac{10,000}{0.19}$ = 52,000 amp per sq in. Stress in pounds per square inch in the tip = $\frac{650}{0.19}$ = 3400 psi.

When the work and the electrode have nearly the same electrical resistance, they tend to weld together. Problems in heating effects arise when two pieces of different thickness must be spot-welded. The thicker sheet has the higher resistance and will receive more heat. This condition may be corrected by using a tip of a smaller diameter in contact with the thinner sheet to increase the current density, thus ensuring more uniform heat distribution. A similar problem arises when two metals of different electrical conductivity must be spot-welded. The material of higher conductivity must have the heavier gauge in order to achieve heat balance.

In theory, the penetration of a spot weld needs only to be a few thousandths of an inch to ensure joining of the two sheets. Welds made with such minimum penetration are not consistent in diameter or strength, however, and therefore a minimum penetration of 20% of the sheet thickness is usually required. Full penetration produces a strong weld, which is nevertheless unsightly owing to embedding of the electrode in the work, and is more damaging to the electrode tip. Maximum penetration is held to 80% of sheet thickness.

The HOLD time in the welding sequence has a number of functions. During HOLD, the sheets are held in contact by the electrode pressure until the fused nugget can harden and strengthen sufficiently to take over this function. The HOLD time also prevents cracking and reduces porosity.

Successful spot welding is influenced by many conditions and variables, such as current, electrode pressure, electrode diameter, number of WELD cycles, number of HOLD cycles, and others. One of the most important welding conditions sometimes is ignored: the surface condition of the metal. Dirt, contaminants, and oxides may result in alloying of the electrode tip and burning or cracking of the work. Surface coating, such as treating with phosphate, galvanizing, or aluminizing, greatly increases the difficulty of making quality welds. Galvanized steel requires greater electrode force, higher current, and longer weld time than the same gauges of uncoated carbon steel do, and the zinc can under adverse conditions produce alloying of the electrode tip. Similarly, aluminized steel requires more current and pressure. In thinner gauges of steel, the galvanized or aluminized coating is a greater proportion of the thickness of the sheet, and welding requirements may conform more to those of the coating than of the base metal of the sheet.

Indentations in the workpiece due to electrode pressure are sometimes caused by *insufficient* electrode pressure, with a resulting higher resistivity at the contact with the work, rather than *excessive* pressure.

Distortion cannot be avoided by substituting spot welding for arc welding. Spot welding distortion is best controlled by spot welding from the center of the sheet toward the edges.

The following tables are typical practice for spot welding. Considerable variation from these tabular values is possible, especially if specifications are not too rigid. The small and inexpensive spot-welding machines that deliver a fixed current at a varying number or a fixed number of cycles are still able to weld a wide range of thicknesses in many metals. A casual reading of the following tables would seem to suggest that such a range of spot welding could not be done on such machines. In all cases the tabular values assume good surface condition and good fit-up of the sheets to be welded. The column for minimum spot-weld spacing indicates the shortest distance between spots without significant short-circuiting from the adjacent spot weld to the spot weld being made.

Gauge in.	Tip Diameter, in.	Electrode Force, lb Plain	Galv.	Weld Cycles Plain	Galv.	Current Amp Plain	Galv.	Diameter of Fused Zone, in.	Minimum Spotweld Spacing, in.
0.021	3/8	300	400	6	9	6,500	10,000	0.13	3/8
0.032	3/8	400	600	8	12	8,000	12,000	0.16	1/2
0.040	1/2	500	700	10	14	9,000	14,000	0.18	3/4
0.060	1/2	800	1000	14	18	12,000	16,000	0.25	1
0.078	5/8	1100	1300	17	24	14,000	19,000	0.28	1 1/4
0.094	5/8	1300	1600	20	28	15,000	23,000	0.30	1 1/2
0.109	5/8	1600		23		17,500		0.32	1 5/8
0.125	7/8	1800		26		19,000		0.33	1 3/4

SPOT WELDING OF AUSTENITIC STAINLESS STEELS

Gauge	Tip Diameter, in.	Electrode Force, lb	Weld Cycles	Current, amp	Diameter of Nugget, in.	Minimum Spot Spacing, in.
0.021	1/4	400	4	3,000	0.10	5/16
0.031	3/8	650	5	4,800	0.13	1/2
0.040	3/8	900	6	6,200	0.16	5/8
0.060	1/2	1500	10	9,000	0.20	1
0.078	5/8	1800	14	11,000	0.27	1 1/4
0.094	5/8	2400	16	12,500	0.28	1 3/8
0.109	3/4	2800	18	14,000	0.28	1 1/2
0.125	3/4	3200	20	15,500	0.30	2

SPOT WELDING OF ALUMINUM ALLOYS
(Aluminum Company of Canada)

Gauge	Tip Diameter, in.	Electrode Force, lb	Weld Current Start	Weld	Weld Cycles Slope	Weld	Taper	Diameter of Fused Zone, in.
0.020	5/8	350	12,000	25,000	2	3	12	0.12
0.032	5/8	500	14,000	39,000	3	4	15	0.16
0.040	5/8	600	14,000	40,000	4	5	15	0.18
0.064	5/8	750	15,000	42,000	6	6	16	0.25
0.081	7/8	860	15,000	45,000	7	10	20	0.30
0.102	7/8	1050	17,000	60,000	10	14	22	0.36

15.9 projection welding

Projection welding is a variation of the spot-welding method. Projections or bosses are preformed on one of the sheets to be welded—on the thicker of the two sheets if they are of different thickness. These projections thus determine the exact position of the weld and its area. When the weld current is fired, the projection collapses under the electrode force so that the two sheets are welded tight together. It is usual to use high welding currents and a minimum number of weld cycles for projection welding, as well as large electrodes and a relatively low current density. Projection welding is especially advantageous when multiple welds are to be made simultaneously.

Projection welding is performed by spot-welding machines of the press type. The rocker-arm machines are not suitable. Projection welding dies are usually custom-made for the work.

A rather common application of projection welding is *cross-wire welding,* used to join crossed wires in the manufacture of wire guards, food racks, range grates, etc. The points of contact of the crossed wires constitute the localized areas for the welds. The welds are made by standard flat spot-welding tips or tips with a V groove. Special tips for producing several such welds at a time are also in use.

Metals with low hot strength, such as aluminum or some copper alloys are rarely projection-welded. Projections must not be so rigid that they will not collapse, nor so small that they are unable to conduct sufficient heat into the sheet.

15.10   seam welding

In seam welding, the two electrodes in the spot-welding machine are replaced by copper alloy rollers, and the work is rolled between them (Fig. 97). Thus a seam welding machine can weld a continuous seam in the two sheets. One roller or both may be motor-driven. The seam is

Fig. 97 An older model of a seam welder, the two copper wheel electrodes may be noted at the front of the machine.

made by a series of overlapping spot welds or spots spaced at short intervals by switching the welding current on and off without removing pressure from the circular electrodes. The latter method of spaced spots is termed roll spot welding. The roll-spot process is similar to spot welding, except that WELD and HOLD times are shorter and currents are larger. The spacing of the welds is obtained by adjustment of electrode rotational speed and current OFF time. The welding current may be

SEAM WELDING OF MILD STEELS

Gauge	Electrode Width, in.	Electrode Force, lb	On Cycles	Off Cycles	Weld Speed, ipm	Welds per in.	Current, amp
0.021	3/8	500	2	2	75	12	11,000
0.031	1/2	700	3	2	72	10	13,000
0.040	1/2	900	3	3	67	9	15,000
0.062	1/2	1100	4	4	63	7	17,000
0.078	5/8	1500	6	5	55	6	19,000
0.094	5/8	1800	7	6	50	5½	20,000
0.125	3/4	2200	11	7	45	4½	22,000

SEAM WELDING OF AUSTENITIC STAINLESS STEELS

Gauge	Electrode Width, in.	Electrode Force, lb	On Cycles	Off Cycles	Weld Speed, ipm	Welds per in.	Current, amp
0.021	1/4	700	3	2	50	13	8,000
0.031	3/8	1000	3	3	50	12	10,500
0.040	3/8	1300	3	4	45	11	13,000
0.062	1/2	2000	4	5	38	10	15,000
0.078	5/8	2400	4	6	36	9	16,000
0.094	5/8	2700	5	6	36	9	16,500
0.125	3/4	3500	6	6	35	8	17,000

SEAM WELDING OF ALUMINUM ALLOYS

Gauge	Electrode Force, lb	On Cycles	Off Cycles	Weld Speed, ipm	Welds per in.	Current, amp
0.020	550	1	3½	40	20	24,000
0.032	700	1	4½	40	16	29,000
0.040	750	2	5½	35	14	32,000
0.064	900	3	8	30	10	38,000
0.081	1100	4	11	25	9	41,000
0.102	1200	5	15	22	8	43,000
0.128	1300	7	21	18	7	45,000

applied either when the electrodes are moving or when they are stopped. Wheel speeds cannot be too high, or pressure will be removed from the spot weld too soon, a condition that may produce shrinkage cavities or cracks.

Continuous butt-welded seams by the resistance method are possible and are used for welding the longitudinal seams of pipe and tubing, where a lap seam is not desired. Figure 98 is a sketch of the rolls and

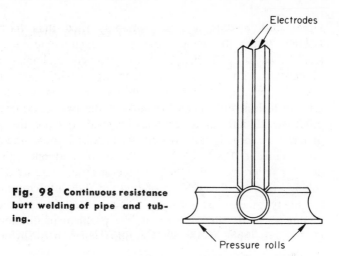

Fig. 98 Continuous resistance butt welding of pipe and tubing.

electrodes for such tube welding. Pressure rolls close the seam, and passage of a heavy current across the two roller electrodes through the work provides welding heat. The metal in the region of the seam is heated to plastic condition but is not melted. Other methods are also employed for seam welding of butt joints, including the induction heating method described in Chapter 16.

15.11 upset butt welding

This method is like flash welding in Sec. 15.12 and welds butt joints on the ends of pipe, tubing, bar, rod, extrusions, wire, and sheet. The two metal parts are gripped in jaws and forced together end to end, and a current is passed through the two workpieces across the joint. Current densities range from about 2000 to 5000 amp per sq in. When the joint is heated by means of its contact resistance, the butt pressure is increased and the joint is upset. Final pressure may be as high as 8000 psi. This pressure must be closely controlled: a pressure too low may produce a porous joint of low strength, while a pressure too high may give too much upset and produce a joint of low impact resistance. The metal in the joint is not melted, but is heated only to plastic condition. The resulting upset must be machined to size after the welding operation.

15.12 flash welding

Upset butt welding is less commonly used than flash welding. Flash welding serves the same purpose of making end butt joints. The two workpieces to be flash-welded are clamped, and their ends are just out of contact with one another. Current densities are approximately the same as those used in upset butt welding. The current arcs across the joint in a flash that melts the ends of the two workpieces. A pressure of 5,000 to 25,000 psi is suddenly applied to close the joint, and as the material is forged, the current is increased to as much as double the initial current. Flash welding is used to weld one coil of stock to the next for uninterrupted rolling of pipe or other material through continuous rolling mills, for the welding of railroad rails into continuous lengths, and for many other such purposes. The process is an excellent method of joining dissimilar metals without the problem of dilution. Figure 99 is a photomicrograph of the flash-welded joint between a stellite exhaust

Fig. 99 Photomicrograph of a flash-welded joint in an exhaust valve of a large stationary diesel engine.

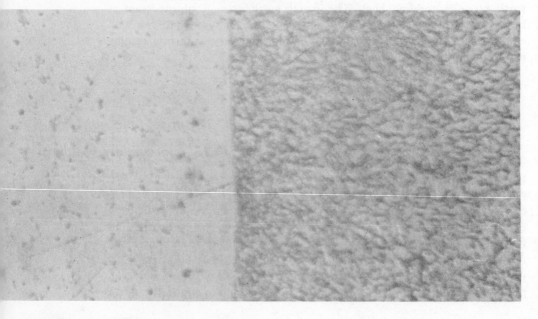

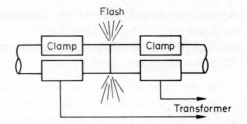

Fig. 100 Flash welding.

valve head and its martensitic stainless steel stem in a large stationary diesel engine.

When two workpieces of different electrical resistance are butt-welded, the material of lower resistance is made to project out farther from its clamping electrode in order to lengthen its resistance path.

FLASH WELDING OF SOLID ROUND OR SQUARE BARS

Bar Diameter, in.	Initial Distance Clamping Electrode to Butt Joint, in.	Flash Time, sec.
$\frac{1}{4}$	0.20	2
$\frac{1}{2}$	0.42	$4\frac{1}{4}$
1	0.83	13
2	1.63	90

The sequence of operations in flash welding may be the following:

1. Load work into machine and clamp work.
2. Apply welding voltage.
3. Flash.
4. Upset.
5. Interrupt current.
6. Unclamp work and unload.

15.13 percussion welding

Percussion welding is somewhat similar to flash welding, since it too uses a sudden electrical discharge across the joint to generate welding heat. When the surfaces to be joined are plastic, they are joined by a percussive blow produced by a spring or pneumatic cylinder. The electric arc is extinguished at the moment the ends are joined. The arc is established by one of the following three methods:

1. Contacting the workpieces, then separating them to draw out an arc

2. Application of sufficiently high voltage to ionize the gap between the workpieces
3. Passage of current across a nib connecting the workpieces
4. High frequency arc starting

The arc is maintained for only a small fraction of a second, and therefore only a small heat-affected zone, about 0.010 in., results in percussion welding. This method therefore is particularly recommended for stainless steels of all types: carbide precipitation is limited in the austenitic steels, grain growth is not pronounced in the ferritic types, and the hardened region is small in martensitic stainless steels. Percussion welding too is very successful in joining dissimilar metals. The short-duration current is almost always provided in percussion welders by capacitor discharge or sometimes electromagnetic energy storage in the welding transformer.

Stud welding, described in Chapter 12, is of course very similar to percussion welding in principle, though it uses an arc welding machine as a power source.

PROBLEMS

1 In Sec. 15.2 spot-welding data for 0.032-in. sheet in four different metals were compared. Calculate the current squared time cycles required for one spot in each metal. Are these wattage values proportional to the specific electrical resistances of the four metals?

2 Explain how the time-delay circuit of Fig. 90(c) works.

3 What is the time constant in seconds in the following circuits:
(a) a 400-μf capacitor discharging through a 100,000-ohm resistor
(b) a 250-μf capacitor discharging through a 25,000-ohm resistor?

4 Why is a HOLD time period needed in the spot-welding sequence?

5 Why is slope control used when spot-welding aluminum?

6 What three methods of producing multiple spot welds are in use? Which is the commonest method, and why is it preferred?

7 For what reasons must spot welds be made in a relatively few cycles of current?

8 Why is a larger tip diameter required for spot-welding aluminum than for spot-welding steel of the same thickness?

9 Calculate the approximate current density for spot-welding aluminum sheet 0.032 in. thick.

10 What is the maximum duty cycle for seam welding any of the thicknesses of mild steel given in the table of Sec. 15.10, "Seam Welding of Mild Steels"?

11 List as many welding methods as you can that use high frequency arc starting.

16.1 low temperature welding methods

Soldering, brazing, and adhesive bonding are metal joining methods with at least two characteristics in common:

1. They do not require fusion of the metal to be joined.
2. They are excellent methods of joining unlike materials. Soldering and brazing can even be used to join metals to a few ceramic materials such as glass, and adhesive bonding will join almost any kind of solid material.

Brazing means the joining of metals by means of a nonferrous filler metal with a melting point above 800 F but below the melting point of the workpiece. The filler metal flows between the closely fitted surfaces of the joint by capillary action, the most familiar use of which is in the brazing of a copper pipe slipped into a copper elbow in a domestic plumbing system. The filler metal flows into the joint between the two fittings even against the pull of gravity. *Braze welding* uses the same filler metals that brazing does, in such joints as fillet, groove, and butt, but the filler metal, being fused where it is deposited, does not flow by capillary action.

Soldering employs a filler metal with a melting point below 800 F and below the melting point of the metal to be joined.

BRAZING,

SOLDERING,

AND ADHESIVE BONDING

16

Adhesive bonding is the joining of metals by the use of organic cements.

Few metals at present cannot be brazed, and all can be adhesive-bonded. For the presently nonbrazeable metals, brazing formulations could be developed if ever the need should arise. Both brazing and adhesive bonding can produce strong and dependable joints. A brazed joint may be as strong as a welded joint. Although tensile strengths as high as 6000 psi are possible for soldered joints, they are never considered to be structurally dependable.

These low-temperature joining methods offer certain advantages over fusion welding, as follows:

1. Fusion methods create metallurgical problems, both in the joint and in the heat-affected zone. The low-temperature methods usually circumvent such difficulties. Dilution of weld metal rarely occurs. Steels need not be heated to their transformation temperature. Preheats and postheats are not required. Brazing rods do not have to be matched to the composition of the base metal.
2. Distortion is much less because of the lower temperature.
3. A wide range of brazing metals with different melting points are available, so that in general brazing may be done at any temperature within the brazing range that is desirable.
4. These methods are especially well adapted to the joining of thin-gauge materials, even metal foil, and to the joining of small parts.
5. The locked-in stresses of welded joints are absent or negligible with low-temperature joining.
6. Whole assemblies can be brazed, soldered, or bonded at the same time, without the necessity of running a bead, by such methods as furnace brazing, induction brazing, and similar methods.
7. These low-temperature methods are easily adapted to mass production techniques.
8. They will all join unlike materials.
9. Low-temperature joints are thin, unobtrusive, and virtually invisible, and brazing material matching the color of the parent metal may even be selected if necessary.

The Handy & Harman Company illustrates the advantages of brazing with the copper bus-bar contact sketched in Fig. 101. This

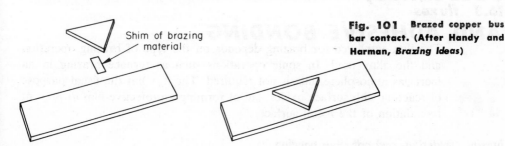

Shim of brazing material

Fig. 101 Brazed copper bus bar contact. (After Handy and Harman, *Brazing Ideas*)

simple case speaks for itself. By means of capillary action the small piece of brazing material covers the bonding area completely, thus providing minimum resistance to the flow of electric current. Such a joint could be adhesive-bonded equally well, except that bonding cements do not conduct electricity.

16.2 *brazing clearances*

To make a strong brazed joint in which capillary action will be effective, the clearance between the mating parts must be between 0.0005 and 0.008 in. in general. The shear strength of a brazed joint is influenced by this clearance dimension, the relationship between clearance and strength being that shown in the graph of Fig. 102. The maximum strength occurs

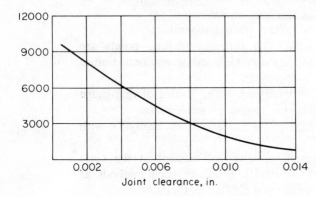

Fig. 102 **Typical relationship between razing clearance and shear strength (psi) of the brazed joint.**

with a rather close clearance. The clearance dimension must be that at brazing temperature, allowing for any thermal expansion. Generally clearances of less than 0.0005 in. are desirable for copper and silver brazing alloys. Commercially pure brazing copper is very fluid, and fine clearances are therefore possible with this material.

16.3 *fluxes*

The flux employed for brazing depends on the type of brazing operation and the alloy used. In some operations such as furnace brazing in an inert gas atmosphere, flux is not required. The flux has the usual purpose of reacting with surface oxides and of forming a protective film to prevent reoxidation of the metal surface.

brazing, soldering, and adhesive bonding

Most of the brazing fluxes fall into three groups: (1) borax and borates, (2) chlorides, and (3) fluorides and fluoborates. This grouping does not include certain special-purpose fluxes, such as the familiar rosin flux usually applied as a rosin-core solder for soldering electronic components. Borax is a general-purpose flux for higher brazing temperatures but will not remove the refractory oxides. Sodium, potassium, and lithium borates are used in fluxes with a melting point of 1400 F or higher and are good oxide-removers. For the difficult oxides, fluoborates are used, but like most of the strong fluxes they are toxic and also attack metals if not removed. It is generally true that any chemical that can dissolve refractory oxides can also attack metals if moisture is present. Chloride fluxes such as zinc and ammonium chloride and, even better, fluorides will remove refractory oxides. The following brief tabulation shows fluxing requirements for brazing various metals:

copper, copper alloys (not including aluminum bronze), nickel, stainless steels, carbon and alloy steels, cast iron	boric acid, borax, borates, fluorides, or fluoborates
aluminum bronze	chlorides, fluorides
aluminum, magnesium	chlorides, fluorides
titanium, zirconium	chlorides, fluorides

Inability of soldering or brazing filler metal to "wet out" on the parent metal indicates either improper fluxing or too high or too low a joining temperature. A common difficulty is the attempt to solder high-nickel wire with rosin-core solder, which is not successful because the flux is not sufficiently aggressive. Acid-core solder will do the job.

Many of the brazing rods used for torch brazing are flux-coated. For other types of brazing the flux is supplied in paste or powder form in 1-lb bottles or cans under brand names. Fluxes are removed with hot water and stainless steel brushes, or by the use of dip tanks containing trisodium phosphate or other chemicals in water.

16.4 brazing filler metals

All brazing metals are alloys of two or more pure metals, usually copper, silver, aluminum, tin, and lead. The metal constituents of the brazing or soldering alloy are partially or completely soluble in each other. The behavior and characteristics of such alloys are usually explained by means of "equilibrium diagrams," "constitution diagrams," or other such diagrams. Several such alloy systems have already been explained in this book. Figure 23 is the equilibrium diagram for the alloy system iron-carbon in the solid state. Figure 39 presents an equilibrium diagram for the nonaustenitic stainless irons, and Figs. 40 and 43 show such diagrams for copper alloys. Every diagram is a graph of temperature plotted against alloy composition. In order to describe the characteristic behavior of brazing alloys, we shall examine the equilibrium diagram for tin-lead solders, which is shown in Fig. 103.

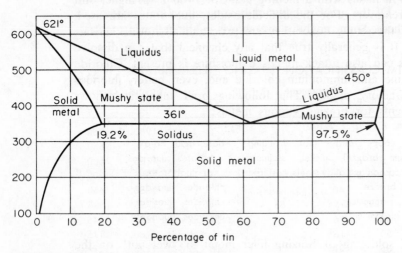

Fig. 103 Phase diagram for tin-lead solders.

Pure lead is not suitable for soldering because it does not wet other metals. Pure tin may be used for soldering but is too expensive. Hence the use of tin-lead mixtures for these purposes.

Pure lead melts at 621 F and pure tin at 450 F. Tin-lead solders are alloys of these two metals in various proportions. But whereas the pure metals melt and freeze at a definite temperature, the tin-lead alloys, like all alloys, freeze and melt over a range of temperatures. They begin to solidify at a temperature called the *liquidus* temperature and continue to solidify until a lower *solidus* temperature, at which freezing is complete, is reached. This freezing range between the liquidus and solidus temperatures is useful when metals are joined by brazing or soldering, since a fast freeze at a definite melting point gives no time for adjustment or manipulation of the work. However, metals can be mixed in a proportion that produces an alloy mixture with the same solidus and liquidus temperatures, that is, with a definite melting point. Called the *eutectic* composition, this is the alloy composition that has the lowest temperature of freezing or melting. For lead-tin solders the eutectic composition is 61.9% tin, 38.1% lead, this mixture melting at 361 F. All this information is conveyed by the diagram of Fig. 103. Notice that the longest freezing range is given by a solder composition of 20% tin.

The American Welding Society and the American Society for Testing and Materials use a special designation for the brazing alloys. The designation symbol begins with a B (for brazing) followed by the symbols for the principal alloy ingredients. The percentages of the alloys are not designated. Thus BCuP is a phosphor bronze brazing material, BNiCr is a nickel brazing material containing chromium, and BAg-1 is one of several silver brazing alloys, the 1 merely signifying that this alloy is first in the list. Of the great number of brazing alloys only a few can receive mention here. Some analyses are shown in the following table:

AWS-ASTM CLASSIFICATION: BRAZING FILLER METALS

Class	Percentage								Solidus Temp.	Liquidus Temp.
	Cu	Ag	P	Zn	Cr	Ni	Al	Other		
BCu	99								1980	1980
BCuP-1	95		5						1305	1650
BCuP-3	89	5	6						1195	1500
BCuP-5	80	15	5						1185	1300
BCuZn-1	60			40					1650	1660
BNiCr-2					7	86		4 Si, 3 B	1750	1825
BAg-1a	15	45		16				24 Cd	1125	1145
BAg-1b	15½	50		16½				18 Cd	1160	1175
BAg-2	26	35		21				18 Cd	1125	1295
BAg-3	15½	50		15½		3		16 Cd	1170	1270
BAg-4	30	40		28		2			1220	1435
BAlSi-1	4						95	5 Si	1070	1165
BAlSi-3	4						86	10 Si	970	1085
BAlSi-4	4						88	12 Si	1070	1080

The high melting point of copper, 1980 F, limits its use as a brazing filler metal to the joining of metals that melt above 2000 F. The copper-phosphorus alloys have much lower solidus temperatures and are used principally for brazing copper and its alloys. These BCuP alloys must not be used to join steel or nickel because phosphorus has a hardening and embrittling effect on these metals. However, BCu without phosphorus is a useful material for brazing unstabilized austenitic stainless steels. Because of the high melting point of BCu, brazing must be done at temperatures above the range at which chromium carbides are precipitated.

The phosphor bronzes BCuP are self-fluxing when joining pure copper. BCuP-3 and 5 contain some silver in order to improve corrosion resistance. These brazing alloys are used for joining copper pipe and tubing and for air-conditioning and refrigeration work. The familiar Sil-Fos grades produced by Handy & Harman belong to the phosphor bronze–silver group of brazing alloys, as their trade name suggests.

The silver filler metals BAg are often called silver solders. These

brazing, soldering, and adhesive bonding
293

can be used to join virtually all ferrous and nonferrous metals, with the exception of aluminum, magnesium, and others with melting points below the useful range of the silver solders. BAg-3, with 50% silver, is widely used for the brazing of cemented carbide cutting tips. Most of the BAg grades in the classification table above contain cadmium. Since cadmium forms toxic compounds, the use of such brazing alloys is not allowed for the fabrication of hospital and food equipment. The cost of the silver brazing alloy will of course increase as the silver content is increased. The color becomes whiter with increased silver content and may be important if the alloy must match the color of a stainless steel.

The BAg solders with the highest brazing temperatures have the highest numbers. There are a great many of these alloys because a range of brazing temperatures is necessary in much assembly work. A sub-assembly can be made with a higher-temperature silver solder, the final assembly using a lower-temperature alloy in order not to melt out the previously deposited brazing materials.

For brazed joints that must hold at higher temperatures or resist oxidation, the high-nickel brazing alloys are used. These have only limited ductility but good strength up to 2000 F. It is not always easy, however, to obtain good wetting conditions on many high-temperature base metals containing aluminum and titanium.

The BAlSi brazing alloys are used for the brazing of aluminum, although brazing is not recommended for the high magnesium or high copper and zinc alloys of aluminum, since these are heat-treatable. The silicon-aluminums are the only alloys use for aluminum brazing. The alloys with higher silicon content are more suited to torch brazing. If anodized, these silicon alloys of aluminum will produce a dark color that will not match that of the of base metal, though the lack of color match may be less important in a hairline brazed joint.

Brazing filler metals are available as round or square rod for torch brazing, coiled wire, rings, washers, foil, strip, or preforms (special flat shapes). In small quantities, the silver solders may be bought by the ounce. Because silver is a precious metal, the ounce is a troy ounce, weighing about 10% more than the standard or avoirdupois ounce.

16.5 brazing practice

In brazing with the oxyacetylene torch, the whole area to be brazed is raised to brazing temperature by keeping the torch continually in motion over the area. A soft, slightly reducing flame is used. The brazing rod is melted by applying the end of the rod to the joint and putting the flame on the part of the joint through which the alloy must flow. Temperatures much above the required brazing temperature must be avoided, since high temperatures may cause loss of some of the constituents of the filler metal or the flux or may have adverse effects on the parent metal.

The work must be clean before the operation begins, for it is not the function of the flux to remove dirt or surface contaminants other than oxides.

Furnace brazing is better suited to production runs of brazed joints. In this method flux and filler metal are applied, the parts are jigged together, and the brazing completed in a suitable furnace. Stopoffs compounded from engine oil, graphite, or other materials are used to prevent the filler material from brazing the wrong surfaces, such as those of the holding jigs and racks. Close temperature control is generally required, for if a great many assemblies are to be brazed, the parent metal melts at a temperature only slightly above the required brazing temperature. Volatile components in the flux tend to condense in the firebrick lining of the furnace and sometimes attack the metal parts of the furnace, although ordinarily maintenance is not a problem. Flux deposits on furnace metal should be removed. Because the more aggressive fluxes will corrode metal jigs, assemblies may have to be self-jigged by bolts, rivets, spot welds, bent tabs, or other such devices.

In some furnace brazing operations a protective atmosphere or vacuum may be used instead of a flux. Although an atmosphere or a vacuum will not remove an oxide film, it will prevent such a film from reforming. A protective atmosphere is one that contains no gases that will react chemically with the metals to be brazed, such as water vapor or oxygen. Protective atmospheres are produced either from ammonia gas generators, which supply an atmosphere of inert nitrogen and oxide-reducing hydrogen, or from natural gas burned in a deficiency of air and with the water vapor then removed. Only a vacuum is suited to the brazing of reactive metals such as titanium and zirconium. A significant advantage of vacuum or atmosphere brazing is that the brazed assemblies come out of the furnace bright and clean without the need for a subsequent flux-cleaning operation.

Dip brazing employs a hot bath of molten flux, into which the assembly is dipped to remove the oxide film and supply the brazing heat. For dip brazing, assemblies must generally be self-jigging. Parts must be securely held together because the buoyant effect of the molten flux can dislodge parts of the assembly that are loosely fitted.

16.6 induction brazing

Induction heating is the fastest of all the methods of melting, heating, welding, brazing, and soldering metals. This method requires a high frequency alternating current generator with a frequency usually between

10 and 1,000 kc and an input power between 3 and 25 kw for brazing. Higher-input power capacities are required for induction welding. Output capacities are a little difficult to specify, since the output depends on the shape of the work being heated and other factors but not more than half the input power will appear as useful work output. This indicates a maximum efficiency for induction heating of 50%, a figure that few heating methods can match. The high frequency generator itself is considered a somewhat expensive item of equipment, but if enough production work is available to keep it busy, it pays for itself very quickly. A summary of the virtues and advantages of induction heating, as applied to metal joining only (the method may also be used for heat treating, melting, and other operations) would include the following:

1. very high production rates
2. reduced labor costs
3. less material handling
4. minimum maintenance and housekeeping
5. minimum floor space
6. small energy cost per piece
7. minimum scrap and rejects
8. minimum damage due to heating effects, since the heating cycle requires only seconds of time

Figure 104(a) shows a 25-kw (input power) Philips high frequency induction generator, with a heating coil made of copper tubing and a carbon rod inserted in the coil for heating.

The remarkably fast heating rates of the induction heater come as a surprise to anyone unacquainted with this type of equipment. The induction heater shown in Fig. 104(b) will heat the surface of a ¾-in. round steel bar to 1500 F in 6 sec from cold. Besides being rapid, the induction heater is a remarkably versatile general-purpose heater of any electrically conductive materials, metal or nonmetal. It is not restricted to any particular shape of metal or any particular operation: it will solder, braze, weld, heat, case-harden, heat-treat, stress-relieve, or melt in a crucible most of the common metals. For many years the cost of this equipment discouraged its use, but speed and versatility, the two paramount characteristics of the induction method, are among the most valued industrial virtues, and this method has had more extended use recently.

The induction heating principle was briefly mentioned in Chapter 11. The piece or assembly to be heated is actually the secondary of an air-core transformer, the primary being a copper tube coil about ¼ in. in diameter wound to fit around the workpiece. Details are shown in Fig. 104(b), where the work coil has three turns. The workpiece is always a one-turn secondary. The setup then is a step-down transformer, like a welding transformer, to induce a low voltage and a high current in the workpiece. The induced current in the workpiece will be very large, several

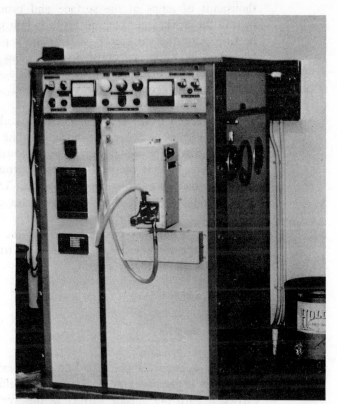

Fig. 104 (a) **25 kw high frequency induction generator. (Courtesy Philips Electronics, Inc.)**

Fig. 104 (b) **Close-up of induction coil for induction heating of the bar shown inserted in the coil.**

thousands of amps at the surface and producing a powerful resistance heat in the workpiece: the end result is that induction heating is resistance heating using the workpiece itself as the resistance. Work coils are easily wound in the shop and consume only a few cents worth of tubing. Such coils are always made of copper tubing and are water-cooled.

Induction generators for brazing and soldering are high frequency machines producing alternating current in the long-wave radio range. They may be likened to a radio transmitting station with the antenna removed and replaced by a copper heating coil. The high frequency is generated from standard 60-cycle power in the following way. The 60-cycle three-phase power is first rectified to direct current by means of six mercury vapor rectifier tubes, two for each phase. The direct current is then fed to an oscillator circuit. The basic oscillator circuit, wherein an induction coil and a capacitor continuously recharge each other, has already been discussed. To make up circuit losses and the power withdrawn as a result of heating the workpiece, a large gas-filled triode tube constantly reinjects power into the oscillator circuit.

16.7 reference depth

The high frequencies used for induction brazing and welding produce a skin effect in the workpiece. By this skin effect almost all the current is carried toward the outside surface of the workpiece and very little by the center of the workpiece, although the interior of the workpiece is heated owing to the high thermal conductivity of the metal. The distribution of the current in the workpiece from the surface to the center is similar to the curve of Fig. 91 and follows the same mathematical relationship, the high current at the outside and little current at the center. It is arbitrarily assumed that only a certain thickness of surface metal carries the whole current. This arbitrary depth, or thickness, is given by the formula

$$d = 3160 \sqrt{\frac{\sigma}{\mu f}}$$

Here $\sigma =$ the specific resistance of the workpiece in ohms per inch cube.

$f =$ the frequency of the oscillator in cycles per second.

$\mu =$ the magnetic permeability of the workpiece. This is equal to 1 for the paramagnetic metals such as copper and austenitic stainless steel. For magnetic steels, the permeability is very large (over 1000) but generally not known. Brazing temperatures, however, are above the Curie point of steel, so that the permeability of ferromagnetic steel may also be taken as 1. The Curie point is the temperature above which a metal loses its ferromagnetism.

d = reference depth, in inches. This is actually the depth from the surface at which the current is 36.8% of the current at the surface.

The following example illustrates the use of this formula. Consider the heating of a ¾-in. round bar of type 302 stainless steel, in which $\sigma = 29 \times 10^{-6}$ (at room temperature) and $\mu = 1$, at a frequency of 540 kc per sec.

$$d = 3160 \sqrt{\frac{\sigma}{\mu f}}$$

$$= 3160 \sqrt{\frac{29}{10^6 \times 1 \times 540 \times 10^3}}$$

$$= 0.023 \text{ in.}$$

This is about ¼₀ in. Thus a skin of about ¼₀ in. is carrying a few thousand amperes, so that the heating effect is very rapid.

The commonsense conclusions that can be drawn from this formula should be noted. First, the reference depth, and therefore the depth of the heating effect, will be greater if the frequency is lower. For example, at 10 kc the reference depth d for the above stainless bar is 0.170 in. For melting, forging, or other operations requiring through heating, low frequencies, possibly as low as the standard 60-cycle line frequency if the thickness of the workpiece is considerable, must be used. For brazing a copper pipe into a pipe elbow, both fittings being hollow, a high frequency, such as the 540,000 cycles of the example, is suitable. Second, the depth of heating will be greater for those metals with a high electrical resistance, such as the stainless steels, and small for highly conductive metals such as copper and aluminum. If the metal bar under discussion were copper instead of stainless steel, at 540 kc the reference depth would be only about one-thousandth of an inch. Since all metals show an increase in specific resistance as temperature increases, the reference depth will increase somewhat as the metal heats up, an effect that promotes faster heating.

It has already been noted that the eddy currents in the bar, and therefore the resistance heating effects, are not actually restricted to the reference depth d from the surface. To obtain a notion of how the induced currents in an induction heated bar are distributed through the bar, we shall consider a stainless 302 solid bar 2.16 in. in diameter and 3 in. long induction-heated at 10 kc and at 400 cycles. We imagine the bar to be divided into nine concentric sleeves, sleeve 1 being the outside sleeve with an outside diameter of 2.16 in. and an inside diameter of 1.92 in., and sleeve 9 being the center sleeve with an O.D. of 0.24 in. and an I.D. of zero. Each of the nine imaginary sleeves into which we have divided the bar has a thickness of 0.24 in. Because the calculations for the current in each sleeve are rather complicated, only the results will be tabulated here.

Sleeve	Amp at 10 kc	Amp at 400 cps
1	6280	1308
2	3270	1142
3	1740	976
4	925	830
5	496	674
6	279	526
7	159	374
8	89	225
9	29	75

The greater skin effect at higher frequencies should be noted.

The heating effect in each imaginary sleeve is given by the wattage I^2R in each sleeve. The resistance of each sleeve must be determined first. Each sleeve has a cross section perpendicular to the flow of current of $0.12 \times 3 = 0.36$ sq.in., but because the sleeves have different diameters, the length of the current path around the sleeve circles varies.

The average diameter of the first, or outside, sleeve is 2.04 in. The length of the current path is $\frac{22}{7} \times 3 = 2.04 = 6.4$ in. The resistance of the first sleeve equals

$$R_1 = \frac{\sigma \times L}{A} = \frac{29 \times 10^{-6} \times 6.4}{0.36} = 0.000516 \text{ ohm}$$

where 29×10^{-6} is the specific resistance of type 302 or 304 stainless steel in ohms per cubic inch.

The voltage drop due to eddy current in this first sleeve $= E = IR$
$= 6280 \times 0.000516 =$ about $3\frac{1}{4}$ v

The heating effect in watts equals

$$P_1 = I \times R = (6280)^2 \times 0.000516 = 20 \text{ kw}$$

This is a great deal of heat to apply to the small quantity of metal of the first sleeve and accounts for the rapidity of induction heating.

At 10 kc, the heating effect in each sleeve due to the induced eddy currents can be tabulated as shown in the next table. Note that about 75% of the heat is developed in the first sleeve at a frequency of 10 kc.

For a comparison, consider the same size copper bar at 242 cps. This odd frequency is selected in order to have the same eddy currents

Sleeve	Amp	Ohms	Watts
1	6280	0.000516	20,400
2	3270	0.000455	4,860
3	1740	0.000395	1,200
4	925	0.000334	286
5	496	0.000273	67.2
6	279	0.000212	16.5
7	159	0.000152	3.8
8	89	0.000091	0.7
9	29	0.000055	0.05

as in the stainless steel bar. The resistance of the copper sleeves is much less, since the specific resistance of copper is 0.7×10^{-6} at room temperature, only $1/41.4$ of the resistance of the stainless steel. For the copper bar at 242 cps:

Sleeve	Amp	Ohms	Watts
1	6280	12.5×10^{-6}	491
2	3270		
3	1740		
4	925		
5	496		
6	279		
7	159		
8	89	1.4×10^{-6}	0.09
9	29		

The copper bar does not have enough resistance to develop a marked heating effect.

As we have already noted, induction heating is actually *resistance heating* with induced currents in which the workpiece itself is the heat-producing resistor. Efficiency is very high compared with the 5 to 10% efficiency often experienced in placing the resistors in the walls of a furnace for heating the workpiece. Induction heating efficiency can be estimated in the following simple fashion. The wattage developed in the workpiece is all useful heat, whereas the watts developed in the copper heating coil are all wasted. If the workpiece is copper, then the resistance of the workpiece is about the same as the resistance of the coil, giving an efficiency of about 50%. Suppose the workpiece is carbon steel. This material has a specific resistance about six times that of copper, giving an estimated efficiency of $6/7$ or 87%. Transformers are always efficient devices, and the induction heater is a kind of transformer.

16.8 induction welding
and brazing practice

To solder or braze with induction heating, the parts to be joined are jigged together with the solder and flux in place. Filler metal preforms cut to the desired shape are commonly used. A short length of round or square copper tubing, usually ¼ in. in diameter, is wound to the shape of the workpiece in one or two coils. The coil must have connections to the terminals of the induction generator both for electric power and for water cooling of the coil. Standard work coils are not available, and because of the wide variety and size of articles that are induction-heated, standard coils are not practical. Every shop therefore winds its own coils, though this is a simple operation. A gap of about ⅛ in. is allowed between workpiece and coil so that the workpiece will not accidentally short the coil. Usually there is no hazard to personnel. Though the workpiece becomes hot, the coil does not because of its internal water cooling. As the voltage across the coil is very low, there is no electrical hazard in touching the coil. Because heating cycles are very short, the heated metal does not form scale or oxides to any serious degree.

Induction welding is less common than induction brazing. The most important use of induction welding is the making of longitudinal butt welds in pipe and tubing. In this process the induction coil surrounds the pipe, which is passed through the coil at speeds of 50 to 500 ft per minute. Radio frequencies of 250 to 450 kc are normally used, though a few installations use a low frequency of 4 to 10 kc. The induction generators used for pipe welding have power ratings that range from 50 to 600 kw.

Thermatool pipe welders also produce longitudinal butt welds in pipe and tubing, using 450-kc radio frequencies for direct resistance heating without induced currents. The arrangement for Thermatool welding is shown in Fig. 105. Two contacts or electrodes ride on the two edges of the pipe being welded. The path of least resistance for the high

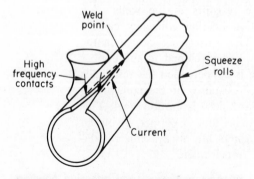

Fig. 105 **Thermatool high frequency resistance welding. The high frequency current follows the path of least inductance along the edge of the sheet.**

frequency current is from one electrode around the circumference of the pipe to the other electrode. The current does not follow this path of least resistance. Such a path forms a loop and creates inductance. The inductive effect in a circuit is directly proportional to the frequency; at a frequency of 450,000 the inductive effects vastly exceed the resistive effects. Therefore the current follows the path of minimum inductance and highest resistance along the edges of the tube as shown in Fig. 105.

16.9 soldering

Soldering is done with tin-lead alloys (except for aluminum and magnesium solders) at temperatures below 800 F. The ASTM designations and characteristics of the tin-lead solders are given in the following table:

TIN-LEAD SOLDERS

ASTM No.	Tin, %	Lead, %	Solidus Temp.	Liquidus Temp.
5A	5	95	572	596
10A	10	90	514	573
15A	15	85	437	553
20A	20	80	361	535
25A	25	75	361	511
30A	30	70	361	491
40A	40	60	361	455
50A	50	50	361	421
60A	60	40	361	374
70A	70	30	361	378

The 5A solder is the lowest in cost, but the high proportion of lead gives it poor wetting characteristics. Solders 10, 15, and 20 are better wetting solders and can use lower temperatures. The 35, 40, and 50 grades give the best combination of characteristics and are used as general-purpose solders. Solder 40A is used in sheet metal work, and 60A for fine instrument work.

In addition to these, are the B-grade solders, 20B, 30B, etc., which contain about 0.5% antimony. These solders have much the same applications as the A-grade solders. They are not recommended for soldering galvanized steel, however, as they form brittle soldering mixtures with zinc. The C-grade solders contain more than 1% antimony.

For soldering aluminum, several solders, including tin zinc, cadmium silver, and zinc aluminum, are available. High-temperature solders with joining temperatures in the range 700 to 800 F are available for general-purpose work. These are usually zinc-base solders with small amounts of other metals. They will produce joints stronger than soldered joints made with tin-lead filler metal. A few solder formulations will even join nonmetallic materials. A 50% indium–50% tin alloy adheres to glass and is used for glass-to-metal and glass-to-glass soldering. Finally, if very low soldering temperatures are necessary, below the solidus temperature of tin-lead, 361 F, bismuth-base solders are available.

Most solder is bought as wire, either solid or flux core. Flux-core wire is available either as rosin core or as acid core and in a range of flux contents by weight. The metal solder melts before the flux melts. This disadvantage can be overcome by scrubbing the joint with the soldering iron. This problem however, is more serious in induction soldering, since eddy currents cannot be developed in the flux. Flux-core solder therefore is not often used in induction soldering. A very large range of wire sizes is available in solder, from 0.007 to 0.250 in. in diameter.

16.10   adhesive bonding

Metals or any other solid materials may be joined with cements by adhesive bonding. The use of adhesive bonding has grown rapidly in recent years as its advantages and reliability have become better known. But as with any other welding method, the production of successful and strong adhesive-bonded joints requires that proper techniques be followed. Probably most people have bought a 25-cent tube of cement that "will bond to anything" only to have no success whatever with it.

The use of structural adhesives was pioneered by an industry in which reliability of joining materials is a matter of life or death—the aircraft industry. Such adhesives are used for a wide range of aircraft components, such as wing flaps, fuel tanks, wing trailing edges, and bulkheads.

The reliability of structural adhesives has led to the widespread use of the type of construction known as "sandwich panel." Such panels consist of two thin skins of metal with a lightweight core between them, the core being a material such as foamed plastic or honeycomb paper. Sandwich construction provides remarkable strength with minimum weight and good thermal insulation. Applications for sandwich construction are many and include aircraft and rocket panels, semi-trailers, wall panels for refrigerated spaces, and walls for prefabricated housing for the Arctic and Antarctic areas. If a Styrofoam (foamed polystyrene plastic) block will sustain a 500-lb load in compression (see Fig. 106), the same block will sustain ten times this load if its two faces are reinforced with a bonded skin of aluminum only 0.032 in. thick. By itself, neither

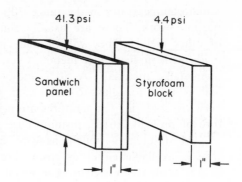

41.3 psi   4.4 psi

Sandwich   Styrofoam
panel   block

1"   1"

Fig. 106 Compressive strength comparison between a foamed polystrene block and the same block sandwiched between aluminum sheets 0.032 inches thick.

the aluminum sheet nor the Styrofoam can sustain a large load, but when bonded together, each supports the other to produce an integral sandwich panel of great strength and small deformation.

The techniques of adhesive bonding are best understood in the light of the problems of mending a broken article.

Suppose a cast iron engine block has been broken. If the two broken parts are brought together in proper alignment, this does not mend the block. We take it for granted that nothing can be mended this way. Yet it is rather remarkable that broken articles cannot be mended in this manner. If the atoms in the engine block attracted each other so powerfully that considerable force was needed to separate them, then an equal force ought to be sufficient to join the broken surfaces again. But a joining force equal to the fracture force is not sufficient to mend the break, though metals are sometimes joined by mashing them together with very large compressive forces in the method known as cold welding.

The two parts of the broken engine block cannot be joined merely by fitting them together for two reasons: mismatch and surface contamination. First, the broken surfaces are rough. It is not really possible to fit every hill of one surface exactly to the valley of the other surface to the degree necessary to restore the original interatomic bonding forces that originally held the engine block together at the break. Only the severe deformation of cold welding can enforce such a perfect fit. In addition some plastic deformation always takes place before fracture, and as a result of such deformation the hills do not actually match the shape of the valleys. In sum, the two fracture surfaces cannot be matched. Second, when the engine block or any other solid is broken, the two fracture surfaces very rapidly adsorb or pick up a layer of gases from the atmosphere. Water vapor is the chief gas thus adsorbed on the surface. Thus when the two fractured surfaces are fitted together again, there is no longer cast iron to cast iron contact; instead a film of water vapor and other gases intervenes and makes bonding impossible.

The action of a bonding cement can be understood from these considerations. The bonding cement must fill between the two solids by means of its fluidity to establish continuous contact between the two surfaces that are to be bonded. In addition, it must remove or dissolve surface impurities to establish contact with the atoms of the solid it must join, thus forming a new three-layer solid of material-adhesive-material. To assist the adhesive cement in making the intimate contact required to establish a strong joint, metal-cleaning techniques must be executed before bonding. It is almost never possible to make a sound cemented joint on an uncleaned surface. The required cleaning techniques will be discussed presently.

16.11 *characteristics of cemented joints*

Cemented joints share at least one characteristic with brazed and soldered joints: a thin layer of filler cement produces a stronger joint than a thick layer (see Fig. 102). A cemented butt joint, like a brazed or soldered butt joint, is weak in cleavage. If a butt joint must be used, the joint should be some type of tongue-and-groove joint so that a part of the joint will be stressed in shear. Cemented joints give greatest strength and reliability in shear, therefore wherever possible, lap joints are employed. The simple lap joint of Fig. 107(a) is offset, and the shear forces are not aligned. Under sufficiently high stress such a joint could peel open. The joggle lap joint of Fig. 107(b) eliminates peeling possibilities and is preferred. All metal bonding cements have very high strengths in shear but low strength in cleavage or peel (see Fig. 107). The epoxy cements have shear strengths in the range of 2500 to 10,000 psi at room temperature but have poor peel strengths. Other bonding cements in general

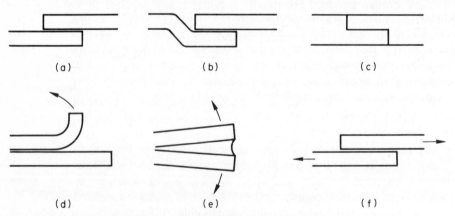

Fig. 107 Lap joint design for adhesive bonding. (a) Straight lap, (b) joggle lap, (c) double butt lap, (d) peel stress, (e) cleavage stress, (f) shear stress.

brazing, soldering, and adhesive bonding

have lower shear strengths but frequently higher peel strengths than the epoxies. Few of these cements can sustain temperatures much above 200 F, but the epoxy cements will hold their bond up to 300 F, though they lose strength as the temperature is increased. Most cements become brittle at low temperatures. The silicones are an exception. These may be used even at very low temperatures, but unfortunately their maximum shear strengths do not reach 1000 psi.

If the coefficient of expansion of the cement must match that of the metals to be joined, filler materials of some inert type may be added to the cement to adjust the expansion coefficient.

16.12   cements for bonding metals

The number of bonding cements, like the number of available steels, is increasing continually. Only a restricted range of cements is suited to the bonding of metals with any degree of reliability and strength, however. The elastomeric cements (rubber cements), for instance, will bond to metals but will not provide metal-to-metal joints of sufficiently great strength. Neglecting a few exceptions, only two classes of cements are suited to bonding metals: these are the *thermoplastic* and the *thermosetting* plastic cements.

All cements, except mortars for bonding brick, are long-chain molecules (called polymers) containing carbon. Such polymers are made by linking characteristic or module molecules called monomers. Actually a wide range of organic materials are polymers, including wood, fuels, foods, drugs, fats, lubricating oils, perfumes, soaps, and others, including the molecules of the human body. The structure of any polymer is easiest understood by taking for an example the simple one of polyethylene, which happens to be a thermoplastic material unsuitable for bonding purposes. The monomer molecule from which polyethylene is made is ethylene, shown in Fig. 108. Each carbon atom has four electrons in its outer shell. In common with other atoms, it has a tendency to fill out its outer electron shell to a count of eight by sharing electrons of other atoms. This is indicated by the four bonding lines from each carbon

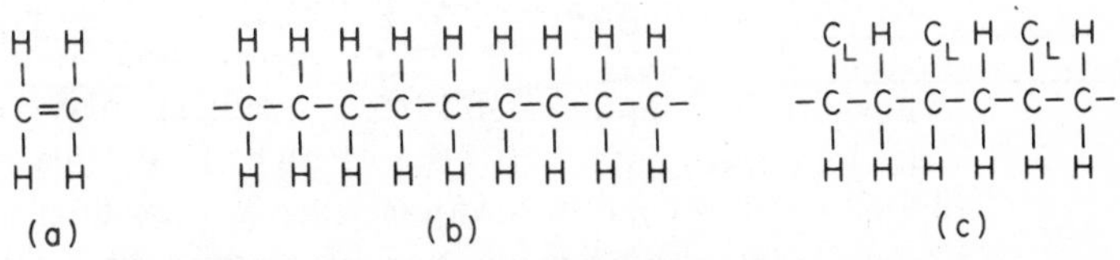

Fig. 108 Polymers. (a) Ethylene, C_2H_4, (b) polyethylene molecular pattern, (c) polyvinyl chloride.

atom, indicating connections for four more electrons. Polyethylene is made by causing about a thousand ethylene monomers to polymerize into a single long polymer molecule as shown in Fig. 108. The molecule is drawn as a straight long-chain molecule but is actually more in the shape of a corkscrew. It will also have a few random branches off the main chain of monomers, but these are not shown in the figure.

Polyethylene is a thermoplastic material, "thermoplastic" meaning that the material may be softened by heating. The thermoplastic adhesives, such as polyvinyl acetate or cellulose nitrate, have a similar molecular structure, a chain of carbon atoms to which are attached atoms of hydrogen, chlorine, or other elements, always in the repeating polymer pattern. Some of the common thermoplastic cements for use with metals include polyvinyl acetate, cellulose nitrate, various polyamides, and vinyl cements. These are all air-drying cements, the curing of the cement being accomplished simply by the escape of solvents.

Thermoplastic cements do not offer the high strengths or good heat resistance of the thermosetting cements. The thermosetting materials are likewise long-chain polymers, generally with a much more complicated monomer molecule than the thermoplastic cements have. The thermosetting cements set by a chemical process called cross-linking, actually the same process as the vulcanizing done on rubber. Cross-linking is explained by the diagrams of Fig. 109. For cross-linking to occur, some of the carbon atoms in the polymer must be unsaturated, that is, in a condition that allows them to bond to other atoms not in the polymer chain. Figure 109 (a) shows an unsaturated carbon atom in the chain: in order to share

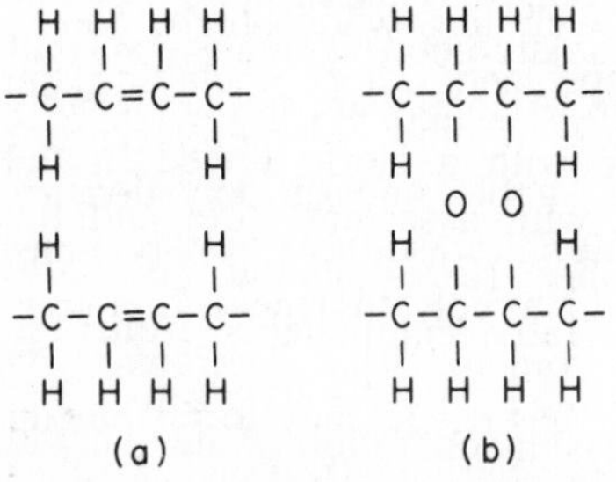

Fig. 109 Cross linking of thermosetting material. (a) Two molecules before cross-linking, (b) cross-linking by means of oxygen atoms.

four extra electrons, it must establish a double bond with the next carbon atom in the chain. Now when the thermosetting cement is removed from its container and exposed to the oxygen of the air or mixed with a catalyst, either the catalyst or the oxygen provides an atom with two outer electrons to share. This atom establishes a chemical link between two polymer atoms to join them into one (Fig. 109(b)). In this manner all the polymer atoms link up and in so doing, cure to their final hardness. Such a bonding cement cannot be resoftened by heating, and this is the meaning of the term *thermosetting*.

The most commonly used of the thermosetting cements are the epoxies, isocyanates, phenolic-vinyls, polyesters, and thiokol-epoxies. These all form excellent bonds to metal surfaces.

Though not the cheapest of cements, the epoxies have become popular because of a number of excellent characteristics. The epoxies do not shrink when curing, a particularly important characteristic in a cement. In addition to their high shear strength, they are resistant to a wide range of solvents, particularly to moisture. They have an almost unlimited shelf life, that is, they will not cure until they are mixed for bonding. They are available in a variety of formulations: room-temperature curing, heat curing, two-component epoxy and one-component epoxy. They are, however, extremely messy to use and extremely difficult to remove after they have cured. It is often said that epoxies will bond anything except themselves, but this is not true: epoxy will bond to epoxy.

Most of these cements are heat curing, an operation which must be performed in accordance with the directions of the manufacturer.

16.13 bonding practices

Before the bonding cement is applied to any metal surface, the surface must be cleaned.

If the maximum possible strength in the bonded joint is not required, the surface of the metal may simply be degreased. This assumes that the surface is free of paint, rust, and mill scale. Any good degreasing solvent will serve, such as Varsol or trichlorethylene. Alcohols are not sufficiently powerful degreasers. If degreasing is done with a cloth dipped in the solvent, the surface should be rubbed dry with a second cloth and the applicator cloth changed frequently. Rubber gloves should be worn, since degreasing compounds will remove fatty components from the human skin.

To test the effectiveness of the degreasing operation, water should be run over the metal surface. If the surface will hold a continuous sheet of water without breaks, then it is degreased. But if the water draws into beads or droplets on the surface, the degreasing operation has not been successful.

Degreasing is the minimum possible surface preparation. To produce the best possible bonded joints, either abrasive or chemical etching treatments must be used. The abrasive treatment may employ sandblasting or abrasive discs or belts. If abrasive cloths or papers are used, a degreasing operation usually must follow before the surface is ready for bonding.

A variety of good chemical etching methods may be used, from which the following methods are selected:

Steel

1. Sandblast or treat with abrasives if possible.
2. Degrease.
3. Hold for 10 min in hot (not boiling) solution of equal parts by weight phosphoric acid and methyl alcohol.

The final surface on the steel is an iron phosphate film, an excellent surface for either bonding or painting.

Alternately, the steel surface may be etched with hydrochloric acid and then rinsed.

Aluminum

1. Degrease or abrade.
2. Immerse for 10 min at 150 to 160 F in acid-dichromate solution: 25 parts by weight sulfuric acid, 2½ parts sodium dichromate, 75 parts water.
3. Rinse with water and dry.

Stainless steel

Treat like aluminum, except use a much stronger acid. Simple degreasing is sometimes sufficient with stainless steels.

The cement should be applied as soon after surface treatment as possible. Treating one day and bonding the next is poor practice. Application is by various methods, chiefly brush, roller, doctor blade, spray, or flow gun. The curing range of temperature for most bonding cements is 150 to 350 F, but room-temperature curing cements are used for sheet metal that may warp at a high temperature. Curing may also be carried out at lower temperatures if considerably longer curing times are used. A light pressure is required during the cure for the following reasons:

1. To obtain uniform thickness of adhesive
2. To overcome the high viscosity of the adhesive and ensure flow throughout the area of the joint
3. To remove variations in flatness of the metal surfaces to be joined

A typical example of curing requirements is H. B. Fuller two-component epoxy formulation 7004. For bonding of metals, two parts of component A are mixed to one part of component B. Only a minimum pressure is required during the cure. Cure times are as follows:

12–48 hr at 85 F
50–60 min at 150 F
30–50 min at 200 F
5–10 min at 300 F
3–5 min at 400 F

The great increase in curing time as the curing temperature is lowered is a characteristic of all metal-bonding cements.

16.14 welding of thermoplastics

Most of the thermoplastic materials, including polyethylene, polyvinyl chloride (vinyl), polystyrene, and acrylonitrile-butadiene-styrene (ABS plastic), can be welded. Filler rod of the same material as the parent plastic is used. The plastic-welding gun is usually the kind that heats the material with a jet of hot air or nitrogen. The welding technique is similar to that used in oxyacetylene welding. However, thermoplastic welding suffers from two disadvantages. First, it is not possible to produce welded joints of the neat appearance demanded in the welding of metals. Second, both the filler metal and the parent metal are somewhat degraded by the temperature required to produce the welded joint, so that the joint is not as strong as the parent metal before welding nor as corrosion resistant.

PROBLEMS

1 Differentiate between brazing, braze welding, and soldering.

2 What are some of the advantages of brazing over welding?

3 What effect does the amount of joint clearance have on capillary action of the brazing filler metal?

4 Explain the terms solidus, liquidus, and eutectic.

5 Why should brazing filler metals containing phosphorus not be used for joining steels?

6 What is a brazing preform?

7 Calculate the reference depth when induction-heating both copper and type 410 stainless steel at 250,000 cycles to a temperature of 1800 F. At 1800 F the specific resistance of copper is 0.0000037, and of 410 stainless steel 0.000050, ohms per cu in.

8 The specific resistance of mild steel is 0.000005 ohm per cu in. at 70 F and 0.000045 at 1800 F. What is the reference depth of mild steel at these two temperatures, at a frequency of 540,000 cycles during induction heating? Take the permeability of mild steel to be 3600 at 70 F and 1 at 1800 F.

9 Explain why induction heating is actually resistance heating.

brazing, soldering, and adhesive bonding

10 Why is pure lead not used as a solder?

11 What is the difference between a thermosetting and a thermoplastic plastic material? Which type of plastic has the higher temperature resistance?

12 Explain the water test for determining whether a metal surface is clean.

13 Why is it not possible to weld thermosetting plastics with filler plastic in a fused joint?

Although fusion welding methods have as their purpose the joining of metals, virtually all these methods may also be used for thermal cutting of metals. In addition there are special cutting methods that are not used for welding purposes, such as the Arcair method and the oxygen lance. Moreover, just as joining by welding may be either manual or automatic, so may thermal cutting.

Thermal cutting of metals is one of the most expensive cutting methods. It is slow and consumes large quantities of oxygen and fuel gas. A mechanical shear is perhaps the cheapest method of cutting, followed by nibbling and punching. Other methods include sawing and cut-off grinding. However, thermal cutting is far more versatile than these mechanical methods and offers these advantages:

1. Thermal cutting can be used to cut metal of great thickness, beyond the capacity of any shear. Indeed, there is no practical limit to the thickness of metal that may be flame-cut.
2. Any shape can be cut by thermal methods, and almost any line can be followed, depending on the requirements of the cut for accuracy. Holes and slots of circular and noncircular shape present no difficulties. Even microholes a few thousandths of an inch in diameter may be produced by thermal cutting methods, though not with an oxyacetylene cutting torch.

THERMAL

CUTTING

OF METALS

17

3. Rarely can the mechanical type of shear be taken to the work, whereas oxygas cutting equipment can be taken virtually anywhere (as in the criminal business of safe cracking) and will cut metal in any position—flat, horizontal, vertical, or overhead—or even under water.
4. Flame-cut edges, if properly executed, present a sufficiently smooth finish for most purposes without further machining or grinding.
5. Accuracies of a few thousandths of an inch are obtainably by thermal cutting with machine control.

When all these advantages are noted, it is easy to understand why thermal cutting is universally practiced.

17.2 the oxygas cutting process

This is still by far the most used of the flame-cutting methods. There are two operations to gas cutting with the oxygas flame. First, the heat of the flame raises the temperature of the metal to its ignition point, not to the melting point. For steel, this ignition temperature is a red heat of about 1600 F. Second, a stream of pressure oxygen is directed onto the hot metal to oxidize or burn it to magnetite, Fe_3O_4. Since this second step is a combustion process using iron as the fuel, heat is generated in addition to the heat of the oxygas flame. Iron oxides have melting points approximately in the same range as those of the carbon steels, and as a result the oxide melts and is blown out of the cut by the oxygen stream. The heat that keeps the cut going is derived both from the oxygas reaction and the iron oxidation. Because of erosion in the kerf, not all the metal in the kerf is oxidized, about one-third being simply washed out in the form of molten metallic iron.

The oxycut surface of any steel plate is always flame-hardened since the high thermal conductivity of steel produces a quenching. The cut surface of even a mild steel will be somewhat hardened by cutting. If such quenching is the cause of cracking in higher-carbon or low-alloy steels, preheating may be necessary before cutting.

Low-alloy steels, manganese steels, and steels with as much as 5% chromium may be oxygen-cut. Steels with a high chromium or tungsten content, such as the stainless steels, cannot be cut by this method. Stainless clad steels, if clad one side only, may be oxygas-cut from the backing metal side. The heat from the oxidation of the backing plate, plus the erosive effect of the ion oxide produced, enable the cladding to be severed.

Flame cutting must necessarily consume more oxygen than gas welding does. For oxyacetylene welding of $1/4$-inch mild steel plate, oxygen and acetylene pressure will be about 5 psi each, consumption of both acetylene and oxygen being at the rate of about 25 cu ft per hr. To flame-cut the same plate, an acetylene pressure of 3 psi may be used, whereas oxygen pressure must be raised to 30 psi. The acetylene consumption will be reduced to about 10 cu ft per hr, whereas oxygen consumption will be doubled to 50 cu ft per hr. The average welder in the average welding shop will manually cut this ¼-in. plate at a rate of about 12 in. per min., although somewhat higher manual cutting speeds are possible, perhaps as high as 18 in. per min. Heavier plate requires higher oxygen pressures.

OXYACETYLENE CUTTING CONDITIONS

Metal Thickness, in.	Oxygen, psi	Acetylene, psi	Oxygen, cu ft/hr	Acetylene, cu ft/hr	Typical Manual Cutting Speed, ipm
¼	30	3	45	10	12–16
⅜	30	3	75	12	12–15
½	40	3	90	13	12–14
¾	40	3	120	14	12–14
1	50	3	140	15	8–11
1½	50	3	180	16	6–7
2	50	3	230	17	5–6

A distinguishing characteristic of a flame-cut edge is the drag lines on the sides of the kerf, as sketched in Fig. 110. The meaning of "drag" may be understood from this sketch; it is the dimensional lag between the

Fig. 110 Drag lines on a flame-cut edge.

Drag
Direction of cut

position of the cut at the top and at the bottom of the plate. The drag must not be too long for a clean cut, and when cutting complex shapes, such as toothed racks that must mesh with other gearing, the drag must be as short as possible. Drag may be reduced by increased oxygen consumption, though this involves higher cutting costs. Drag tends to increase with thickness of the cut plate. A good average drag for straight-line cutting would not exceed ³⁄₃₂ in. for ½-in. plate and ¼ in. for 2-in. plate.

Many shops that employ acetylene for welding use propane for

thermal cutting of metals
315

cutting. Propane is cheaper than acetylene. The two gases require different torch tips because of differing characteristics, such as specific gravity and oxygen-fuel gas ratio. Propane consumes more oxygen. A propane kerf is slightly narrower than an acetylene kerf, a factor that may sometimes be advantageous.

17.3 cutting torches

In manual cutting it is usual to attach a cutting attachment to the acetylene torch body and to insert the proper size cutting tip in the end of the attachment. Cutting tips are made of tellurium copper, are chrome-plated, or are made of other material that will not be burned or damaged by hot iron slag. Most such cutting torches and attachments are adaptable to a wide range of cutting gases.

Cutting torches mix acetylene and oxygen for preheating the plate to be cut. In addition, the torch must supply a stream of pure oxygen for the actual cutting. This oxygen supply must be brought to the tip in a third tube. The construction of a typical cutting attachment is shown in Fig. 111. The oxygen stream is discharged from the center of the torch tip, and the preheating mixture from small preheating holes arranged

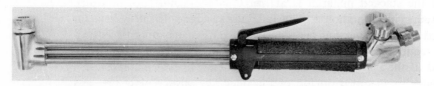

Fig. 111   Oxyacetylene cutting head. (Courtesy Smith Welding Equipment Division of Tescom Corp.)

around the oxygen jet. The torch body is equipped with hand valves for acetylene and oxygen, and the cutting attachment has an oxygen valve to control the supply of preheating gas mixture and a lever to control the cutting oxygen. The torch body oxygen valve is kept full open, because oxygen flow is controlled by the cutting-valve lever and the preheating oxygen valve. The metal is brought up to white heat with the preheating flame, and the cutting valve lever is then operated to commence cutting.

Special tips are available for cutting rivets, sheet metal, and cast iron. There are also special tips and torches for foundry work, such as the cutting of sprues and risers. Gouging tips are used for removing imperfect welds, grooving, and veeing. The gouging tip can vary the depth of gouging depending on the angle at which the torch is held. Flame

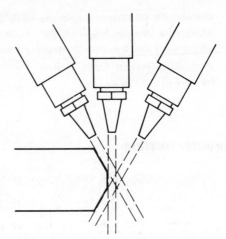

Fig. 112 Multiple torch edge preparation

gouging is sometimes referred to as flame machining. The use of multiple torches for edge preparation of welds is shown in Fig. 112, the three torches following one behind the other.

Stack cutting is the cutting of several pieces of plate simultaneously while stacked. The plates must be clean, they must lie tight against each other, and the edges must be in alignment where the cut is started. Frequently the stacked material is delivered in the same piles in which it was stored in the warehouse. The long storage time in the warehouse ensures that the sheets in the pile lie close against each other, thus providing the requirement for a quality cut. The pile of material must always be clamped. If the plates to be stack-cut are thin, a thicker plate, called a "waster plate," is clamped on top of the pile. The waster plate prevents burning and buckling of the top sheet and serves to maintain ignition by its own combustion.

17.4 oxygen lancing

Oxygen lancing is used chiefly for heavy cutting. This technique will cut the same types of metal that oxygas will cut. The lance is simply a length of 1/4- or 3/8-in. black iron pipe fitted with a globe valve at the oxygen supply. Oxygen pressure of 40 psi or higher is used. Preheating is done by a welding torch with a large tip, and then the oxygen stream from the lance is directed against the heated area. The lance can sustain the cut without further preheating. A minor disadvantage of lancing is the short life of the pipe, which is consumed by the oxygen

thermal cutting of metals

stream. It is simply replaced with another pipe as often as required. Moreover, consumption of the steel pipe contributes to the heating effect, which may be somewhat increased by using a pipe of heavier wall thickness. The oxygen lance is used to open frozen tap holes in steel melting furnaces.

17.5 powder cutting

Stainless steels have alloy blends specially designed to provide resistance to oxidation. Such steels thus have a built-in resistance to oxygen cutting. If oxygen-cutting of such steels should be attempted, a skin of refractory chromium oxide will form, the melting point being roughly a thousand degrees higher than that of iron oxide. The result will be that the metal is protected against further oxidation and the cut is stopped. However, oxygen cutting is possible if the chromium content does not exceed about 5%. For steel with somewhat higher chromium content, the waster-plate technique can be used to cut the alloy material, if the plate is not too thick. The waster plate is laid on top of the material to be cut, combustion of the waster plate providing the additional heat needed to cut the alloy plate. Since this is a rather expensive method of cutting, however, it is not too often used.

Oxygen cutting is ineffective also against other oxidation-resistant metals such as aluminums and bronzes. Because nickel too does not readily oxidize, the high-nickel alloys cannot be torch-cut. To oxycut these difficult metals, a variant of the waster-plate method is employed. Iron powder is fed into the oxygen stream in the technique known as *powder cutting*. Other powders may also be mixed with the iron powder. As much as 40% aluminum is used for cutting heavy brass, copper, high-nickel alloys, concrete, and firebrick. The advantage given by aluminum in the powder is that it releases much more heat than iron does when it oxidizes. However, iron powder is best for general use. It does not produce refractory oxides, it is highly fluid, and it readily fluxes the other oxides formed in the cut, thus lowering the melting temperature of the oxide mixture.

Figure 113 shows a small powder-cutting torch with the added powder tube, nozzle, and powder valve along the top of the tube. The powder valve is cracked first, then the oxygen valve. Preheating is not usually needed to start the cut. Powder-cutting attachments are available for standard hand-cutting torches of the oxyacetylene type if needed.

Powder cutting of stainless steels is as fast as oxygen cutting of carbon steels of the same thickness. On cast iron powder cutting produces a better finish than straight oxygen does. The iron powder must be dry and free-flowing, however. If it should pick up moisture it will sinter,

Fig. 113 Linde "Oxweld" cutting torch with powder-cutting attachments.

resulting in irregular cutting. Powder dispensers use either vibratory feeding troughs or pneumatic feeding by means of dry air or nitrogen.

Powder-cutting unstabilized austenitic stainless steel will produce a narrow heat-affected zone which has been heated through the sensitizing temperature range where chromium carbides form. This zone may be removed, or the stainless steel may be subsequently annealed. If the cut edge is to be welded, the same heat-affected zone would also be produced by welding. The straight chromium steels of the martensitic type should be preheated before cutting to at least 500 F to prevent cracking due to quenching effects. Nickel, aluminum, and copper are not cut well with the powder method and appear to be melted and eroded rather than cut. Copper, as is usual with this metal, requires a preheat operation to overcome its very high thermal conductivity.

Powder cutting may also be employed in conjunction with the oxygen lance for heavy cutting operations.

17.6 arc cutting

Steels may be cut with a manual arc electrode and a sufficiently high current to melt out the metal. Although any arc welding rod will cut, 6010 and 6011 rods are preferred for their deep digging characteritics. Special cutting rods are also available for use with the arc, such as Cut-Trode, Chamfer-Trode, etc. Arc cutting produces a rough cut, however, which if it needs grinding, makes arc cutting too expensive. However, arc cutting is used for emergency purposes and for cutting scrap metal. Carbon arc cutting is also occasionally employed, usually with direct current, though alternating current may also be used.

Welding wire with the MIG method may be used for cutting ferrous and nonferrous metals. A small-diameter wire is fed at a high rate of speed and a high-current arc established between the wire and the work. The inert gas is usually oxygen 20% in 80% argon. The cuts are smooth and can be executed at high speed. Even the tungsten inert gas method may be successfully adapted for cutting by using thoriated tungsten

thermal cutting of metals

electrodes and direct current. In these inert gas methods the cutting speed is proportional to the arc current.

The *oxyarc* process uses hollow or tubular electrodes, usually with a d-c power source. A stream of oxygen is discharged through the bore of the electrode. In effect the arc preheats, and the oxygen removes the metal. The oxyarc method may be used on most metals, ferrous and non-ferrous, except those obviously unsuitable such as titanium, but like many other arc-cutting methods, the cut edge is not as smooth as a standard flame-cut edge on carbon steel and requires further surface preparation.

The *Arcair* process is a more commonly used method for cutting, gouging, removing defective welds, and edge preparation. By this method a carbon or graphite electrode is connected to a DCRP supply to draw an arc with the work. A cable brings both current and compressed air to the Arcair torch, the air valve mounted on the torch. Air pressure of 60 to 100 psi must be supplied to the torch and is used to blow the melted metal. The oxyarc method may be used on most metals, ferrous and non-ferrous, except those obviously unsuitable such as titanium, but like many heavy work. Since the Arcair process is a melting process, it may be used on most of the common metals, including the stainless steels. The cut surface is slag-free and smooth. However, the use of a carbon electrode may raise problems of carbon pickup in metals that cannot tolerate additional carbon, such as austenitic stainless steels. The carbon-enriched areas may then have to be ground off.

17.7   plasma arc cutting

This is a more recently developed cutting process that may also be used for metal melting, surfacing, and welding. Basically, this method is an extension of the tungsten inert gas process.

The plasma arc torch is a special type of TIG torch using a non-consumable tungsten electrode that does not project beyond the end of the torch. The power supply is direct-current straight polarity, the work-piece being cut as the positive electrode. The usual welding machine is not a suitable power supply, since plasma arc cutting requires an open-circuit voltage of about 150 v, exceedingly high for arc welding machines, and current capacity of 500 amp or more at 100% duty cycle.

In the plasma torch, the tip of the electrode is located within the nozzle. The nozzle has only a small opening. The cutting gas must first flow through the arc, being then heated to more than 15,000 F, a temperature far higher than that of any flame. But instead of expanding as a result of this great heating, the gas is forced under high pressure to flow through the small constricting nozzle and as a result is accelerated to supersonic velocity of about 4000 ft per sec. This exceedingly hot jet of gas can melt any metal or ceramic material (such as concrete or fire-brick), and the high gas velocity blows the molten material quickly and cleanly out of the kerf to produce an exceedingly smooth cut, clean and free of metal oxides.

A "plasma" is a gas that has been heated to such a high temperature that it is ionized and can carry an electric current. In the plasma torch only about 1% of the gas atoms are ionized, but this seemingly small amount of ionization is sufficient for conducting an electric current.

More familiar types of plasma include lightning and the arcs used in arc welding. Virtually all the matter of the universe is in the plasma state, since all the stars are plasmas. Solids, liquids, and gases exist only on a few small planets, which are relatively cold by comparison with the stars. The plasma state is considered as a fourth state of matter in addition to the solid, liquid, and gas phases. When matter changes from one of these states to another, latent heat is always involved, just as latent heat is required to change water into steam of the same temperature as the water. In the same way, the plasma torch supplies energy to its gas in order to change the gas into a conducting plasma. When the plasma changes back into a gas at the workpiece, heat is released.

The cutting gas used with plasma arc cutting depends on the metal to be cut. Compressed air is preferred for cutting carbon and low-alloy steels. Some high-alloy steels, such as the maraging steels, may be cut with compressed air. In compressed-air cutting, heat is provided from the iron-oxygen combustion as well as from the plasma arc. Nitrogen-hydrogen or argon-hydrogen mixtures are used to cut stainless steels. For manual cutting, 80% argon and 20% hydrogen is recommended. For cutting the nonferrous metals, the same gas mixtures as those for stainless steels are used.

The plasma arc cutting process offers two advantages of outstanding importance: no warping or distortion of the plate and high cutting speed. The high speeds of the cut are the reason for the lack of distortion. Typical cutting speeds with the plasma arc are shown in the following table:

TYPICAL PLASMA ARC THERMAL CUTTING

Metal	Thickness, in.	Speed, ipm
carbon steel	¼	200–300
	½	80–180
	1	40–80
stainless steel	¼	100
	½	40
aluminum	¼	250
	½	180
copper	¼	75
magnesium	¼	150

17.8 machine cutting

Mechanical or automatic guiding of the thermal cutting torch is desirable in much flame-cutting work. If great accuracy is a critical requirement, as in the flame-drilling of holes and slots in die plates and die sets used for the punching and forming of metals, manual cutting is out of the question. But in addition to much higher accuracy, speed, and economy of cutting, machine cutting produces better workmanship. Further, mechanized cutting is not limited to the direction of one cutting torch; any number can be controlled by one operator, all torches making the same movements and producing the same cut on multiple work. Figure 114 is a photograph of a machine-cutting operation producing multiple cuts in a

Fig. 114 Machine cutting with five oxyacetylene cutting heads.

large fabricating plant. In the preceding section, plasma arc thermal cutting speeds of 200 to 300 in. per min were mentioned. Obviously such cutting speeds cannot be realized unless the cutting process is mechanized.

If a considerable amount of pipe cutting and beveling must be done, it is usual to install a pipe-cutting and beveling machine. These machines are usually limited to a range of nominal pipe sizes of 1½ to 36 in. The machines are fastened around the pipe, and either the pipe rotates or the cutting machine rotates around the pipe.

For cutting flat pieces of any shape and thickness, tracer machines are used to guide one or more cutting torches. The simpler machines, which are only required to cut straight lines and circles, mount the torch on a small guided tractor with knurled wheels for traction. Such machines will produce straight cuts, bevels up to 45°, or circles. Speed is usually controlled with an adjustable knob.

For cutting complex shapes more elaborate machines are used. These will reproduce the shape of a steel template or will follow a line drawn on a sheet of drafting paper. Three tracer principles are in use on these machines:

1. A line can be followed by hand-guiding around a template.
2. A magnetic follower is driven along the edge of a steel template.
3. A photoelectric cell follows an inked or penciled line on a sheet of paper. For this no template is required.

Again, one torch or multiple torches may cut the shape dictated by the template or drawing. Correction for the width of the kerf is available on machines that must produce highly accurate work, since it is not convenient to design kerf correction into the template or drawing. Figure 115 is a sketch of the Airco Servograph, a typical machine of the electronic tracer type. The drawing of the part to be flame-cut is fastened to the aluminum template table. The photoelectric scanner is mounted on a long arm, called the main carriage, the cutting torch or torches being fastened to the other end. Spark ignition can be provided for the torches by a high-voltage transformer and spark electrodes. Two tractors drive the main carriage in the X or transverse direction (right- and left-hand motion) and Y or longitudinal direction (back and front motion) under the control of the scanner. Virtually any shape can be cut by this machine in plate up to 12 in. thick and 144 in. wide in any length from an ink or pencil line. If the photocell line follower should lose the line, the cutting action is stopped. The machine will cut straight lines and circles

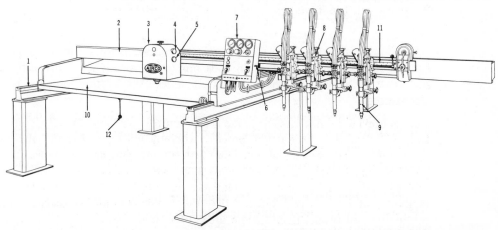

Fig. 115 Airco servograph for automatic flame-cutting. 1. Main carriage and template-table track. 2. Main carriage. 3. Electronic tracer. 4. Speed-control potentiometer. 5. Mode selector. 6. Switch for automatic electric torch ignition. 7. Control panel. 8. Torch holder—motorized. 9. Torch. 10. Template table. 11. Guide rule for lateral positioning of torches. 12. Template table, lock-release lever.

thermal cutting of metals

as well as complex shapes but does not require a template drawing for such simple shapes.

The Servograph is a good example of a *servomechanism*, a mechanism which controls the position and movement of a device. The scanning device has a light bulb to reflect light from the template paper into a photocell, also located in the scanning device. The photocell is vibrated back and forth across the template drawing line by means of an electromagnet. In its excursion across the dark line on the white paper, the photocell passes from the light area of the paper through the dark area of the line into the light area of the paper again. If the photocell sees light on one side of the line for the same length of time as on the other side of the line, the cutting torch or torches are directed in the same direction as before. But if the length of time differs between one side of the line and the other, the mechanism automatically corrects and rotates the mechanism to come back to the line.

If very close accuracy is necessary in the flame cutting, then the template must be drawn on a type of paper that is dimensionally stable under changes in relative humidity. The line to be followed must be drawn with a soft pencil and should have a width between 0.020 and 0.040 in. Reasonably good drafting standards must be followed. If a curve on the line is not exactly tangent to the straight line it connects with, the photocell may lose the line. When trying to follow through such drafting errors, photocell tracers have been known to turn around and retrace the line back toward the starting point. Other sources of error are caused by a cutting torch being out of plumb, by thermal expansion of the plate as it is cut, and by dirt or smudges on the drawing.

17.9 n/c

The abbreviation n/c means "numerical control" or "numerically controlled." This is a production process whereby machines execute their work under the control of machine instructions punched as holes in punched paper tape. Numerical control is rapidly taking over machine tool operations. It is, however, relatively new as a welding and cutting method, but it is to be expected that the momentum of its success in machining will propel it into some areas of welding also.

The operations of numerical control are rather easily learned and understood. To understand how n/c would be applied to a cutting operation, we shall set up a specific example. In Fig. 116 a steel plate measuring 24 by 18 in. is required to have the two slots shown burned at the locations indicated, with an accuracy of a few thousandths of an inch, as might well be required for a die plate to be produced for a die shop.

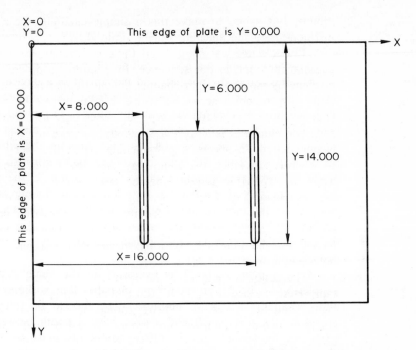

Fig. 116 An example of numerically controlled flame cutting. **See text.**

To make the example simple, suppose the slots are to be only as wide as the torch kerf.

Numerical control uses X and Y coordinates measured from a fixed location on the machine bed, the "origin," which has the location measurements $X = 0.000$, $Y = 0.000$. Figure 116 shows one corner of the plate located at this origin by means of pins or stops dropped into holes in the machine bed. The torch must execute the following movements:

1. move to location $X = 8.000$, $Y = 6.000$
2. ignite torch
3. commence cutting
4. cut in the Y direction to location $X = 8.000$, $Y = 14.000$
5. cease cutting
6. move to location $X = 16.000$, $Y = 6.000$
7. ignite torch
8. commence cutting
9. cut in Y direction to location $X = 16.000$, $Y = 14.000$
10. cease cutting
11. move off plate to shut-down position and close all gas valves

In addition to these instructions, the machine must be instructed about the required height of the torch nozzle above the machine bed, oxygen and acetylene flow requirements, and cutting speed in inches per

thermal cutting of metals
325

minute, but again, to make this a simple example, these supplementary instructions to the machine will be omitted.

Under numerical control, all these operations would be carried out automatically and in this sequence. Instructions to do so are given to the machine by means of eight-channel punched paper tape, that is, tape with eight rows of holes across its width. N/c tape is 1 in. wide, similar to teletype tape, except that teletype tape uses only five channels. The tape code for numbers, letters, and symbols is shown in Fig. 117. The tape is punched on a special tape-punching typewriter, such as the Friden Flexowriter, in much the same way that one would type a letter, and while the typewriter is punching the tape instructions, these instructions are also being typed on a sheet of paper inserted into the typewriter. Because of the tape-punching facility, such a typewriter costs more than $3000. The n/c machine reads the instructions punched into the tape by feeling for the punched holes by means of small pins or some other hole-reading method.

The following might be the instruction program punched into the tape. Here we are using DNC for the instruction "Do Not Cut," C for "Cut," and SD for "Shut Down," though in an actual tape program a single or two-digit number (not letters) would be used for such instructions.

```
DNC X 08000 Y 06000
  C X 08000 Y 14000
DNC X 16000 Y 06000
  C X 16000 Y 14000
 SD
```

This short program of instructions would require only about 6 in. of tape. The program punched into the tape of course must contain no errors. If a wrong number should be typed, the tape is backed up and an error, or DELETE, key is punched, making a complete set of holes across the tape where the wrong number is located. The correct number is then punched on the tape following.

Numerical control is as remarkably simple to program as it seems to be. All programming and planning, however, must be done before the work is executed; none is done at the machine, though the controls can be switched to manual operation if that is desirable. Note that through numerical control flame cutting will not be faster than any other type of machine cutting. The economies of n/c lie in the fact that the flame-cutting machine need not be shut down while the operator lays out the work. All the layout work is done in the drafting office and on the Flexowriter, relieving the machine for the purpose for which it was bought—flame cutting. Another possible misconception is that with n/c the welder operator is replaced by a woman typist. This is not true.

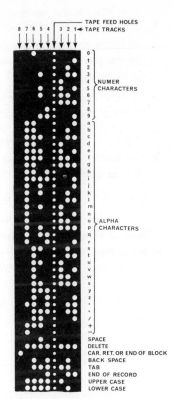

Fig. 117 Eight-channel tape for numerical control of manufacturing processes.

Since machines require adjustment and maintenance and general supervision, an operator is still needed, particularly since his output is greatly increased with numerical control. A last misconception is to suppose that n/c is a mass-production method. It is not. It is a job-shop, general-purpose method. Mass production is best done with special-purpose machines set up to execute one kind of operational sequence and one only. Numerical control, being automation for short runs, has never yet been applied to long production runs.

PROBLEMS

1 What advantages does thermal cutting offer over mechanical methods of cutting plate? What are the disadvantages of oxyacetylene cutting? Does mechanical shearing produce a better finish than machine cutting with the torch?

2 Explain how steel is cut by the oxygas process.

3 How and why can stainless-clad steel be oxygas-cut?

4 Why can stainless steel plate not be oxygas-cut?

5 Since oxygas cutting is actually combustion of the steel plate with oxygen, the oxygen consumption should be proportional to the thickness of the plate cut. Is this actually the case?

6 Consumption of acetylene does not increase much with increasing thickness of plate. Is this to be expected?

7 What is a plasma?

8 For cutting steel plate, how much faster is plasma arc cutting than oxyacetylene cutting?

9 What three tracer methods are used in machine cutting?

10 In the example given in Sec. 17.9 of n/c flame cutting, assume that ¼-in. plate is being cut with oxyacetylene. Estimate the total machine-time hours for layout and cutting for manual layout and for numerical control. Accuracy of ±0.005 in. is required.

Any wave energy that can be radiated through space as a voltage wave accompanied by a magnetic field is called electromagnetic radiation. The radiation of radio and television signals from a transmitting antenna to be picked up by a receiving antenna is perhaps the most familiar example of electromagnetic radiation.

Figure 118 is a composite diagram of information on all electromagnetic radiation. Actually all types—radio, infrared, visible light, and so on—are identical and differ only in frequency and wavelength. There is no clear-cut distinction between any two types. Certain ranges of radiation, however, are transmitted or received by special devices, and such ranges have names. Thus if the radiation can be received by the human eye, it is called *visible light*. If the radiation comes from an X-ray tube, it is called *X radiation*. If it has a heating effect, it is called *infrared* or *radiant heat*. The prominent natural types of radiation in the world around us range from infrared to ultraviolet, the human eye being sensitive to a narrow band of radiation in the middle of this broad band of natural radiation.

All electromagnetic radiation shares a few simple characteristics.

1. Such radiation includes both an alternating electric field and an alternating magnetic field. As always, the magnetic field is at right angles to the electric field (Fig. 119).
2. All electromagnetic radiation travels at the same velocity through space. Light was the first kind of radiation to be studied by scientists, its velocity being called the *speed of light*, 300 million meters per sec,

ELECTROMAGNETIC RADIATION
AND
THE ELECTRON BEAM

18

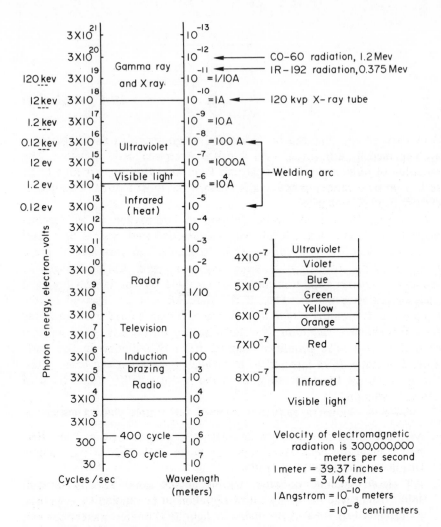

Fig. 118 Electromagnetic radiation.

or 186,000 mi per sec. The speed of light is symbolized by the letter *c*.

3. One positive and one negative half-wave of the alternating wave are together termed one wavelength, as in 60-cycle alternating current. The frequency is the number of wavelengths that pass any point in one second. The product of the frequency times the wavelength is equal to the velocity *c*:

$$fL = c$$

Thus to determine the wavelength of 60-cycle a.c.,

$$60 \times L = 186{,}000 \text{ mi/sec}$$
$$L = 3100 \text{ mi}$$

electromagnetic radiation and the electron beam

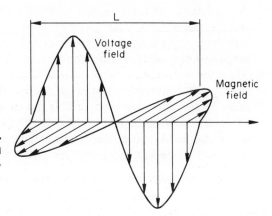

Fig. 119 Relationship of electric field, magnetic field, and wave velocity in electromagnetic radiation through space.

4. Such radiation has both the characteristics of a wave and a particle. One cycle can be considered either as a single wave or as a particle. This particle is called a *photon*.

18.2 relativity and the photon

The theory of relativity, developed about the time that welding itself was developed, about 1905, is concerned with the speed of light. Two conclusions or "laws" of relativity apply to welding technology.

1. The faster the velocity of a body, the greater its mass. However, the increase in weight is negligible until the velocity approaches about one-sixth of the speed of light, or about 30,000 mi per sec. Such velocities are produced by some types of welding equipment. For an example, an electron in an X-ray tube that is accelerated by a voltage drop of 100,000 v (not a high voltage for welding radiography) will hit the target of the X-ray tube at a velocity of about 100,000 mi per sec. This speed is more than half the speed of light, so that the electron must "weigh" more at this speed than it does when it is at rest. The formula that relates traveling mass to mass at rest is

$$M = \frac{M_0}{\sqrt{1 - (v/c)^2}}$$

Here M = the traveling mass of the body
M_0 = the mass of the body when at rest (rest mass)
v = the actual velocity of the body
c = the speed of light

electromagnetic radiation and the electron beam
331

According to the formula, any body that moves at the velocity of light has an infinite mass. This does not occur. Actually the only entities that can (and do) travel at the speed of light are those that have no mass when standing still, or have zero rest mass.

2. Mass, or weight, can be converted into energy. All mass is basically energy. To convert from mass to energy, the famous formula of Einstein applies: $E = mc^2$, where E is the energy produced by conversion of the mass, M is the rest mass, and $c^2 = $ (velocity of light)^2. Since c^2 is an enormous figure, the formula indicates that a small amount of mass will produce a relatively enormous quantity of energy.

These relativity concepts can explain the otherwise unexplainable particle called the *photon*. Each a-c wave of radiation can also be considered a photon, an actual particle. The photon contains all the energy of the wave, indeed, it is the wave. The photon necessarily travels at the speed of light, a characteristic which makes it one of the most interesting of the fundamental particles. Since it travels only at the speed of light, it has no rest mass and therefore ceases to exist when it is stopped. Its mass is 100% energy and 0% mass. The energy of the photon is transferred to the object which stops the photon: thus an infrared photon will heat the object which intercepts it.

18.3 the electron volt

The electron-volt (ev) is one of the many units of energy like watts, horsepower, foot-pounds, etc. and is one of the easiest to understand and apply. It may be taken as a kind of watt measurement through the following reasoning:

$$\text{watts} = \text{volts} \times \text{amperes},$$

and amperes are units of 6.28×10^{28} electrons per sec. Now if we consider only 1 electron and multiply it by the voltage applied to the electron, we have a wattlike measurement called the electron-volt. Thus an electron moving across a welding arc of 18 v drop has an energy of 18 ev at the instant it completes its travel across the arc. Halfway across, its energy would be 9 ev. Voltages are actually forces that accelerate charged particles. Doubling the voltage increases the electron velocity by four times. High voltages therefore account for the tremendous speeds of electrons in X-ray tubes, electron beam welding machines, and other high voltage equipment.

For converting into larger units of energy,
$$1 \text{ ev} = 1.60 \times 10^{-19} \text{ joules} \quad \text{and} \quad 1 \text{ w} = 1 \text{ joule/sec}$$

The following is a comparison of some familiar energy producers rated in electron-volts:

1 molecule of water falling over Niagara Falls = 0.00015 ev
1 carbon atom burned to carbon dioxide   = 4 ev
1 uranium atom disintegration   = 200 million ev

The electron-volt is the most convenient energy unit to use in connection with the photon. The relationship between the energy of a photon in electron-volts and the frequency of the electromagnetic wave of radiation is simple:

$$\text{photon energy (ev)} = h \times f$$

where h is some constant and f is frequency in cycles per second. It is perhaps not important to welding technology to know what value to put on the constant h. Instead, we make use of a slightly different formula that seems to serve our purposes better. Since $f = c/L$ from Sec. 18.1, the photon energy is proportional to $1/L$. Electromagnetic radiation of frequency higher than the radar range, beginning with infrared radiation, has wavelengths much shorter than 1 mm, and for these very short wavelengths, the Angstrom (abbreviated A) is the most convenient unit of length: $1 \text{ A} = 10^{-8}$ cm, or one ten-millionth of a cm. We can now relate the electron-volt energy of the photon to the Angstrom length of the radiation wave.

$$\text{photon energy in ev} = 12345/L \qquad \text{where } L = \text{Angstroms}$$

Example: What is the energy of a photon of red light with a wavelength of 8000 A?

$$\text{ev} = 12345/8000 = 1.55 \text{ ev}$$

Figure 118 shows the photon energy of the high-frequency types of radiation. In the X-ray range this radiation becomes very powerful, the energies exceeding 10,000 ev.

18.4 *biological and photographic effects of electromagnetic radiation*

Radio, television, and radar waves propagated through space are of very low energy, measured in electron-volts, because of their relatively long waves. The human body is insensitive to them. Infrared radiation is more powerful, having energies up to about 1 ev. This radiation we can sense as radiant heat. Still farther up the scale of radiation is visible light, with energy as high as 3 ev. This is powerful enough to make the retina of the eye respond.

Damaging radiation begins at ultraviolet energy levels. The ultraviolet components of the sun's radiation can produce sunburn. The more powerful ultraviolet radiation from the welding arc can produce a variety of reactions in the human skin and eye. Both the retina (the light-receiving portion of the eye) and the cornea (the lens of the eye) are especially sensitive to the high energy of ultraviolet radiation, and if exposed, the result can be retinitis, conjunctivitis (inflammation of the inner lining of the eyelid), or keratitis (a thickening of the cornea). Serious reactions of the skin to radiation from the arc are not common except in sensitive individuals, but cases of dermatitis and even carcinoma (cancer) have been found.

Ultraviolet radiation is powerful enough to depolymerize and therefore to ruin such organic materials as plastics and rubbers. Carbon black is added to polyethylene pipe to absorb such radiation and thus protect the plastic.

Radiation energies above 10 kev (10,000 electron-volts) are termed X-ray and gamma ray radiation. Such radiation is so powerful that it can penetrate solid matter, its penetrating power increasing with its photon energy. Gamma ray or X-ray radiation above 1 Mev (1 million electron-volts) can penetrate 6 in. of steel: even at 100 Kev some radiation will penetrate completely through a quarter-inch of steel. The radiation hazards of X radiation are a study in themselves and will be deferred to the chapter on nondestructive testing.

All types of electromagnetic radiation above the general radio range are used in photography. That is, a minimum energy of about 1 ev (infrared) is required to develop photographic emulsions. For these long waves, infrared film must be used. Visible light, 1½ to 3 ev, is used for ordinary camera film, which therefore will also be sensitive to the shorter wavelengths of ultraviolet and X radiation. The applications of photography to welding technology will be dealt with later in this book.

18.5   energy levels in the atom

Money exists in two forms, cash and checks. We can write a check for any amount, $4.53, $106.86, or any other. But cash has only a few units: 1, 5, 10, 25 cents, and so on. There is no 29 cent coin, nor a $4.53 bill.

Mathematically we would say that check numbers are continuous and cash is *quantized*, that is, it exists only in certain quanta or amounts. Many other things are quantized, like shirt collar sizes or welding machine current capacities. It was discovered early in this century that many physical quantities, particularly energy, which we had thought were continuous, were actually quantized. A case in point, which must now be discussed, is the energy levels of electrons which revolve around the atomic nucleus. Formerly it was assumed that an electron might taken a position at any distance from the nucleus and that it could maintain such position because the attraction of the nucleus for the electron due to their opposite electric charges would be balanced by centrifugal force tending to pull the electron away from the nucleus. This is not true, however. The electron is restricted to a limited number of positions, specifically the K, L, M, and succeeding energy levels as explained in Chapter 11. The energy levels are not continuous but quantized.

The simplest atomic structure is that of the hydrogen atom. This was shown in Fig. 53(a). The single electron may occupy a position only in the K, L, M, N, and other energy levels up to the infinitieth level, the ionized state or state of complete separation from the atomic nucleus. The electron, in any energy shell, has a specific energy in electron-volts, and these are known. The electron will normally be found in the innermost or K shell, however, unless energy, such as heat, is supplied to move the electron to an outer shell or to ionize it.

The energy of the electron is assigned a value of zero in the infinitieth shell or energy level. This is of course the ionized condition. The energy of the electron in any energy level closer to the nucleus is arbitrarily given a minus value. In the energy level closest to the atom, the K level, the electron has an energy of -13.6 ev. The electron could equally well be assigned an energy of zero in the K shell and $+13.6$ ev in the ionized condition. Either way, the electron is bound to the nucleus by an energy of 13.6 ev when in the K shell, and a minimum energy of 13.6 ev will be required to ionize the atom by pulling the electron off it. This simply means that if single atoms of hydrogen were used as a shielding gas in a welding arc, the shielding gas would ionize if the arc voltage exceeded 13.6. Hydrogen gas, however, consists of double-atom molecules of hydrogen, for which ionization requirements are somewhat different— there are two nuclei to attract the two electrons in the molecule.

The K orbit in which the electron usually moves has a radius of 0.5 A. The electron moves around this orbit at somewhat less than 1% of the speed of light. A moving electron is of course an electric current, and the orbital motion therefore sets up a corresponding magnetic field.

The electron may be moved out of the K shell to one of its other shells by providing energy to the atom from heat, a voltage, or a photon of radiation. The energy of the electron, if it should be found in one of the outer energy levels, is given by this simple relationship:

$$E = 13.6/n^2$$

where $n = 1$ for the K shell
$= 2$ for the L shell
$= 3$ for the M shell, etc.
Thus in the K shell, the energy is $13.6/1$, or 13.6 ev
in the L shell, the energy is $13.6/4$, or 3.35 ev
in the M shell, the energy is $13.6/9$, or 1.5 ev

The energy differences between the outer electron shells become very small. The minimum energy that must be added to the hydrogen atom to cause the electron to move out of the K shell is 10.2 ev, this being the difference in energy between the K and the L shell.

Thus the hydrogen electron can jump to a higher energy level, if supplied with sufficient energy. It can jump back to a low-energy level also but will have to lose energy to do so. The question then arises, where does this lost energy go?

Suppose this hydrogen atom is burned in an oxyacetylene flame as part of the acetylene molecule. The heat of the flame causes the electron to jump from the K shell to an outer shell, say the M shell, 1.5 ev. .As the hydrogen atom travels out of the flame and cools, it loses energy, causing the electron to fall back to the L or K shell from the M shell to which it was raised by the heat of combustion. Let us suppose it falls back to the L shell. To do so, it must lose 1.85 ev, this being the energy difference between M and L. The lost energy of 1.85 ev becomes a single electromagnetic particle, a photon of energy 1.85 ev. The photon carries the energy away as radiation. The wavelength of the radiation is 12345/1.87, or 6700 A. This is red light. If the electron had jumped back to the K shell, the created photon would have had an energy of 12.1 ev, which is ultraviolet radiation. Smaller electron jumps in the outer energy levels explain the origin of infrared radiation.

Figure 118 indicates that about 10 Kev is the minimum photon energy for X radiation. Since the maximum electron jump in the hydrogen atom is 13.6, it is not possible to produce X rays by means of electron jumps in hydrogen atoms.

The above constitutes a somewhat simplified explanation of how radiation originates. It has been explained here in terms of a single atom of the simplest of all elements, hydrogen. The whole subject of quantum differences of energy is called quantum mechanics, a very important field of scientific study that has given us such devices as the fluorescent lamp, the transistor, the X-ray tube, and the laser. We can now turn our attention to the applications of quantum mechanics to welding technology.

A photoelectric cell is a simple application of these quantum concepts. This device is a vacuum tube diode that can create a small electric current of a few millionths of an amp if exposed to radiation with a certain minimum photon energy that is in the range of visible light to ultraviolet. The current is produced by a flow of electrons from a radiation-sensitive cathode (not a heated cathode) to a collecting anode. The cathode material is some metal easily ionized by the loss of one electron. Such metals are cesium or rubidium, which have only a single electron in their outermost populated energy level. Such electrons can be separated from their atoms by photon energies as low as 1 or 2 ev. The released electrons are attracted to the anode by a positive voltage, thus creating the small current in the photocell.

The photoelectric cell receives radiation. The purpose of an X-ray tube is to produce radiation, specifically the very high-energy radiation known by the peculiar name X rays. X rays are produced when electrons make jumps of 10,000 ev or more, thus releasing very high-energy photons of the same energy. A simple hydrogen atom does not have the capacity for such large electron jumps in its permitted energy levels. Much heavier elements of higher atomic number and a multitude of electrons are required for the production of X rays. Figure 120(a) shows the approximate K, L, and M energy levels of sodium, an element with 2 electrons in the K shell, 8 in the L shell, and 1 in the M shell. The

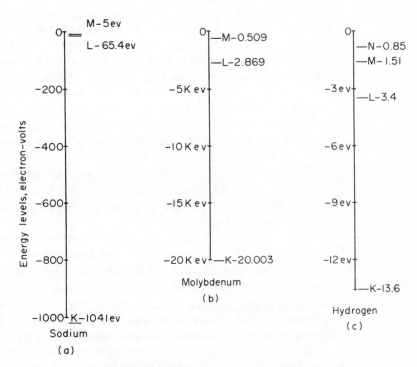

Fig. 120 Energy levels in the heavier atoms of sodium and molybdenum compared with hydrogen.

maximum electron jump in such an atom is 1041 ev, from the infinitieth level to the K level. This would release a photon of ultraviolet radiation. As in hydrogen, X radiation is not possible from electron jumps in sodium. Figure 120(b) is a similar diagram for the metal molybdenum, which has 42 electrons. Since the K level has an energy of 20,000 ev, it is possible to obtain long-wave X rays from this metal in an X-ray tube. However 20-Kev X rays are not powerful enough for the radiography of metals, castings, and welds.

18.6 laser welding

Every small boy has tried using a magnifying glass to concentrate the rays from the sun in order to char a piece of paper. Electromagnetic radiation is energy. The laser, using the concepts of quantum mechanics, is a more technical substitute for the magnifying glass. Early in its development, the laser was found to be useful as a welding tool. Considerable research is being expended on the laser in order to improve its performance. The word *laser* means light amplification by stimulated electromagnetic radiation.

Consider a heating element in an electric stove after current is switched through it. It radiates a certain amount of red visible radiation and a considerable amount of infrared (heat) radiation. The atoms of the heating element receive energy from the electric circuit, this energy having the effect of moving electrons from inner energy levels close to the nucleus to energy levels farther removed from the nucleus. Photons of red light are created when an electron jumps back toward the nucleus through an energy difference of about 1 ev. Those electrons that return toward the nucleus through smaller energy differences emit photons of infrared radiation. The radiation occurs over a very broad band of wavelengths and is not very intense. Certainly it is not possible to join metals by exposing them to such radiation.

The most important part of a laser suitable for welding or cutting is a transparent crystal. Suppose that the electrons typically inhabit, two characteristic energy levels, a higher energy level when the electrons receive photon energy and a lower energy level when they release photon energy. Three processes are possible.

1. When radiation interacts with electrons in the lower energy level, a photon is absorbed and the electron is raised to the upper level.
2. An electron can spontaneously emit a photon by dropping back to the lower level.
3. Radiation can interact with an electron in the upper level, causing it to emit a photon of radiation. The photon thus emitted will travel in the

same direction and be in phase with the stimulating photon. The radiation will then be twice as powerful, that is, it will be amplified. This is what happens in the laser.

The laser solves the problem of producing huge amounts of power by means of radiation because of two characteristics: the electron jumps all give the same photon energy level, and all the electrons make the jump at the same instant. On first acquaintance, however, the laser is not an impressive piece of equipment, despite the great publicity it receives. High-power lasers consist of either a ruby (aluminum oxide) crystal that has been doped with a few billion chromium atoms or a certain type of glass doped with the rare earth metal neodymium. Such crystals are about the size of the human thumb. The back end of the crystal is heavily silvered to reflect any internal radiation; the front end face, from which the intense beam of radiation is emitted, is partially silvered. These crystal end faces must be ground flat and square to approximately a millionth of an inch. A xenon-filled flash tube is either wound around the laser crystal in helical form, or it may be a straight tube parallel to the crystal. The radiation from an electrical discharge through xenon gas very closely resembles that of sunlight; however, the important characteristic of a xenon tube is its high power capacity. The xenon tube is the "trigger" that fires the laser, and the laser output depends on the power output of the xenon tube. The best xenon tubes are limited to about 10,000 w at present, not enough if the laser is to develop its applications in the field of welding. However, if the power of the xenon tube is further increased, keeping the temperature of the ruby crystal down to a suitable level will be difficult.

Figure 121 represents a laser of the type under discussion. The laser is fired by discharging the capacitor through the xenon tube, which then puts out a powerful pulse of light. The chromium atoms in the ruby crystal absorb the yellow and green fraction of the visible radiation. This

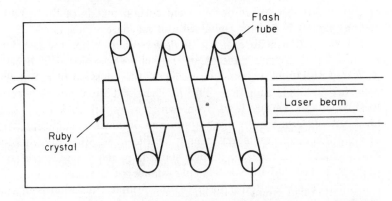

Fig. 121 The ruby laser, with helical xenon flash tube.

electromagnetic radiation and the electron beam

absorption "pumps" vast numbers of electrons from a lower energy level 1 to a higher energy level 3. The more powerful the flash, the greater the number of electrons excited to the higher level. From energy level 3 the electrons rapidly fall back to an intermediate energy level 2. This is a small energy drop measured in electron-volts, appearing as heat in the crystal. A few electrons fall back to energy level 1, creating photons of red light. This light is reflected back and forth between the ends of the crystal, stimulating the electrons in energy level 2 to fall in unison back to level 1 and producing a pulse of red light of enormous power. The laser may be fired again after the fifth of a second or more required to charge the capacitor. Present high-power lasers fire in pulses like a spot welder, although much research is being done on continuous lasers. Pulsed ruby lasers with outputs as high as 1500 joules represent the maximum output in present laser technology.

One limitation of the welding laser is apparent. Highly reflective materials such as aluminum are not easily welded with the laser since the surface of the metal reflects the greater part of the radiant energy of the laser. Since metals must be cleaned before welding, the cleaning operation makes the metal surface more reflective. Other problems also arise. The laser beam may well punch a hole through the metal instead of producing a weld if the pulse duration is not closely controlled to a few thousandths of a second. The ideal laser pulse for welding appears to be a rapid upslope to maximum power, terminated by downslope. Successful welds depend too on the characteristics of the metal, such as the thermal conductivity and the boiling point. All welding methods have their problems and limitations, but the laser welder has one difficulty not shared by other devices: more heat is generated in the welding machine than in the work, indeed, the laser is so inefficient that only about 1 to 2% of the input power can be transferred to the workpiece.

Nevertheless, the laser is a new development and will undergo much improvement in its presently limited applications in welding, cutting, and drilling. It has been used chiefly for microwelding, either for butt welds or spot welds. Moreover, it can weld certain metals of the reactive type, such as tantalum and tungsten, without an inert atmosphere.

Laser action is an example of *fluorescence*. When the laser crystal is irradiated with shorter-wave green and yellow radiation, it delivers longer-wave red radiation. This is fluorescence—the emission of radiation during exposure to other radiation. The incident radiation pumps electrons up to some higher energy level, from which they fall back to their original level, usually in more than one jump, one of which is sufficiently powerful to yield detectable radiation, usually visible light. Virtually all substances can be made to fluoresce, though some may require powerful radiation, such as X rays, to do so. The persistence of the emission of radiation from the substance after exposure to the primary radiation is discontinued is called *phosphorescence*.

Phosphors are chemicals that emit visible light, when irradiated at high photon energies such as ultraviolet. In parts of our country phosphorescent wood that glows green in the dark can be found. Such wood has been caused to phosphoresce by ultraviolet radiation from the sun, the phosphorescent material being certain salts in the wood, perhaps zinc sulfide. Fluorescent light bulbs have a phosphor painted on the glass bulb which fluoresces when irradiated by the ultraviolet discharge through the mercury vapor of the lamp. Similarly, cathode ray tubes, such as television picture tubes, are coated with a phosphor surface. The use of fluorescent dyes for inspection of welds will be discussed in a later chapter. Fluorescence even creates a problem in the X-raying of welds, also to be discussed later, the problem being the protection of the X-ray film from fluorescence caused by the powerful X radiation. The laser itself may be summed up in the remark that it is the most technically complex method yet in use for putting fluorescence to work in science and industry.

18.7 electron beams

An electron beam is a controlled stream of electrons (that is, an electric current) accelerated across a vacuum by means of an accelerating voltage. The electrons are expelled from the cathode and are attracted to a positive anode, moving at a constantly increasing velocity so that the maximum speed of the electrons occurs at the instant of impact with the anode. If the accelerating voltage is very high, of the order of many thousands of volts, the impact of the electrons on the anode produces considerable heat, and in extreme cases the anode may have to be cooled with oil, water, or air. Every vacuum tube operates by means of an electron beam of course, the electron beam in the tube being controlled by a voltage placed on a third electrode called a grid. Vacuum tubes have already received some discussion in this book. This chapter will focus attention on three electron beam applications in the field of welding: the cathode ray oscilloscope, the X-ray tube, and the electron beam welder.

If the accelerating voltage applied to a beam of electrons reaches a magnitude of about 10 kv, the electron impact generates heat, but also a small amount of X radiation, in the anode. The X radiation may be used for the examination of welds, the electron beam device being called an X-ray tube. The heat of impact may be used to make welds, the electron beam device then being called an electron beam welding machine. In principle therefore, the electron beam welder and the X-ray tube are the same device, though not so in practice, one device rejecting the anode heat and the other device rejecting the X rays.

electromagnetic radiation and the electron beam

The cathode ray oscilloscope is a low-power electron beam device used for inspection and testing, or as the television picture tube, simply for entertainment. The oscilloscope might almost be called a "pictorial voltmeter," for it usually draws graphs of voltage on its fluorescent face.

18.8   the cathode ray oscilloscope

The construction and operation of a cathode ray oscilloscope, or "scope," may be understood from the diagram of Fig. 122. The scope tube is about 1 ft or more long and 3 to 5 in. in diameter at the large front end, where the fluorescent indications appear.

The source of electrons is the hot cathode, and the oscilloscope also has a control grid and an anode. So far then, this tube is another type of vacuum triode. The voltage between the cathode and anode may range from 1100 to 6000 v or more. The electrons are traveling at a high speed when they reach the anode. The anode, however, has an opening in the front, through which most electrons shoot, striking the front face of the tube. This face is coated with a fluorescent coating that emits visible radiation when "excited." At the area struck by the electrons this fluorescent material emits visible radiation to produce a spot of light.

The combination of cathode, control grid, and anode, is called an *electron gun*. An electron beam welder likewise obtains its electron beam from an electron gun, though its electron current and accelerating voltage are greater than those used in scope tubes. Just past the electron gun are two pairs of deflecting plates. (In a TV picture tube electromagnetic coils may be substituted for deflecting plates.) One pair of plates is vertical, one pair horizontal. The electron beam may be deflected by a voltage impressed on these plates. If a positive voltage is applied to one of the four plates, the electron beam will be deflected toward it and will strike the fluorescent screen at some point other than the exact center. A negative voltage applied to the same plate will repel the electron beam in the

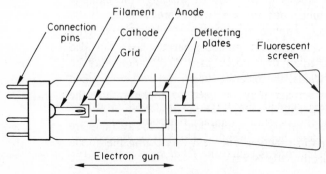

Fig. 122 The cathode ray oscilloscope.

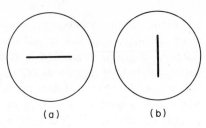

Fig. 123 Oscilloscope patterns. (a) 60-cycle applied to the vertical deflecting plates, (b) 60-cycle applied to the horizontal deflecting plates.

(a)   (b)

opposite direction. If 60-cycle voltage is applied to the vertical pair of plates, the electron beam will draw a straight line across the tube, as shown in Fig. 123(a), as the beam oscillates. A 60-cycle voltage applied to the horizontal plates will produce a vertical line, as shown in Fig. 123(b).

Perhaps the two most important uses of the cathode ray oscilloscope in welding are the checking of welding currents and the ultrasonic testing of welds. In ultrasonic testing, a pulse of sound waves is fired into the weld. If the weld is cracked, an echo will be reflected back to the instrument from the crack. This sound echo is converted into a voltage, the voltage then being applied to the vertical plates of the scope. The electron beam traces a horizontal line back and forth across the face of the scope. Any vertical deflection of this horizontal line indicates a sound echo off a weld defect.

18.9 the X-ray tube

The X-ray tube is simply a high-vacuum tube diode with an unusually high voltage difference between cathode and anode. The filament is heated by a 6- or 12-v transformer supply, and is located in the open front of a focusing hood. The focusing hood is negatively charged to repel electrons released by the cathode and thus aims the electron beam at a small area of the anode (the focal spot). The X-ray anode must be designed to produce the maximum amount of X-ray energy and to direct these X rays in the desired direction. A more difficult problem is the removal of the large amount of heat produced by the electron bombardment. The efficiency of these X-ray tubes is only about 1% or so, since nearly all of the output is heat instead of X rays. The efficiency is highest when heavy metal such as tungsten is used for the anode and is improved somewhat at higher tube voltages.

The face of the anode is called the *target*. The target is usually tungsten, this metal offering the desirable characteristics of good X-ray output, high melting point, and heavy weight. The small area of the target that is bombarded by electrons is called the *focal spot,* and in order to obtain sharply defined radiographic pictures, this focal spot is made as small in area as possible without causing melting of the metal. The tungsten target is embedded in a large copper anode. Copper is selected for its high heat conductivity, its purpose being to remove heat from the target. The stem of the anode passes through the wall of the tube, where it is sealed by a leak-proof glass-to-metal joint, and terminates in a bath of cooling oil. Very large X-ray tubes have a hollow stem and head with cooling passages. If the anode is allowed to become too hot, it will act as a cathode and emit electrons on reverse cycles of alternating current. Such action would mean bombardment of the cathode and destruction of the tube.

Figure 124 shows that the tungsten target is inclined at about 20° to the electron beam. By this arrangement the focal spot is foreshortened when viewed from the direction of the photographic film; the effect is to

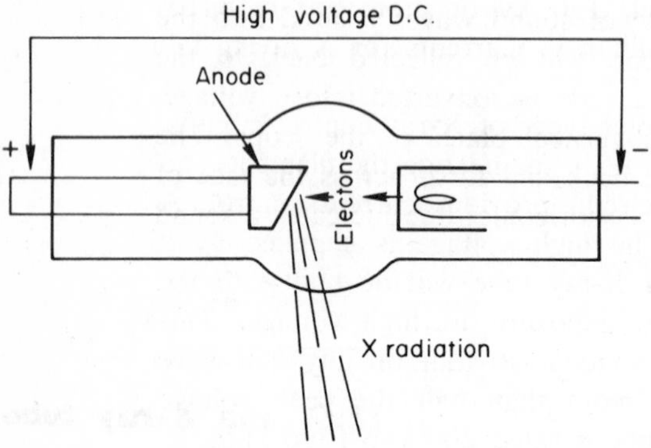

Fig. 124 Construction of an X-ray tube.

sharpen the image on the film by reducing the apparent size of the focal spot to a minimum.

All X rays do not pass through the window of the tube. Some radiation is scattered in all directions. For the safety of personnel therefore, the tube head is lead-lined except for the "window" made of a light metal such as beryllium, which is transparent to X rays.

An X-ray tube must have controls for current and voltage and an on-off switch. A timer device for shutting off the tube is also included. To protect the operator from X radiation, the controls are mounted in a box connected to the tube by a long cable. By controlling the voltage, the electron-volt energy of the electrons is determined: higher voltages produce more penetrating (harder) X rays for the examination of thicker sections of metal. By controlling the current, the quantity of X radiation is controlled. Twice as much current will produce twice as many electrons and twice as much X radiation. Controlling the time controls the exposure of the film as in ordinary photography. For very thin and light metals, like those used in the aircraft industry, voltages as low as 50 kv may be

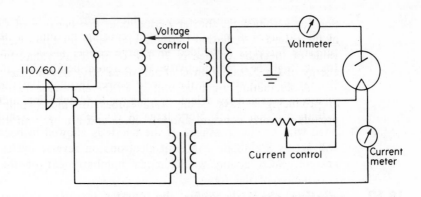

Fig. 125 X-ray tube control circuit, with the X-ray tube acting as its own rectifier.

used. To X-ray half an inch of steel, 150 kv or more are required. Maximum X-ray voltages exceed 1 million v. Currents for X-raying fall within the range of 4 to 20 ma.

Figure 125 shows one of the simpler types of X-ray control circuits. A step-down transformer provides 6 or 12 v for heating the filament, and a variable resistance in the filament circuit provides current control. A milliammeter indicates the current. The high voltage is supplied by a step-up transformer, which in a small X-ray tube will be built into the tube head so that there may be no exposure to high voltage. This transformer has its center winding grounded, so that on any half-wave of voltage, no part of the system is more than half the peak voltage above ground or zero voltage. If the tube is rated 200 kvp (200 kilovolts peak), one end of the transformer will go to +100 kv and the other end to −100 kv. X-ray tubes are never rated by effective voltage but always by peak voltage.

The voltage control is a line voltage transformer of the autotransformer type with a single coil. By picking off the appropriate number of turns on the single coil, the desired voltage, proportional to the number of turns, is obtained. Like all vacuum tubes, the X-ray tube can operate only on direct current. In this circuit the tube acts as its own rectifier, and as a result X rays will be emitted only on those half-waves when the anode is positive. Further, the X-ray energy will not be constant over the half-wave of voltage. No radiation will be emitted until the voltage climbs to about 10 kv. This very soft radiation will not penetrate any significant thickness of metal. As the voltage builds up toward peak voltage, the X rays continually become harder and more penetrating because of their decreasing wavelength until maximum voltage is reached, after which the radiation becomes softer, again ceasing when the voltage drops below 10 kv. With such a circuit, the tube target will radiate less than 50% of the a-c cycle, and the photographic film will receive radiation for a somewhat shorter period than this because of the filtering out of the softest X radiation by the metal being photographed. The effective value of the tube voltage is 70.7% of the peak value, but the effective energy of the X radiation is about 40 to 50% of the peak kev.

A fluctuating a-c tube voltage is therefore not an efficient method of producing X rays. Some X-ray tubes use more complex circuits to provide a nearly constant anode voltage and a more uniform X radiation.

18.10 radiation characteristics
of X-ray tubes

If an X-ray tube is operated at a potential of 100 kv, then electrons strike the focal spot with an energy of 100,000 ev. Suppose that such an electron strikes an atom of tungsten in the target and that the atom absorbs the maximum possible energy from the electron, 100 Kev. This energy will move an electron in the tungsten atom from an inner energy level to a remote outer energy level. Let us suppose that an electron jump of 100 Kev is possible in all the permitted levels of the tungsten atom. Then if the same electron later falls back to its inner energy level from which it started, it will release a 100-Kev photon with a wavelength of 0.12 A. This will be the minimum possible wavelength emitted by the tube.

Actually only a few X-ray photons of this maximum energy will be emitted. The energy of the bombarding electron will usually be absorbed by several atoms in several impacts as the electron gradually slows down. The electron jumps will be smaller, and the wavelengths of the radiation will be longer. Since perhaps 99% of the electron energy is converted into heat (infrared radiation), many of the electron jumps will be small. Also, if an electron in a bombarded atom of tungsten is removed from the K level to perhaps the S level, it will not necessarily jump back again to the K level. An electron from an L level may move into the empty K position instead, producing a photon which may or may not be in the X-ray range. Perhaps the original K electron may then leave the S level for the now empty position in the L level. Again, the resulting photon may or may not lie in the X-ray range of radiation.

Thus the maximum photon energy (that is, hardness) of the X rays from the tube will be fixed by the voltage, but there will be a continuous distribution of X rays lower in energy than this maximum and therefore a continuous distribution of wavelengths. Typical wavelength distributions are shown in Fig. 126. Note that the higher voltage produces a greater quantity or intensity of radiation. The most frequent wavelength is about

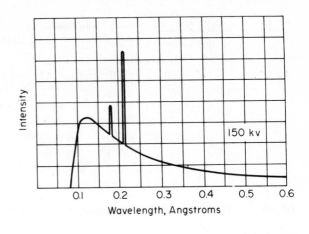

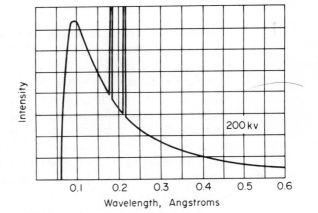

Fig. 126 Radiation spectrum from a tungsten X-ray target at 150 and 200 kv.

1½ times the minimum wavelength, or for a half-wave type of tube as in Fig. 125, about 2½ times the minimum wavelength.

In addition to this continuous spectrum of radiation, the target metal produces characteristic radiation, socalled because such radiation is specific to the target material. Shown as the two narrow emission lines in Fig. 126, these characteristic radiation lines are independent of the voltage. For a tungsten target the characteristic wavelengths are always 0.18 and 0.21 A and are always present at any voltage above 70 kv. The minimum voltage at which these lines will appear is termed the excitation potential. Similar lines are found in the radiation spectrum for any target material, though each metal has different characteristic wavelengths. For molybdenum they are 0.71 and 0.63 A, which correspond to lower tube voltages. The wavelength in Angstroms of the characteristic radiation for any metal is given roughly by

$$\frac{1200}{(Z-1)^2}$$

electromagnetic radiation and the electron beam
347

where Z is the atomic number of the metal, found in any periodic chart of the elements. For tungsten the atomic number is 74, that is, tungsten is the 74th element.

The characteristic radiation is simply the radiation corresponding to an electron jump from the L, M, or N levels to the K level. The energies corresponding to these levels in the tungsten atom are

K level	69.3	Kev
L level	12.1	Kev
M level	2.8	Kev
N level	0.6	Kev

The electron jumps and their corresponding X-ray photon energies are as follows:

L to K $69.3 - 12.1 = 57.2$
M to K $69.3 - 2.8 = 66.5$
N to K $69.3 - 0.6 = 68.7$

The corresponding wavelengths are:

L to K, $12345/57200 = 0.216$ A, called the $K\alpha$ line
M to K, $12345/66500 = 0.187$ A, called the $K\beta$ line
N to K, $12345/68700 = 0.18$ A, called the $K\gamma$ line

These wavelengths agree with the wavelengths of the characteristic radiation shown in Fig. 126. Similar characteristic lines for the L or M levels do not lie in the useful X-ray range.

The excitation voltage necessary to produce this characteristic radiation is simply the electron-volt energy necessary to displace an electron from the K shell, creating the conditions for an electron jump to that shell.

18.11 gamma rays

An alternative to the X-ray tube for purposes of radiography is the use of artificial radioisotopes, chiefly cobalt-60 and iridium-192. The nuclei of the atoms of these metals disintegrate at a certain rate, and in the act of disintegration gamma rays are emitted from the nucleus. Such gamma rays do not have the continuous and characteristic radiation of the X-ray tube but have only a few wavelengths at certain very sharply defined frequencies. An X ray therefore is produced by a change in energy level of an orbital electron, whereas a gamma ray is produced when the nucleus of the atom disintegrates.

Suppose a gamma ray from an isotope has an energy of 300 Kev.

An X-ray tube can also produce 300-Kev radiation, called X rays. The two emissions have the same energy. What then is the difference between them? There is no difference. Both emissions are really X rays. Both are also gamma rays. If the emission comes from a tube, it is called an X ray. If it comes from an isotope, it is called a gamma ray. Just as identical welding transformers can be bought under two or more brand names, so the terms "X ray" and "gamma ray" are simply different brand names for the same product, identical in every respect except for their origin.

18.12   the electron beam welder

Since electron beam welders use kilovoltages in the X-ray range, they emit radiation, and the machine operator may have to be protected from this radiation by a lead lining in the machine. In the electron beam welding machine, as in the X-ray tube, the source of heat is a narrow beam of electrons emitted from a heated cathode in an electron gun. The beam of electrons is focused by means of an electromagnetic coil. Since the electron beam is to be used for welding, drilling, or cutting, the workpiece is made the anode. To make a continuous weld, the workpiece may be traversed under the electron beam, the electron gun may be traversed, or the beam itself may be deflected to trace the path of the weld.

If electron beam welding is performed in a gas atmosphere, the energy of the electrons in the beam will be dissipated by collisions with gas molecules. Therefore, with minor exceptions, all electron beam welding must be performed under vacuum conditions. Since neither shielding gas, filler wire, nor electrode is used, it is virtually impossible to contaminate the workpiece. However, a high vacuum is required. Vacuum pressures used are less than one three-millionth of atmospheric pressure, or 10^{-4} mm of mercury pressure. (One atmosphere is about 300 mm of mercury.) The size of the vacuum chamber is of course determined by the size of the work to be welded and by the method of completing the weld seam. If the workpiece is to be moved past the electron beam, then the vacuum chamber must be twice as long as the workpiece, but if the electron gun is traversed over the workpiece, then the chamber need only be large enough to fit the workpiece inside it.

Electron beam welding must necessarily be an automatic welding method. To set up the work and machine for welding, the work must be fixtured in the vacuum chamber, the chamber door closed, and the chamber pumped down to the required pressure. Time spent pumping down is not available for welding. Vacuum pumps of ample capacity are therefore supplied, and pump-down times are about 10 min.

Unfortunately, an industrial vacuum of the order of 10^{-4} to 10^{-5}

mm of mercury pressure requires a pumping system that is neither simple nor inexpensive. The required vacuum system is diagrammed in Fig. 127. Two pumps are required in series, since it is not possible to reach the low vacuum needed with a single type of pump. The roughing pump, a vane pump, is first cut in to bring the vacuum down to about one-tenth of a mm of mercury (about one three-thousandth of an atmosphere), after which the second pump, a diffusion pump, pumps down to final vacuum pressure. The diffusion pump pumps up to the vane pump which then pumps to atmosphere. The diffusion pump uses oil to entrap gases from the vacuum. As the vacuum pressure drops, the oil will increasingly tend to vaporize and back-stream into the vacuum chamber. This tendency is prevented by the cold trap, a section in the vacuum piping which is kept cold with dry ice or liquid nitrogen for the purpose of condensing any vaporized oil or water vapor. The piping system itself must be specially constructed to prevent even the smallest leaks. Rubber or plastic gaskets are not usually suitable, because such organic materials contain components which boil out (outgas) at extremely low vacuum pressures. Butt welds in vacuum systems are usually welded from one side only; if welded from both sides, any lack of penetration between top and backing welds will provide a leak path for gases along the weld seam.

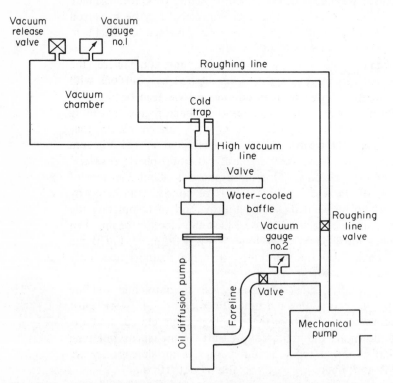

Fig. 127 Vacuum pumping system for an electron beam welder.

electromagnetic radiation and the electron beam

The oil diffusion pump (Fig. 128) has an unusual type of construction. The pumping effect is produced by means of oils of special formulation and containing a minimum of low-boiling constituents. Fig. 128(a) shows the construction of an oil diffusion pump. Such a pump is readily identified by the pipe elbow projecting from its side. The pump has a water-cooled casing and, in the base of the pump, an electric heater for evaporating the oil. The vaporized oil travels up the concentric tubes and issues from the venturi jets at the top of these tubes at high speed, entraining gases from the vacuum piping and propelling them to the discharge elbow leading to the mechanical pump. The latter pump finally pumps these gases out of the system to atmosphere. The vaporized oil condenses on the water-cooled wall of the pump and returns to the base, com-

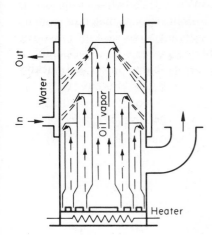

Fig. 128(a) **Construction of an oil diffusion vacuum pump.**

Fig. 128(b) **Series of Balzers' oil diffusion pumps. The large pump has sixty-five times the pumping capacity of the small pump. (Courtesy Philips Electronics, Inc.)**

electromagnetic radiation and the electron beam

pleting the cycle. The diffusion pump is thus an oil boiler. The oil vapor jets may be considered as umbrellas or diaphragms separating the higher pressure below them from the lower vacuum pressure above them. When the condensed oil flows from the water-cooled wall back toward the center of the pump, the most volatile oil fraction is vaporized first and issues from the lowest jet; the heaviest oil fraction is boiled last and issues from the uppermost and central jet. The top nozzle thus has the oil with the lowest vapor pressure, an arrangement that minimizes back-streaming of the more volatile constituents of the oil into the vacuum chamber.

The vacuum chamber is usually made of stainless steel since this alloy is easy to keep clean and does not scale. Dirt and scale both tend to absorb gases at atmospheric pressure and release them under vacuum conditions. A vacuum gauge must be installed to indicate the vacuum pressure. Such a gauge has a special construction and in no way resembles the more usual gauges attached to welding gas cylinders. Finally, an optical viewing system allows the operator to observe the welding process.

The high vacuum required in the electron beam welder creates a few special problems with certain metals. Such metals as zinc cannot be welded by this method, since they boil readily in a high vacuum and deposit on the electron gun, the optical system, or other parts of the welding machine. Aluminum and magnesium give trouble also but can be electron-beam-welded. Special construction, such as isolation of the electron gun, can prevent damage due to deposited metals vaporized in the vacuum chamber.

18.13 work fixturing and beam deflection

In the making of electron beam butt welds, since there is no filler metal, the edge preparation consists simply of machining the butting surfaces flat, straight, and square. This type of joint is inexpensive to prepare in thick metal, as compared with a V, U, or J edge preparation. However, poor fit-up cannot be tolerated in electron beam welding, since no joint will be produced if the very narrow electron beam can pass between two metal edges.

After edge preparation, the two workpieces to be welded are then tight-butted in a welding fixture. The fixture need not be of heavy construction, since it does not have to resist the heavy distortion forces that accompany other types of fusion welding. No matter how thick the material, it is possible to complete the joint in one pass, although sometimes special reasons exist for a light backing pass on the other side of the joint. The workpiece is usually clamped to a worktable having two variable-speed motors that traverse the work in either the X or the Y direction. Other methods use a worktable that traverses in one direction only, the motion at right angles to the worktable movement being provided by movement of the electron gun across the top of the workchamber. For rotary motion a variable-speed motor-driven turntable is used.

The electron beam can be operated in any of three "modes" or methods:

1. A steady beam for continuous welding
2. A pulsed beam for ceramic and metal cutting, using pulse cycles ranging from about 1 to 15,000 per sec
3. Single pulses for spot welding or small-hole drilling

Electronic beam deflection systems are standard on electron beam welders. With these beam deflection controls, the beam can be made to weld along a straight line or around a rectangle or circle or follow a zigzag or other path. Some electron beam welders have been fitted with the pantographs and tracer controls more familiar in machine shop work in order to weld or cut along complex paths. The automatic methods for cutting complex shapes using photocells or punched-tape control were briefly described in Chapter 17. Both these automatic methods have been used for electron beam welding and cutting. The worktable, or the electron gun, or the deflection of the electron beam can be thus guided.

18.14 characteristics of the electron beam

Electron beam welding is a fusion welding process. Most welding methods may also be used for thermal cutting, and so may the electron beam, although for cutting the beam is pulsed. There is no practical limit to the thickness of metal that may be electron-beam-welded. A current of 10 ma with 150,000 v is sufficient to weld 1-in.-thick stainless steel with full penetration. The width of the fusion zone is only a few thousandths of an inch. A section through such a weld is shown in Fig. 129.

It was noted earlier that an electron accelerated by 100,000 v finally reaches a velocity of about half the speed of light. At such velocities, impact of the electron on the workpiece melts and even boils the metal. The local temperature is so high that even ceramic materials may be welded or cut. Figure 130 shows the sequence of penetration of the electron beam into the metal. The stream of electrons penetrate a thin layer of material of the order of one-thousandth of an inch. As they travel deeper into the material, they are scattered and stopped by collisions with the atoms of the crystal structure, thus heating a pear-shaped

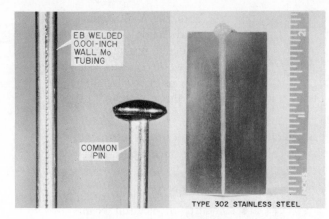

EB WELDED
0.001-INCH
WALL Mo
TUBING

COMMON
PIN

TYPE 302 STAINLESS STEEL

Fig. 129 Application of electron beam welding to either microwelding applications or to heavy sections. (Courtesy Hamilton-Standard Division of United Aircraft Corporation)

volume of metal. Some of the heated metal is vaporized, and the vapor pressure thus generated bursts the unaffected surface layer membrane. Thus a hole is "burned" in the material. This process is repeated in the second and following layers of metal until complete penetration occurs. The depth of penetration of each such cavity depends on the accelerating voltage of the electron beam, being greater for higher voltages. Higher voltages also produce a narrower width of penetration. Many of these pear-shaped cavities can be seen in the cross section of Fig. 129. Some appear to be wider than others, and this is accounted for by segregation and nonuniformities in the composition of the metal, resulting in irregular scattering of the electrons of the beam.

If the electron beam traverses the workpiece, this same penetration sequence is repeated at neighboring points along the weld seam. The

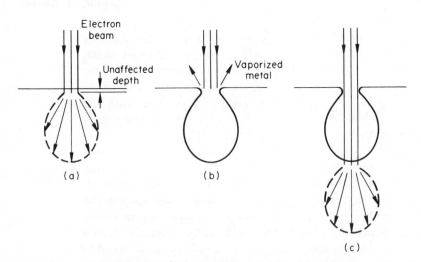

Electron beam

Unaffected depth

(a)

Vaporized metal

(b)

(c)

Fig. 130 Penetration of the electron beam into the workpiece.

electromagnetic radiation and the electron beam

metal that is melted and vaporized redeposits in the previously melted hole, so that electron beam welding is sometimes described as the transportation of a very small hole along the seam. For cutting, all that is necessary is to increase the voltage (thus increasing the power of the beam) to the point at which a permanent hole rather than a resolidified weld results. The required voltage and current for electron beam cutting of course depends on the material and the thickness being cut. Virtually any metal or ceramic material may be cut or drilled by the electron beam, including diamond.

Obviously the fastest electron beam welding will be given by concentrating the welding heat, which is the wattage of the electron beam, into the smallest possible diameter spot, thus producing the highest possible power density in watts per square inch or per square millimeter. For extremely high power densities, it is necessary to use higher voltages, which reduce the size of the welding spot, rather than higher currents, which increase the spot size. With higher voltages, there are fewer electrons for the same power and therefore less spreading of the electron beam due to repulsion of like electric charges in the electrons. Electron beam voltages range from 10 to 150 kv. Spot sizes vary but may be made as small as 0.01 in. or as large as a sixteenth of an inch. The heat-affected zone is correspondingly small, in one instance being determined as 0.0007 in. in width. The heat-affected zone is smaller for larger accelerating voltages.

With the exception of very high voltage electron beam welders, the following relationships hold:

$$I = KE^{3/2}$$

where $K =$ a constant, and since

$$\text{power} = EI, \ P(\text{watts}) = KE^{5/2}$$

For an example of power density per square inch, consider electron beam welding with 30 kv and 250 ma, spot size 0.030-in. diameter.

$$\text{spot area} = \frac{\pi}{4}(0.030)^2 = 0.000705$$

$$\text{watts} = 30,000 \times 0.250 = 7500$$

$$\text{power density} = \frac{7500}{0.000705} = 10,600,000 \text{ w/sq in.}$$

Such power levels are more than adequate to vaporize metals. Yet the electron beam welding machine demands about the same electric power as an electric stove cooking a turkey dinner. To compare electron beam (EB) welding with shielded metal arc welding, note that the above 7500 w is the wattage of an ordinary electric arc operating at 25 v and 300 amp. However, the shielded metal arc spot size is far larger, and only a fraction

electromagnetic radiation and the electron beam

of the arc heat is released at the workpiece. Sciaky Bros., Inc, manufacturers of electron beam welding equipment, report the following heat input comparison for welding half-inch-thick aluminum 2219 butt joints:

	Heat Input
Process	Kilojoules/in.
TIG	57.25
EB	3.97

18.15 electron beam welding

The electron beam method is often referred to as the "ideal" method of welding. It is no doubt the best of all welding methods, though it too has its limitations. Difficulties with the more volatile metals such as zinc, lead, aluminum, and magnesium have been mentioned. Such metals will boil out of the weld zone. Nevertheless aluminum and magnesium are EB-welded, and in alloys containing small amounts of these metals, such as the maraging steels, any such losses are negligible. The most serious disadvantage of the electron beam method is the cost of the equipment: small EB welders start at about $75,000, and this price does not buy a very large vacuum chamber. Despite this high initial cost, electron beam welding is often enough competitive with other welding methods.

Distortion and shrinkage are at a minimum in EB welding. The weld zone and the heat-affected zone are both very narrow, so that only a few thousandths of an inch width of metal is subject to distortion. Distortion is always proportional to the width of the fusion zone. The weld too is completed at extremely low heat inputs in joules per inch. In other fusion welding methods, to minimize distortion, butt joints should be welded from both sides, preferably simultaneously. Electron beam welding (like electrogas or three o'clock welding) meets the requirement of minimum distortion actually by completing the whole depth of joint in a single pass, without the types of edge preparation that require addition of filler metal to contribute to distortion. Butt joints in stainless steel (a particularly easy metal to weld with the electron beam) as thick as 4 in. have been completed in one pass, using 150 kv and 165 ma at a rate of 7 in. per min. The welding heat for such a pass is

$$\frac{150,000 \text{ v} \times {}^{1}/_{6} \text{ amp} \times 60}{7 \text{ ipm}} = 21,430 \text{ joules/in.}$$

which is about the maximum heat input used in EB welding. Probably no other method of welding could join this material in one pass. Further, the savings in expensive stainless steel filler metal are substantial.

The freedom of the weld zone from contamination is an outstanding advantage of EB welding, particularly in the joining of such metals as titanium and zirconium.

Control of arc length is a requirement of any arc welding method, and in general the arc must be very short. The electron beam offers a very wide latitude in arc length. Welding may be done a fraction of an inch from the electron gun, or perhaps 18 in. away from it. This is an advantage in repair and maintenance, for the beam can enter highly confined spaces inaccessible to other types of welding. The Hamilton Standard Division of United Aircraft Corporation, also manufacturers of electron beam welding machines, reports many interesting cases of electron beam repairs in otherwise totally inaccessible locations. In one instance an expensive finished machine part hand an oversized hole drilled in it. The electron beam had to reach about six inches into the interior of the part to make a circular weld of a sleeve in the oversized hole. Actual welding time was only 10 sec. The weld produced no warping of the finished part, nor damage to the machined surfaces. In another case a blind hole in a finished machine part was drilled too deep. The hole was 5 in. deep and $\frac{1}{2}$ in. in diameter. Nevertheless with the electron beam a plug was welded into the bottom of the hole. Again there was no damage to the machined surfaces and no distortion. Fatigue cracks in machinery parts have also been repaired by the electron beam method. Even weld cracks in welds produced by the electric arc method have been repaired by the electron beam. Broken drills and taps can be removed from holes by vaporizing a hole in the tool to provide means for grasping it.

Porosity can hardly be a problem in any welding done under high vacuum conditions. Starter and runoff tabs are therefore rarely used when welding with the electron beam.

Almost all welding methods are limited to a minimum thickness of metal: below this thickness the metal is burned through. The electron beam has no such limitation. It is equally suited to thin foil and wire, and has wide uses in microwelding.

Welding speed affects weld quality in electron beam as well as other methods of welding. Increased welding speed reduces the depth of penetration. Too low a travel speed provides more time for heat to conduct into the surrounding metal, resulting in a wider fusion and heat-affected zone. Too high a travel speed results in irregular penetration and may cause undercutting.

A very important part of the setup operations for electron beam welding is the focusing of the electron beam. The electrons must be brought to a sharp focus at the weld zone by meant of a deflection coil in much the same way that a beam of light is focused with a lens. Since the workpiece may be positioned any distance from the electron gun, the point of focus of the electrons in the beam must be adjustable for distance from the gun. Generally in setting up, the point of focus is established at the surface of the workpiece, but it may have to be adjusted below the surface, especially if a fusion zone with parallel sides is desired.

TYPICAL ELECTRON BEAM WELDING CONDITIONS, SQUARE BUTT JOINTS

Material	Thickness, in.	Voltage, kV	Current, ma	Welding, ipm	Speed, Joules/in.
stainless 321	1.0	30	500	40	22,500
stainless 304	0.5	29	330	63	9,100
stainless 302	⅛	31.5	32	56	1,080
AISI 4340	0.095	100	6	60	600
Inconel 718	0.080	30	26	39	1,200
18 % nickel maraging steel	0.625	30	400	63	11,400
6061 aluminum	0.050	18	33	100	360

Summing up the case for electron beam welding, the advantages appear to be as follows:

1. ability to weld or cut any metal or ceramic
2. absence of weld contamination
3. no gas porosity problems
4. no filler metal
5. low heat input
6. very low distortion and shrinkage
7. remarkable penetration
8. one-pass welding
9. simple edge preparation
10. access of the electron beam to confined spaces
11. suitability to heavy sections or microwelding
12. high welding speeds
13. no preheat requirements

The disadvantages of the electron beam method are these:

1. good fit-up required
2. difficulty in welding volatile metals
3. not suited to joints which require filler metal
4. vacuum conditions required
5. possibility of set-up time and vacuum pump-down time exceeding actual welding time

electromagnetic radiation and the electron beam

Electron beam welding is a relatively new method that is still developing. It is to be expected that much welding now done by other methods will in the future be given to the electron beam. Quality standards grow more rigorous, a trend that influences more extensive use of the electron beam for joining.

18.16 a famous case of electron beam welding

An outstanding application of the electron beam welding method was the welding of the four large circular stiffener rings for the frame of the Saturn V S-IC booster rocket. These rings are 33 ft in diameter, weighing 3700 lb each, and composed of four quadrants butt-welded to make the complete ring. Because the least possible distortion was a critical requirement, these four butt joints were electron-beam-welded, and it is doubtful whether any other welding method could have resulted in lower costs. The whole ring was too large to place in a vacuum chamber, so that a small clampon chamber was employed, only large enough to house one butt joint and its fixturing.

The cross section of the heaviest ring was a shape resembling the letter Y about 24 in. high. The thickest section was $2\frac{2}{5}$ in. and the thinnest $\frac{3}{8}$ in. Material of the ring was 2219 aluminum alloy. Since the cross section of the ring was nonuniform, automatically programmed electron beam power was used, the beam power in kilowatts being approximately proportional to the metal thickness. The electron beam machine had a maximum power rating of 30 kw and maximum current of 1 amp. The finished weld was made in one pass for each leg of the Y section and was about $\frac{1}{16}$ in. wide despite the depth of $2\frac{1}{2}$ in. Welding time was *less than 1 min* per joint.

The best competitive method of making these joints would be MIG welding, although distortion would be excessive with MIG. For MIG welding, a double-U joint preparation and a 3-in. width of edge preparation would be needed. Almost 100 MIG passes would have been required, successive passes being made on opposite sides of the joint to reduce distortion. Cleaning would have been a requirement, and radiography would have been necessary every few passes. Against a setup and welding time of 8 hr for EB welding, it is estimated that MIG welding would have required ten times as long and about 30 lb of filler metal per joint. Besides producing poorer weld quality, it appears therefore than MIG welding would have been much more expensive.

18.17 electron beam welding
in inert atmospheres

Some progress has been made with electron beam welding in an inert atmosphere. When an atmosphere replaces a vacuum, the electrons in the beam will collide with atoms of the atmosphere gas and lose most of their energy to these atoms. To reduce this energy loss, the workpiece must be positioned close to the electron gun and the losses partially compensated by the use of higher gun voltages. Another unfavorable effect of an atmosphere is the spreading of the electron beam due to collision, resulting in a wider weld zone and a poorer depth-to-width ratio in the weld.

The use of a low density gas such as helium makes possible a deeper weld penetration than heavier gases such as argon or air do. Helium, which is about one-tenth as heavy as argon, results in about three times the penetration realized with argon.

TYPICAL ATMOSPHERE ELECTRON BEAM WELDING CONDITIONS

Material	Thickness, in.	Kv	Current, ma	Welding Speed, ipm	Atmosphere	Distance Gun to Work, in.
SAE 1010	0.010	150	2.5	145	Air	¼
SAE 4340	0.25	175	40	60	3 He to 1 Ar	½
Stainless 304	0.28	175	29	36	Air	¼
Copper	0.008	150	8	145	Air	¼
5052 Alum.	0.009	150	3	145	Air	¼

18.18 sonic transducers

The low hum of a transformer is a familiar sound, signifying that the transformer, or some part of it, is vibrating.

Now any elastic material can be made to vibrate at a certain frequency by striking it with another object. Being simply cyclical strains in the elastic materials, these vibrations set the surrounding air in motion to produce a sound. The loudness of the sound depends on the magnitude of the cyclical strains, and the frequency of vibration, or pitch as it is termed by musicians, depends on the characteristics and dimensions of the vibrating object. This energy of sound—sonic energy or acoustic energy—is yet another form of energy. Like the electron beam, acoustic energy serves a dual purpose in the technology of welding: it can be used as a method of welding or as a method of weld inspection.

For both welding and inspection the frequency, energy, and duration of the acoustic wave must be controllable. Being the most easily controlled form of energy, electric energy of controlled frequency, amplitude, and duration is applied to *a sonic transducer,* a device for converting one type of energy into the other or acoustic type of energy.

Sonic transducers may use either of two principles of operation, magnetostriction or piezoelectricity. Transformer hum is an example of magnetostriction. When an electromagnetic field is induced in a magnetic material, the material strains slightly, less than 0.003%, in phase with the magnetic field. In a steel-core transformer, a 60-cycle magnetic field is induced in the core. However, the sound that is produced is not 60-cycle but the higher 120-cycle tone. This irregular behavior is due to the fact that steel contracts in the same direction on both half-waves of the 60-cycle frequency. This is a kind of magnetostrictive rectification, producing 120 cycles in the same way that a full-wave rectifier produces 120-cycle direct current. Few magnetostrictive transducers are made of steel or iron, however. Nickel is the preferred material since it does not readily corrode. Corrosion products are not necessarily elastic and would interfere with the propagation of the sound wave. Nickel will produce 60-cycle acoustics from a 60-cycle electrical frequency.

Magnetostriction occurs only in ferromagnetic materials. The piezoelectric effect is a characteristic of many ceramic materials, but quartz, barium titanate, or zirconates are usually used for this purpose. If a small voltage is impressed across two parallel faces of such a material, a small strain is produced, that is, the distance between the two faces is altered very slightly. Impressing a 60-cycle voltage across the faces of such a crystal will produce a 60-cycle acoustic wave.

Both magnetostriction and piezoelectricity have the reverse effect also, that is, in addition to sound transmission they will also receive acoustic energy. Each can therefore function both as a "loudspeaker" and as a "microphone." If an acoustic wave impinges on a piezoelectric crystal, a small voltage is produced across the faces. This small voltage can be amplified by a vacuum tube or a transistor amplifier. Similarly if an acoustic wave is received by a magnetostrictive transducer, an induced voltage is produced in a coil wound around the transducer. Transducers of both types are most familiar in the pickups of record players. Since World War II they have been successfully applied to welding techniques.

18.19   ultrasonic welding

The usual 60-cycle electric power frequency is not used in welding transducers for ultrasonic welding. One reason is that this frequency lies in the audible range, and the constant low-pitched sound would be objected to by personnel within earshot. (The human ear has a sound range of about 50 to 15,000 cps.) Higher frequencies for ultrasonic welding are produced by suitable frequency generators or oscillators.

It is a familiar experience that when listening to an orchastra from a distance, the low pitched sounds and the rhythm can be heard at much greater distances than the higher pitches can. This is a practical indication of the fact that large amounts of acoustic energy can be transported only at lower frequencies and that higher frequencies attenuate or dissipate more readily. Therefore ultrasonic welding, which requires sizable amounts of energy for making welded joints, cannot be done at the very highest frequencies. On the other hand, for the detection of defects in welds, very high frequencies must be used.

Ultrasonic welding uses acoustic frequencies in the range from 1000 (in the sonic range) to about 100,000 cycles (ultrasonic, or beyond the range of the human ear). The transducer that fires the acoustic wave into the weld seam may be either the piezoelectric or the magnetostrictive type and is called a *sonotrode,* an abbreviation of sonic electrode. About 15 to 30% of the acoustic power is delivered to the weld area. The acoustic vibration creates a friction effect which bonds the metals together in a lap weld with minimum temperature rise. Power inputs range from several watts to about 8 kw. With such limited amounts of power only microwelding and lightgauge welding are possible by the ultrasonic process.

The maximum sheet thickness possible for ultrasonic welding is about 0.100 in. in light metals such as aluminum. In harder metals the maximum possible gauge is considerably less than this. Aluminum alloys that are difficult to join by other methods, such as 2024 and 7075, are joined without difficulty by the ultrasonic method.

18.20 ultrasonic testing of welds

Sound waves, like electromagnetic radiation, follow the mathematical principle that the product of wavelength and frequency equals the velocity, of the wave. For ultrasonic flaw detection, high frequencies above 1 million cycles per sec are used. If an ultrasonic flaw detector with a frequency of 5 megacycles is searching for defects in a stainless steel weld, the wavelength of the acoustic wave is found as follows:

velocity of sound in stainless steel $= 226,000$ in./sec.

frequency $\times$ wavelength $= 226,000$ in. sec.

$5 \times 10^6 \times$ wavelength $= 226,000$

acoustic wavelength $= 0.045$ in.

The practice of ultrasonic flaw detection is described in Chapter 20. It is considerably more difficult than radiography. In brief, a piezo-electric transducer is connected to a cathode ray tube. A pulse of high frequency sound is fired into the weld area. If there is a flaw, a hole, porosity, a crack, or a piece of slag in the weld, an acoustic echo will be sent back to the transducer from the edge of the flaw. The transducer meanwhile has ceased sending out acoustic waves and is "listening" for possible echoes. A returning echo will produce a voltage signal in the transducer. This voltage pulse is applied to the vertical plates of a cathode ray tube, producing a vertical pip on the face of the tube.

The smallest detectable flaw is of the same order of magnitude as the acoustic wavelength. Therefore to obtain sensitivity for the detection of very small flaws, high frequencies are used, usually in the range of 2.25 to 10 megacycles.

PROBLEMS

1 Determine the wavelength and the electron-volt photon energy of an electromagnetic wave with a frequency of 1 megacycle.

2 Determine the wavelength in Angstroms and the photon energy of red light with a frequency of 5×10^{14} cycles per sec.

3 What is the wavelength in Angstroms from an X-ray tube operated at 300,000 v?

4 A certain photoelectric cell will not be activated by radiation below 4 ev. What is the longest wavelength that can cause this photocell to operate?

5 Cobalt-60 emits two gamma rays with energies of 1.33 and 1.17 million ev. What are the corresponding wavelengths of these gamma rays in Angstroms?

6 Photographic film must not be carelessly exposed to visible light. Why will the magnetic field from a powerful radio transmitter not harm this film?

7 What is the wavelength of the electromagnetic radiation required to displace the hydrogen electron from the K shell to the L shell?

8 If an electron falls from the M shell in a hydrogen atom to the L shell, what type of radiation will be emitted?

9 Why is it not possible to produce X-radiation from electron jumps in the hydrogen atom?

10 What is the difference between a vacuum tube diode and a photoelectric cell?

11 If a photocell in an elevator door is exposed to X radiation, might the cell operate the automatic door system and why?

12 Describe the construction of a laser suitable for microwelding.

13 Why can the laser of question 12 not be operated continuously?

14 Why does a temperature rise appear in the laser crystal?

15 Which would be easier to weld with the laser: hot-rolled or cold-rolled steel?

16 Why can fluorescence not occur at a shorter wavelength than the received radiation that causes the fluorescence?

17 In a cathode ray oscilloscope, does the electron, after traveling past the anode, still accelerate or does it travel at a constant velocity?

18 What is the difference between a vacuum tube diode and an X-ray tube?

19 Why is the high-voltage transformer of an X-ray tube center-tapped?

20 An X-ray tube has a maximum rating of 600 kv and 10 ma. If continuously operated for 1 hr, how many pounds of water must be pumped through the anode to prevent the anode temperature from rising using a water temperature rise of 10 F? Assume the total output of the tube to be heat (which is almost the case).

21 What is the focal spot of an X-ray tube?

22 Why is tungsten used for the face of an X-ray tube?

23 Why are high-voltage X rays more penetrating than low-voltage X rays?

24 Why would you suppose X-ray tubes are rated in terms of the peak voltage of the cycle instead of the effective voltage, as is more usual with electrical equipment?

25 What is the difference between an X ray and a gamma ray?

26 The earth is constantly being irradiated in the X-ray range from the sun and other sources in outer space. Is such radiation X or gamma?

27 Why is electron beam welding performed in a vacuum?

28 What is the purpose of a cold trap in a vacuum system?

29 How does a diffusion pump operate?

30 Why are metal gaskets preferred to plastic or rubber gaskets for a high vacuum system?

31 Explain what happens if the fit-up is poor in a butt joint for electron beam welding.

32 Explain how the electron beam penetrates through thick metal.

33 Explain why electron beam welding is more successful in a helium atmosphere rather than in an argon atmosphere.

34 Why are sonic vibrations not possible in a plastic material?

35 What is the meaning of piezoelectricity and of magnetostriction?

36 What is a transducer?

37 Explain why the following are transducers:
   (a) microphone
   (b) loudspeaker
   (c) trombone
   (d) electric motor
   (e) the human body

38 What is a sonotrode?

39 The velocity of sound in stainless steel is 226,000 in. per sec. What is the wavelength of 40,000-cycle sound in stainless steel?

INSPECTION
AND
TESTING OF WELDS

Part **IV**

Almost all weldments are required to conform to some specifications. Throughout the progress of the job and at its conclusion inspection of the work is often required. Inspectors, employed by the ultimate customer, may visit the shop to examine the work or may be integral members of the field staff at the jobsite. The inspector must continually make decisions about the quality of the workmanship, and unless his judgment is trusted by the welding contractor, his opinions are likely to be contested frequently. He must necessarily be familiar with all the fabrication and erection techniques of welding. In particular, the inspector must be familiar with the particular code of specifications under which the welding operations are conducted. So indeed must the welding crew, especially if they are to defend themselves from the decisions of a hostile inspector. If the job is a boiler, it must meet the specification requirements of the Boiler and Pressure Vessel Code. If it is a steel building frame, construction will be governed by a local structural code.

The day-to-day duties of the inspector include the following and other types of inspection:

1. acceptability of materials
2. proper dimensions
3. conformity of the welding to the procedure laid down for the job
4. acceptable fit-up of parts
5. proper size and contour of fillet welds and reinforcement of butt welds
6. removal of slag between passes

SPECIFICATIONS, INSPECTION, AND TESTING OF WELDS

19

7. qualification of the welding operators
8. conformity of welding electrodes to specifications
9. proper welding sequence
10. suitablility of welding machines
11. proper sequence of the work
12. suitable progress of the work
13. checking for cracks, undercutting, overlapping, unfilled craters, etc.

Figure 131 shows those fillet weld profiles that an inspector would pass and several that would be designated as unacceptable.

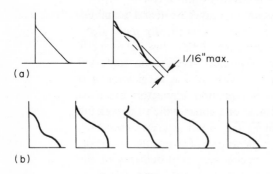

(a)

1/16"max.

(b)

Fig. 131 Fillet weld profiles. (a) Acceptable, (b) unacceptable: insufficient throat, excessive reinforcement, undercut, overlap, and insufficient leg.

In addition to any shop and field inspection, the construction specifications may call for certain tests to be performed on parent metal, welding electrodes, or deposited metal. Such test work is divided into two broad classes:

1. destructive tests
2. nondestructive tests

A nondestructive test is any test that does not damage the material nor impair its usefulness. The recognized nondestructive tests applied to welded joints are as follows:

1. Radiography, a special type of photography using X rays or gamma rays
2. Ultrasonic tests, which reveal flaws by means of acoustic echoes
3. Magnetic particle tests, which reveal flaws by means of the magnetic fields set up in the vicinity of the flaw
4. Dye penetrant tests, which reveal flaws by means of colored dyes

In addition to these are a number of other nondestructive techniques applicable principally to production work in welding, such as the production of tube and pipe. Visual inspection too is a nondestructive testing method. Although it lacks the fascinating hardware with which the human race loves to surround itself, visual inspection can be an excellent and discerning method, which must never be neglected for more sophisticated techniques.

Destructive tests are rarely performed on whole weldments, except when the whole structure is intended as a test specimen. Destructive tests must be performed on samples assumed to be representative of the materials or welded joints on which judgment will be passed as a result of the tests.

19.2 standard construction codes for welding

A contract for the construction or repair of any article or equipment usually requires the setting out and explaining of many specific details. Therefore the full explanation of the work to be done is set out in two sets of contract documents:

1. blueprints, plans, or drawings
2. written specifications

Roughly, the plans explain *what* is to be done, whereas the specifications explain the details of *how* the work is to be done. Thus if the work to be executed is a weldment, the plans will show several full and detailed views of the required work, giving exact dimensions. The specifications provide the descriptive details that cannot be communicated by means of drawings. The following are typical specifications:

Spec. 1.7. The Contractor shall furnish six (6) copies of shop drawings, and all anchor bolts, all labor, material, and equipment necessary to complete the work of all trades, and such other materials as are required by these specifications to be supplied.

Spec. 2.8 All welders employed by the fabricator shall be qualified in accordance with Section IX of the ASME Boiler and Pressure Vessel Code, "Welding Qualifications."

Specifications are written in a somewhat legalistic style, which is in part explained by the fact that they are legally binding for both parties to the contract. In addition, the text of the specifications must be carefully composed so that no party is in doubt about the meaning of the specifications and so that there is no room for dispute in interpreting the specifications. A specification written in foggy language, such as the following, is less than useless: "all welds shall be of adequate strength, of good appearance, and without excessive reinforcement." Nothing is clarified by such a specification, and no inspector can interpret it. How much strength is "adequate strength"? How much reinforcement is excessive? Nobody knows.

The writing of complete sets of specifications to govern the quality of welding work is often an onerous, exacting, expensive, and time-consuming job. To reduce the amount of specification writing that must be done and to provide uniform quality and standard requirements across the country, it is customary wherever possible to use standard specification codes. A very great number of such codes apply to welding fabrication, only a few of the more important of which can be mentioned here.

The American Society for Testing and Materials (ASTM) publishes sets of specifications bound in several volumes, setting requirements for raw materials such as steel plate and pipe and for standard material tests, such as impact tests and tension tests of metals. Thus ASTM Standard E-23 specifies test conditions for Notched Bar Impact Testing of Metallic Materials (the significance of which is outlined in Chapter 5 of this book). If the ASTM Standard number is followed by a T, it means that the Standard is "tentative." If followed by a hyphen and a second number, such as 52, it means that the date of establishment of the test was 1952. Buyers and sellers of materials use these ASTM standards almost universally, since the standards are set up by, and represent the consensus of, American industry. If agreement cannot be reached, no standard can be set up. Chapter 5 briefly described impact, hardness, and tensile test methods for metals—brief outlines of standard ASTM methods of testing.

The American Welding Society, Canadian Welding Bureau, American Standards Association, Canadian Standards Association, Underwriters' Laboratories (AWS, CWB, ASA, CSA, and UL respectively), and others have set up standard construction codes to which fabricators are referred in the manufacture of weldments, such as the AWS *Standard Rules for Field Welding of Steel Storage Tanks*. Other associations publish their own welding specifications. Welded steel tanks for the storage of petroleum products must meet the specifications of the American Petroleum Institute (API), and large welded steel tanks for the storage of water, such as overhead tanks for town and city water supply, are built to the requirements of the American Water Works Association. The latter AWWA tank specifications are very similar to the AWS *Standard Rules for Field Welding of Steel Storage Tanks*. The design and fabrication of a water storage tank to these specifications will be described in Chapter 22.

19.3 the ASME boiler code

The Boiler and Pressure Vessel Code of the American Society of Mechanical Engineers, usually referred to as the "Boiler Code," is a special code, since in some U.S. states and cities and in all the provinces of Canada, it has been incorporated into local statutes and has therefore the force of law.

Until about sixty years ago, the construction and operation of boilers and pressure vessels were unregulated. Boiler explosions were common and were often irresponsibly viewed as one of the inevitable hazards of industrial life, like the frequent railroad accidents of the same period. In 1905 a catastrophic boiler explosion occurred in a shoe factory in Brockton, Massachusetts, killing 58 people and seriously injuring 117 others. As a result of this disaster, the need for steam boiler regulations became suddenly more apparent. In 1907 Massachusetts enacted the first state code for the construction of steam boilers, which of course at that time were riveted, not welded. Ohio passed similar legislation in 1908. Other states and cities followed.

An extensive state of chaos then arose. Regulations varied from state to state. Boiler and pressure vessel manufacturers found it very difficult, even impossible, to construct vessels for use in one state that would be accepted in another. To introduce uniformity, the American Society of Mechanical Engineers was requested "to formulate standard specifications for the construction of steam boilers and other pressure vessels and for their care in service." As is customary in this sort of project, a committee was appointed that represented all interested segments of industry: one boiler insurance engineer, a boiler material manufacturer, two boiler manufacturers, one consulting engineer, and two professors of engineering. As a result of the work of this committee and its advisers, the first uniform boiler code was adopted in 1915.

Because of rapid technological progress, the boiler code must be revised about every three years. The low-pressure riveted boilers of 1915 are now replaced by welded boilers operated at pressures as high as 5000 psi and temperatures up to 1200F, and unfired pressure vessels operate up to 3000 psi and over a temperature range of −350 to 1000F. The boiler code committee must constantly make new decisions on new methods of fabricating, new welding methods, and new materials such as low-alloy steels and titanium. The latest edition of the code is the 1965 edition, divided into seven separate books:

Section   I. *Power Boilers*

       II. *Material Specifications*

      III. *Nuclear Vessels*

      IV. *Low Pressure Heating Boilers*

     VII. *Suggested Rules for Care of Power Boilers*

    VIII. *Unfired Pressure Vessels*

      IX. *Welding Qualifications*

The missing numbers in the sequence are due to the dropping out of obsolete parts of the code, such as *Locomotive Boilers* and others. All in all, the code is a complex document, especially in its provisions on welding. Some insight into the problems of fabricating boilers and pressure vessels may be gained from the description of fabrication and erection procedures in Chapter 22.

The establishment of a uniform boiler code means that a shop authorized under this code to construct boilers and pressure vessels can build such vessels that will be accepted anywhere in the United States or Canada after they have been inspected by an inspector holding a commission from the National Board of Boiler and Pressure Vessel Inspectors.

If a welding shop wishes to build code vessels, application is made to the secretary of the Boiler & Pressure Vessel Committee. The shop facilities and personnel will be inspected by a National Board inspector to determine whether the shop is competent to design and fabricate such vessels. If judged competent, the shop is issued a Certificate of Authorization, permitting it to use the pressure vessel symbols of the code on pressure vessels of its manufacture.

All Canadian provinces and most states require boilers and pressure vessels to be inspected during fabrication by an inspector holding a National Board commission and then stamped with a National Board standard number. Two data sheets for each vessel must be filed with the National Board. One copy is retained by the Board. The other is sent to the administrative authority of the province, state, or city where the boiler is to be used.

For a boiler of American manufacture to be installed in any Canadian province, the following procedure must be followed:

First, the manufacturer must submit in triplicate blueprints and specification sheets for the vessel design to the chief boiler inspector of the province in which the design is to be registered. Boilers cannot be installed until the design is registered. A typical specification sheet is shown in Fig. 132. Among other details, the front and back of the sheet call for information on welding methods, stress relieving, and radiography. The provincial inspector checks the drawings and specifications for conformity to the code and to provincial regulations. If the design is satisfactory, a provincial registration number is assigned to the vessel design. This number must be stamped on the vessel, in addition to the ASME symbol and the National Board stamp. Once the vessel design is approved and registered, any number of vessels of the same design may be built and installed in the province where it is approved.

Second, when a vessel is shipped to the Canadian customer, an Affidavit of Manufacturer for the vessel must be sent to the chief inspector of the province.

There are, however, 10 provinces. If the same vessel design is to be supplied to a customer in another province, the same procedure must

MANUFACTURER'S SPECIFICATIONS
UNFIRED PRESSURE VESSEL
Manufactured to Manitoba Regulations 96/57 and CSA B51 — 1957

Date..........................

Type of Pressure Vessel....................................(To Contain)..........................
(Air, Ammonia, Propane, etc.)

Manufactured by....................................
(Name and address of manufacturer)

Working Pressure....................Temperature............Degrees F.............Dwg. No............

Designs to A.S.M.E. Code year....................Section................Part No............

List registration numbers previously allotted by other provinces........................

Outside diameter............Overall length............Cubic feet capacity............Heating surface............

Outside surface............(Required on Propane and A.A. vessels for checking safety valve)

1. OUTER SHELL AND HEADS:
Note: This section also pertains to simple vessel with no inner shell, tube bank or coil. (See Section 2)

Design Pressure....................................Working Pressure....................

Design temperature....................................Working temperature....................

Inside diameter of shell....................................Min. thickness shell plates....................
(Top, bottom, intermediate, etc.)

Shell material spec. No.....................................
(ASTM-ASME)   (Top, bottom, intermediate, etc.)

Longitudinal joint............Longitudinal joint eff.............Unit stress, psi............
(Single, double or lap welded, etc.)

Heads ....
(Flat, dished, elliptical 2:1, etc.)   (Top, bottom, intermediate, etc.)

Radius of dish....................................Of knuckle............

Inside diameter of heads....................................
(Top, bottom, intermediate, etc.)

Minimum thickness of head plates....................................
(Concave head)   (Convex head)   (Top, bottom, intermediate, etc.)

Head material specification No.....................................
(ASTM-ASME)   (Top, bottom, intermediate, etc.)

Type of head joints....................................
(Single, double or lap welded, etc.)   (Top, bottom, intermediate, etc.)
NOTE: If bolted or riveted construction, give detail sketches with all dimensions, etc., on design drawings.

Corrosion allowance thickness....................................
(On shell)   (On head)

If lined or clad vessel............Lining specification No............
(Thickness of shell lining)   (Of head lining)   (ASTM-ASME)

Safety valve outlets............Required safety valve capacity............
(No. and size)   (ASME, lbs. per hour or cubic feet per minute)

Fusible plug............Drain connection............Manhole............
(Yes or No) (Size)   (Yes or No) (Size)   (Yes or No) (Number)

Number, size and kind of inspection openings....................................
(Free of piping and other attachments)

Nozzles ....
(Type, size, thickness and reinforcing)

Vessel to be stress relieved............In shop............In field............
(Yes or No)   (Yes or No)   (Yes or No)

DL-b-173

(Over)

Fig. 132 Manufacturer's specification sheet as required for registration of pressure vessel designs.

specifications, inspection, and testing of welds
375

Inside diameter of shell .... Minimum thickness shell plate .... Shell material spec. No. ....
.... (ASTM-ASME)

Longitudinal joint .... Longitudinal joint efficiency .... Unit stress per sq. in. ....
(Single, double or lap welded, etc.)

Heads .... Radius of dish .... of knuckle ....
(Flat, dished, elliptical, 2, 1, etc.)

Inside diameter of head .... Minimum thickness of head plates ....
(Concave head)   (Convex head)   (Other heads)

Head material specification No. .... Type of head joints ....
(ASTM-ASME)   (Single, double or lap welded, etc.)

NOTE: If bolted or riveted construction give detail sketches with all dimensions, etc., on
design drawings.

Corrosion allowance thickness ....
(On shell)   (On heads)

If lined or clad vessel .... Lining specification No. ....
(Thickness of shell lining)   (Of head lining)   (ASTM-ASME)

Heating surface of coil or tube bank .... How attached to heads ....
(Square feet)

Number of tubes .... Size .... Thickness or gauge No. .... Spec. No. ....
(ASTM-ASME)

Is separate safety valve from that outer shell required .... Required capacity ....
(Yes or No)   (ASME lbs. per hr. or cu, ft. per min.)

Safety valve outlet .... Fusible plug ....
(Number and size)   (Yes or No)   (Size)

Number, size and kind of inspection openings ....

To be stress relieved .... In shop .... In field ....
(Yes or No)   (Yes or No)   (Yes or No)

To be radiographed .... Spot or complete radiograph ....
(Yes or No)

To be examined by sectioning .... Code year and paragraph this part ....

3. Is the welding procedure to be used registered with the department? .... Regist. date ....
(Yes or No)

   Do welders hold current certificate? ....
(Yes or No)

Remarks, etc ....

....

4. I HEREBY CERTIFY THAT if the design to which the
   foregoing statements pertain is registered by the department, that every vessel manufactured under such
   registration will be constructed strictly in accordance
   with these specifications and related drawings, and
   that each vessel will be stamped in accordance with
   the CSA B51 Canadian regulations for the Construction
   and Inspection of Boilers and Pressure Vessels.

....

(Signature for manufacturer)

....

(Date submitted)   (Leave blank for Department Registration Stamp)

Fig. 132 Cont.

specifications, inspection, and testing of welds
376

be followed. With 10 provinces all requiring forms in triplicate followed by affidavits of manufacturer, all this seems to be reminiscent of O'Flaherty's Test for Completion: "when the weight of paper forms equals the weight of the welded vessel, the vessel is ready to ship." But it is better for 30 file clerks to file 30 forms in 30 file cabinets than to kill 58 people and injure 117 others because of unregulated boilers, and welded boilers of course are used almost everywhere. The registration numbers follow an efficient system. Suppose a vessel is first registered in British Columbia. This most westerly province is number 1 in the registration system, Alberta, the next province east, is number 2, Saskatchewan is number 3, and so on. Suppose British Columbia assigns the number 819 to the design. The full registration number will then be 819.1, the .1 signifying registration only in British Columbia. If the design is next registered in Saskatchewan, the registration number (throughout Canada) becomes 819.13. A registration number 819.1345 indicates registration in British Columbia (1), Saskatchewan (3), Manitoba (4), and Ontario (5), so that the registration number indicates at a glance the provinces in which a competitor does business.

19.4   welding qualification codes for fabricating and contracting firms

Improper welding practices in the fabrication of such structures as ships, buildings, bridges, and pressure vessels may be a serious hazard to life and property. Therefore licensing bodies require prequalification of welding shops and welder operators for such work and the issuance of certificates before shops or welders are allowed to undertake the construction of weldments. Qualification practice, however, varies from area to area and industry to industry. Section IX of the ASME *Boiler and Pressure Vessel Code* sets out the welding qualifications for qualifying welders for pressure vessel work under the code. This qualification code requires three types of tests to establish the ability of the operator:

1. Tension tests for testing weld strength
2. Guided bend tests for testing weld bead ductility
3. A fillet weld test to establish that no cracks or incomplete fusion exist and that the weld contour is satisfactory

In addition, a length of weld must be examined by radiography or sectioning. Section IX of the code must be consulted for full details.

The American Welding Society and the Canadian Welding Bureau, a division of the Canadian Standards Association, have produced codes for qualifying welder operators. These qualifying codes in the two countries are very similar. The AWS procedure is B3.0-41T, *Standard Qualifications Procedure,* and for the CWB is CSA W47-1947, *Welding Qualification Code for Application to Fabricating and Contracting Firms.* Qualification requirements for welder operators under either of these codes closely resemble those of many other welding codes, such as Section IX of the boiler code. Qualification for butt welds calls for:

1. a root-bend test (see Sec. 19.5)
2. a face-bend test
3. a side-bend test
4. or X-ray tests instead of the above

Qualification for fillet welds calls for a fillet weld soundness test. Operators may qualify as

Class O, capable of welding in all positions
Class V, capable of welding in the flat, horizontal, and vertical positions
Class F, capable of welding in the flat butt weld and horizontal fillet weld positions

19.5 the guided bend test
for weld ductility

A complete description of this test may be found in ASTM E190-61T, Section IX of the boiler code, AWS B3.0-41T, or CSA W47-1947. The guided bend test die is shown set up in a testing machine in Fig. 28. The weld specimen should be $1\frac{1}{2}$ in. wide, and any weld reinforcement must be ground away. The specimen is laid horizontally across the supports of the female die with the weld at midspan. The male die is forced down onto the weld specimen until the specimen is bent to a U shape and until a $\frac{1}{32}$-in.-diameter wire cannot be inserted between the specimen and any point on the curvature of the male member of the jig. The convex surface of the specimen is then examined. Any specimen in which after bending a crack or other open defect exceeds $\frac{1}{8}$ in. in length is considered to have failed the test. Cracks on the corners of the specimen are disregarded. Fig. 133 gives details of construction of the guided bend test jig.

To make a face-bend test in this jig, the face of the weld is made the convex side of the bend. For a root-bend test, the root of the weld will be on the convex side. For a side-bend test, the side (root or face) showing the greater defects is made the convex side.

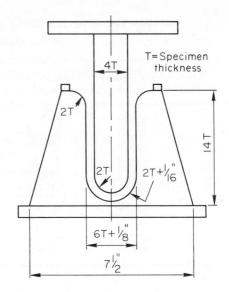

T=Specimen thickness

Fig. 133 Guided bend test jig.

19.6 mild steel arc welding electrodes

Many construction codes specify that mild steel arc-welding electrodes must meet certain standards, usually ASTM A233-58T or an equivalent specification. ASTM A233 is a joint standard of the American Welding Society and the American Society for Testing and Materials. Other similar joint AWS-ASTM standards are A298-55T for stainless steel electrodes and A251-46T for gas welding rods. Still others cover tungsten electrodes, low-alloy steel electrodes, surfacing rods, bare welding wire, and other applicable materials. Lists of band names of welding rods that comply with these requirements are available from such technical societies as the American Welding Society and the Canadian Welding Bureau. Actually, most of the familiar brand names (Fleetweld, etc.) meet these requirements.

Mild steel arc welding electrodes are required to meet three mechanical tests:

1. an all-weld-metal tension test
2. a transverse guided bend test
3. a fillet weld test

The guided bend test procedure has been outlined in Sec. 19.5.

The all-weld-metal tension test requirements for strength and elongation are summarized in the following table, extracted from A233-58T.

specifications, inspection, and testing of welds
379

STRENGTH AND DUCTILITY REQUIREMENTS FOR MANUAL
ARC WELDING RODS

AWS-ASTM Class	Minimum Tensile Strength, psi	Minimum Yield Point, psi	Elongation in 2 In., %
E6010	62,000	50,000	22
E6011	62,000	50,000	22
E6012	67,000	55,000	17
E6013	67,000	55,000	17
E6014	67,000	55,000	17
E6015	67,000	55,000	22
E6018	67,000	55,000	22
E6020	62,000	50,000	25
E6024	67,000	55,000	17
E7018	72,000	60,000	22

In tensile pull tests for qualifying welders, the welder often finds that he can obtain tensile strengths of 70,000 psi with his welds, using E6000 electrodes. According to the table above, this ought not to be too surprising, since many of these rods are guaranteed to give a *minimum* strength of 67,000. Note also that the lower ductilities accompany higher strengths.

The core wire must not vary more than ±0.002 in. from the specified standard size, and the flux covering is required to be closely concentric with the core wire. Under this specification, the manufacturer guarantees that his electrodes conform to this specification, his responsibility being limited to replacement of electrodes failing to meet this specification.

AWS-ASTM Standard A298-55T for stainless steel electrodes requires that stainless steel flux-coated electrodes meet two tests:

1. an all-weld-metal tension test
2. a fillet weld test

Specified minimum strength and elongation levels for such rods, without heat treatment, are these:

AWS-ASTM Class	Minimum Tensile Strength, psi	Elongation in 2 In., %
E308	80,000	35
E308ELC	75,000	35
E309	80,000	35
E310	80,000	30
E316	80,000	30
E316ELC	75,000	30

A wide variety of useful and informative destructive tests are applied to butt welds. Some of these tests have already been discussed, including the notched bar Charpy impact test (ASTM E23-60), the tension test (ASTM E8-61T), and the guided bend test (ASTM E190-61T).

Hardness tests made by taking readings along a line across the weld, from the parent metal on one side through the heat-affected zone, the weld, and the other heat-affected zone to the parent metal on the other side, provide much information on the heat-treating effects of welding. Figure 134 is an example of such a test on hardened aluminum 65S-T6 plate ¼-in. thick welded with 33S filler wire. Because of the softness of this material in the annealed condition, the readings are made in the Vickers Pyramid Hardness scale. This scale uses a diamond pyramid-shaped indentor. The equivalent Rockwell B hardnesses are also shown in the figure, converted from Vickers. The original hardness of the unwelded aluminum sheet is just over Vickers 100, the maximum hardness shown on the hardness curves for MIG and TIG welding. The heat input to the weld anneals the aluminum, reducing the hardness. Hardness readings show that this annealing is greater with TIG than with MIG, though the width of the heat-affected zone is approximately the same with

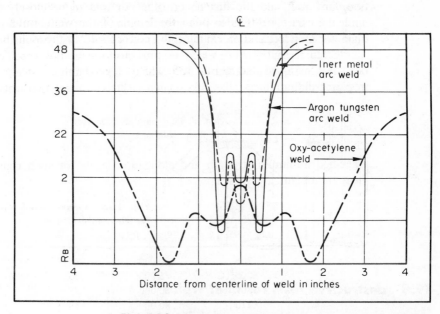

Fig. 134 **Hardness readings across a butt-welded joint in aluminum alloy 6061-T6. (Modified from work of Aluminium Company of Canada, Ltd.)**

specifications, inspection, and testing of welds

both welding methods. The greater heat input of oxyacetylene welding is indicated by the hardness curve for this method, the heat-affected zone exceeding 4 in. The oxyacetylene method also produces more pronounced annealing. The annealing effects of the welding operation indicate that both the weld zone and the heat-affected zone are not as strong as the parent metal is.

In this example the welding operation has resulted in an annealing of the metal. In low-alloy steels, the effect of welding heat in the heat-affected zone is a hardening. If this hardening is too pronounced, it becomes a matter of concern, as it indicates greatly reduced ductility and the possibility of cracking.

All the tests so far mentioned require special test equipment for their performance, but the quality of butt welds may be tested by relatively simple methods also. Most of the simple types of weld tests are fracture tests. The butt weld specimen to be tested may be held in a vise, the weld line just above the vise, and a bend introduced into the plate at the weld line by levering with a crescent wrench or by hammering. A quality weld will take considerable bending before fracturing or cracking. In gauge thicknesses and with most E6000 rods, the sheet should usually bend through 180° in a tight bend without fracture. A variant of this test is the notched-bend or nick-bend test, in which a short notch is sawed into both ends of the weld seam with a hacksaw. After fracture, the weld is examined for any nonuniformity, ductility, incomplete penetration, undercut, slag inclusion, or other defects. Another cracking test applied to butt welds is to bend the length of the weld around a small-diameter mandrel and to examine the convex side of the weld for cracks.

Circumferential butt welds in pipe are sometimes given a tongue-bend test, as illustrated in Fig. 135. This is a good test of root penetration in pipe welding.

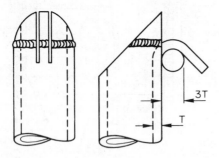

Fig. 135 Tongue bend test for pipe welds.

19.8 destructive tests for fillet welds

Perhaps the commonest test for fillet welds is the fracture test. One leg of the fillet-welded specimen is held in a vise. The other leg is held in the jaws of a crescent wrench, which is used to fracture the weld. The bending direction is such that the root of the fillet is in tension and the face of the weld in compression. After the weld fractures or is bent flat on itself, the fractured surface is examined and should meet the following standards:

1. The weld should indicate penetration into the two plates
2. There should be no evidence of cracks, incomplete root fusion, or gas pockets
3. The two legs of the fillet weld should be equal in length within a $\frac{1}{16}$-in. variation
4. There should be no undercut
5. Convexity or concavity of the weld should not exceed $\frac{1}{16}$ in.

19.9 the controlled thermal severity test (CTS test)

This is a test of sensitivity to cracking of the welded base metal and is therefore only applied to steels with cracking tendencies, such as low-alloy steels.

The general arrangement of the CTS test specimen is shown in Fig. 136. Each specimen contains two test fillet welds, actually lap welds, made

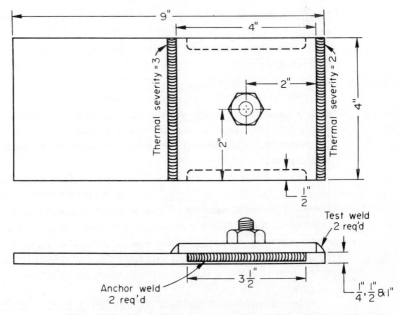

Fig. 136 Test specimen for controlled thermal severity test.

specifications, inspection, and testing of welds

between the two plates as shown. The plates are first machined and bolted together. Then the two anchor welds are placed. These are used to hold the two test plates together with the maximum rigidity, so that the following test welds will not be able to strain and relax any cooling stresses. In the figure the two test plates are $\frac{1}{4}$ in. thick. Of the two test welds, one has a thermal severity number of 2, and the other of 3. A standard series of specimens is made up, one specimen of $\frac{1}{4}$-in. plate, one of $\frac{1}{2}$-in. plate, and a third of 1-in. plate. With these three test specimens, a range of thermal severity numbers is available from 2 to 12. The test welds must have a leg length of $\frac{1}{4}$ in., and the heat input to the test welds must be 32,000 joules per in. (see Sec. 14.2). Since crack-sensitive low-alloy steels are usually welded with 7018 rods, this type of rod is usually employed in the CTS test.

The CTS test is used to determine preheat or postheat temperatures for welding. If the material should show cracks with a thermal severity number of 2, it is crack-sensitive. Should there be no cracking even at the maximum thermal severity number of 12, then there is no risk of cracking during welding operations. Examination of the test welds is done simply by sawing through them.

19.10 quality control
of resistance welds

Destructive tests are considerably more common in the quality control of resistance welds than nondestructive tests are, since the standard nondestructive tests discussed in the following chapter are not well-suited to the assessment of resistance welds. Radiography, however, has occasional use in the examination of spot welds.

Resistance welds are usually examined by sawing through the weld and inspecting for such defects as penetration, porosity, cracking, weld expulsion, and sheet separation. Such an examination is termed a macroexamination, as opposed to a microexamination under a low-power microscope.

In a *shear test* two sheets are spot-welded together and the weld pulled to failure in a testing machine. The resistance weld is tested in shear. The spot weld or welds must be located in the center of the overlap of the sheets for this test. There is always some variation in the shear strength of spot welds, and a deviation from the average shear strength of $\pm 20\%$ is generally allowed. Acceptance is always based on more than one test. Recommended minimum dimensions for test pieces are given in the table.

In the *twist test*, the two sheets, joined with a single spot weld, are twisted apart by rotating one sheet about an axis through the spot weld.

RECOMMENDED MINIMUM DIMENSIONS OF TEST SAMPLES FOR SHEAR TESTING OF SPOT WELDS

Material	In Inches Minimum Width	Minimum Length
up to 0.031	⅝	3
0.032–0.045	¾	4
0.046–0.059	1	4
0.060–0.070	1¼	5
0.071–0.100	1½	5
over 0.100	2	6

This test gives a good indication of weld size, strength, and ductility. Strength and ductility are assessed from the angle of twist necessary to cause failure and the torque required for failure. Spot welds with good ductility will show a rough and torn fracture, whereas a smooth fracture usually indicates low ductility.

A common test of spot welds is the *peel test*. A test specimen with about fifteen spaced spot welds is made up. One sheet is peeled off the other, one spot at a time, with pliers or other suitable tools.

Sectioning of the weld and macroexamination is used for the quality control of seam welds as well as spot welds, examination being made for the same defects that may be found in spot welds. Peel tests and shear tests are likewise applied to seam welds. In addition, a seam weld test for gas tightness or water tightness may be required. The test for this purpose is the *pillow test*. Two sheets of sufficient area are selected, both of the same size. A pipe connection is brazed to the center of one of the sheets. The two sheets are then stacked one on top of the other and seam-welded all around. Air or water is then pumped between the two sheets through the pipe connection. The pressure may be raised to any required value, or increased until rupture occurs. Any convenient method of leak detection may be used if needed.

Figure 137 is a "Spot Welding Schedule and Test Report" required for spot and seam welding to aircraft specifications. All machine settings and sequences must be recorded at the top of the form. In the lower left-hand corner the results of macro- and microexamination are recorded. Destructive shear tests are reported in the lower right-hand corner.

19.11 welding procedures

A welding "procedure" is a written specification stating how the welding shall be done. Procedures are frequently called for, either by standard

BRISTOL AERO-INDUSTRIES LIMITED
WINNIPEG DIVISION
SPOT WELDING
SCHEDULE & TEST REPORT

SCHEDULE NO. R.W. _____ TEST NO. _____
TYPE OF TEST _____ DATE _____
MACHINE NO. _____ [ ] TIME _____

MACHINE _____ CONTROL: _____

PRESSURE MODES

1 SINGLE HIGH	2 SINGLE LOW	3 WELD & FORGE (DUAL)	4 CYLINDER	5 PRE COMP. & WELD	6 PRE COMP. WELD & FORGE (TRIPLE)

TIME SEQUENCES

PRE COMP. OR SQUEEZE	WELD PRESSURE DELAY	FORGE PRESSURE DELAY	PRE HEAT	WELD HEAT	POST HEAT	CHILL	TEMPER HEAT	HOLD	OFF

MACHINE SETTINGS

HEAT

WYE/DELTA _____
LOW/HIGH _____
50 KVA PACKS USED _____
8 TAP SWITCHES A [ ] B [ ]
PRE HEAT LEVEL _____ %
WELD HEAT LEVEL _____ %
POST HEAT LEVEL _____ %
TEMPER HEAT LEVEL _____ %
CURRENTS _____ (Rms) Amps
ADDED SECONDARY RESISTANCE _____ μ Ω

FORCE (LBS.)

CYLINDER FORCE _____
BELLOWS FORCE _____
BUCKING FORCE _____
WELDING FORCE _____
PRESSURE MODE _____

TIME (CYCLES)

SQUEEZE _____
WELD PRESSURE DELAY _____
FORGE PRESSURE DELAY _____
PRE HEAT _____
WELD HEAT (INC. PRE HEAT) _____
POST HEAT _____
CHILL _____
TEMPER HEAT _____
HOLD _____
OFF _____

ELECTRODES

	R.W.M.A. ALLOY	DIAMETER	CONTOUR	COOLING
UPPER				
LOWER				

ELECTRODE HOLDERS UPPER _____ LOWER _____
REMARKS _____

PART & OPERATION

_____
_____
_____
_____

SURFACE PREPARATION _____

MATERIAL UPPER _____ LOWER _____
SPEC. _____
GAUGE _____
CONDITION _____

TEST RESULTS

WELDING SPECIFICATION _____

MACRO SECTIONS

	WELD DIAMETER	PENETRATION UPPER	PENETRATION LOWER
1	_____	_____ %	_____ %
2	_____	_____ %	_____ %
3	_____	_____ %	_____ %
AV	_____	_____ %	_____ %

REQ. _____ MIN. _____ TO _____ %
DEFECTS _____

TEST SATISFACTORY / UNSATISFACTORY

SPOT INDENTATION _____ INS.

SHEAR TEST SPECIMENS (LBS.)

	OBTAINED		REQUIRED
1	_____	AVERAGE	_____
2	_____	MINIMUM	_____
3	_____	REQUIRED	
AV	_____	CERTIFICATION SCHEDULE	
		AVERAGE	_____

VARIATION = $\dfrac{\text{RANGE}}{\text{AVERAGE}}$ = _____ =

SHEET SEPARATION _____ INS.

REMARKS _____
SIGNED - B.A.W. _____ R.C.A.F. _____

2015 MAR/65

Fig. 137 Spot welding schedule and test report.

codes and specifications or by consulting engineers, or may simply be written by someone in the shop in order to control or produce consistent weld quality. By and large, the ability to set up and follow a welding

specifications, inspection, and testing of welds
386

procedure is an indication of shop and supervisory competence in welding. A shop that cannot write up a procedure cannot be trusted to do critical welding. A simple example of a welding procedure might be the following:

1. *Process*

   The welding shall be done by the_____process [shielded metal arc, metal inert gas, etc.], using butt welds.

2. *Base Metal*

   The base metal shall conform to specifications of [ASTM number, etc.]. Base metal shall not exceed_____in thickness.

3. *Filler Metal*

   The filler metal shall conform to [AWS specification, rod numbers, etc.] Electrode size shall not exceed_____in diameter.

4. *Position*

   All welding shall be done in the _____[flat, etc.] position.

5. *Preheat.*

   [Specify preheat requirements and method.]

6. *Edge Preparation*

   The edges or surfaces to be joined shall be prepared by shearing, grinding, or flame cutting. The gap between the plates to be welded shall not exceed half the thickness of the plate. Surfaces to be welded shall be cleaned of all oil, grease, and excessive scale or rust. [Edge preparation may also be shown by means of attached sketches.]

7. *Electrical Characteristics*

   [a.c., ACHF, DCRP, DCSP, etc. Machine characteristics if necessary.]

8. *Cleaning of Passes*

   All slag or flux remaining on any bead shall be completely removed before laying down the next bead.

9. *Defects*

   Any cracks or blowholes that appear on the surface of any bead shall be removed by chipping, grinding, or Arcair gouging before depositing the next bead.

10. *Heat Treatment*

    [Stress relieving, etc. if required, temperature requirements.]

PROBLEMS

1 Explain the difference between a destructive and a nondestructive test. Which is the more expensive to perform?

2 Explain the purpose of (a) plans, (b) specifications, and how the two complement each other.

3 How could you rewrite the following specification clause so that it was clear, meaningful, and interpretable?
"Butt welds shall be of adequate strength."

4 Do the same for the following clause:
"Fillet welds must have a proper contour."

5 What is a "shop drawing"?

6 Boiler explosions still occur. Most are caused by burner and fuel accidents of one sort of another. Few are due to welding and fabrication deficiencies. Explain why.

7 In a tension test on an all weld-metal sample of E6012 rods (Sec. 19.6), how long will the 2-in.-thick length of the sample be after straining to destruction?

8 Try writing a simple welding procedure for the butt welding of ¼-in. mild steel plate using E6011 electrodes with the shielded metal arc process. Specify a rod diameter, current capacity of welding machine, etc.

20.1 *simple nondestructive tests*

Nondestructive testing, often abbreviated NDT, has seen remarkable growth in use and techniques since World War II, and in that time has become an exacting and sometimes difficult technology. In actuality though, nondestructive testing is as old as the human race and is a technique constantly employed by all mankind. The housewife who squeezes the grapefruit on the supermarket shelf, the railroad employee who taps car wheels with a hammer to listen for the characteristic ring of the wheel, the machinist who tests for a cracked grinding wheel by tapping it with the handle of a hammer, the doctor who tests your reflexes (medical inspections must necessarily be nondestructive), and the automobile buyer who looks for ripples in the car roof to see if the car has been rolled are all typical everyday examples of nondestructive inspection. Many of these simple nondestructive tests are visual. Visual tests do not usually require complex equipment, and may require no equipment whatever beyond a sharp pair of eyes and a discerning and experienced mind. Nevertheless the human eye is restricted in its use to a very narrow band of electromagnetic radiation, and other nondestructive testing instruments must be employed to extend the capabilities of the eye, particularly in the inspection of materials opaque to visible light.

In addition to such obvious devices as improved lighting, a variety of special optical instruments are also used:

1. Microscopes to improve the resolving power of the eye
2. Borescopes, which are special small-diameter devices for inserting into long narrow tubes to inspect their internal surfaces

NONDESTRUCTIVE

TESTING

OF WELDS

20

3. Closed-circuit television for inspection in hazardous areas
4. Cameras to make a permanent record of what the eye sees

Finally photoelectric cells and other photosensitive devices may be used as substitutes for the human eye in such operations as automatic opening of doors and automatic flame cutting from draftsmen's drawings.

20.2 welding defects

The business of nondestructive testing is primarily a search for defects. Since materials contain a great many types of defects, an important part of the interpretation of the test results is the identification of the defect. Defects may be said to arise from three sources:

1. *Material defects*, put into the original raw material during its initial processing. An example of a material defect would be a silicon or aluminum oxide inclusion in a steel plate resulting from the deoxidation of the steel with silicon or aluminum.
2. *Processing defects*, which arise from fabrication of the part. Familiar examples would be undercut or slag inclusions in a weld.
3. *Service defects*, which arise from the use of the material in service. Service defects include such items as fatigue cracks or corrosion pits.

The following remarks serve to define some of the defects encountered in welding operations.

1. Material defects

(a) Coarse grain size or grain growth. Grain growth has been noted as a characteristic defect in the welding of the ferritic stainless steels—a processing defect. Coarse grain size may also be a defect in the original material. Fine-grained metals have better toughness or resistance to impact and are somewhat stronger than similar coarse-grained metals. Determination of relative grain size may be done by the nondestructive method of eddy current testing.
(b) Segregation. Segregation means that some regions of the material are enriched in an alloy ingredient, whereas other regions are impoverished. There may, for example, be variations in carbon content or in phosphorus content throughout a steel bar or plate.
(c) Blowholes. Blowholes occur in castings (most welds are castings). These are cavities caused by gas entrapped during the solidification of the metal that can occur during the freezing of weld metal. They may be detected by radiography. Another type of porosity found in frozen metals are pinholes, distributed very small blow-

Fig. 138 Radiograph of an aircraft magnesium casting showing porosity defects. Porosity will be found in the two arms of the wye. The light area in the middle of the casting is a steel insert.

holes. Figure 138 is a radiograph of an aircraft magnesium fitting rejected for porosity in the two arms of the Y.

(d) Pipe in wrought metals has become rare. It is usually found as a long tight crack running the length of a bar or plate. When steel or any other metal cools in the ingot mold, the metal lying against the walls of the mold freezes first. The freezing of steel produces a linear contraction of about 2%. This shrinkage must occur in the last metal to freeze, which is in the center of the ingot, and as a result a shrinkage depression appears in the middle of the top surface of the ingot. If the piped ingot is then rolled into bar, the result is a long fine crack, developed from the original "pipe."

(e) Inclusions. The word "inclusions" as applied to metals means impurities, foreign substances, or nonmetallic materials such as ceramic materials in the metal. Such nonmetallic inclusions as carbides or graphite flakes in cast iron are purposely placed in the metal and are not considered to be defects. Metal inclusions are usually sulfides, oxides, or silicates. Figure 139 shows copper oxide inclusions in cast copper. An inclusion, because it is not an integral part of the metal, has the same effect as a crack. Quenching cracks may start from inclusions if a steel is heat-treated.

nondestructive testing of welds
391

Fig. 139 Copper oxide inclusions in cast copper

2. **Processing defects**

   (a) Lack of penetration. This shows up in a radiograph as a straight line showing the edges of the joined plates, as in Fig. 140. A crack would not appear as a straight line and could not be confused with lack of penetration.

   (b) Cracks. For an example of a crack shown in a radiograph, see Fig. 141.

   (c) Undercut. Discovered by visual examination.

   (d) Crater crack. A surface crack in a weld crater.

   (e) Heat-treating crack.

   (f) Porosity.

   (g) Slag inclusion.

   (h) Arc burn. Discovered by visual examination.

   (i) Distortion.

   (j) Residual or internal stresses. These are produced in the course of fabrication as a result of cold working or rapid cooling. Such stresses always accompany fusion-welding operations but may be removed by stress-relieving heat treatments. Nondestructive methods of revealing residual stresses are available but are not yet in use in industry as routine and standard methods of inspection.

3. **Service defects**

   (a) Fatigue. This is the cracking or failure of metals under repeated applications of stress. Contributory factors to fatigue failure may be inclusions and stress concentrations due to changes of section, holes, fillet welds, and undercuts.

Fig. 140 Radiograph of a butt weld in quarter-inch steel plate showing incomplete penetration.

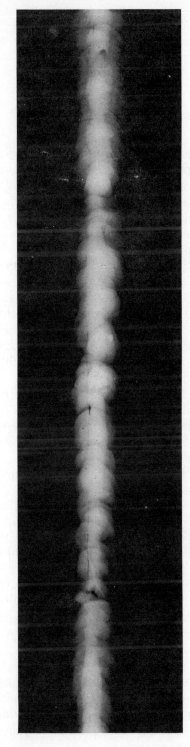

Fig. 141 Radiograph of a cracked weld in steel plate. The crack did not extend to the surface and therefore could be found only by radiography or ultrasonic testing. The narrow crack is difficult to discern in the radiograph.

(b) Corrosion. The thinning and loss of metal due to corrosion may be periodically examined by the method of ultrasonic testing.

20.3 liquid penetrant inspection

This method may be used for the detection of any flaws, cracks, or holes that extend to the surface of the work and may also be used for leak detection in tanks. Liquid penetrants will often reveal flaws not apparent to visual inspection and are especially useful in locating grinding cracks, weld cracks, pinholes, and fatigue cracks.

Most penetrants are proprietary compounds. However, homemade formulations can be put together to do a tolerably good job, though such mixtures are not quite so sensitive as the commercial brands. A simple penetrant test uses kerosene and talc (even finely ground chalk will do). The surface to be tested is first cleaned with any convenient cleaning compound and dried. A thin coat of kerosene or other penetrating fluid is applied. A short time is allowed for the kerosene to penetrate into any defects by capillary action. The penetrant is removed from the surface with a cloth, leaving only penetrant in the cracks. A thin coat of talc or chalk is next sprinkled over the area. After about half a minute, the penetrant liquid will begin to penetrate into the white powder from the cracks, again by capillary action. In the area of a crack the powder will be somewhat yellowed because of absorption of the penetrant, thus disclosing the crack. This staining effect will not persist for more than a short time if kerosene is used, since this material evaporates rather quickly. The sensitivity of the test will be improved if the metal is warmed to reduce the viscosity of the penetrant. To improve the color contrast, a drop of red alizarin dye may be added to the penetrant liquid.

Proprietary dye penetrants all contain red dyes. Among those with which the author is acquainted are Chexall by Sperry Products, Spotcheck by Magnaflux, and Dy-Chek by Turco Products, Inc. Most of these companies offer a variety of dye penetrants to suit different requirements, for example, dye penetrants for the examination of high-nickel alloys must be sulfur free. The general-purpose penetrants usually have a flash point of about 200 F; nevertheless these materials must be stored and used with reasonable care, as there is a degree of fire hazard. The vapors from penetrants may also be mildly toxic, so that if these materials are used in any great quantity, ventilation must be provided. In the rare worker, the oil base of penetrants causes an allergy, which can be prevented by wearing rubber gloves.

Most users of dye penetrants on a limited scale prefer to use these materials in aerosol cans pressurized with Freon-12. Small quantities can

Fig. 142 Set of dye penetrant spray cans.

be bought by the case or in small complete kits. Figure 142 shows the aerosol cans of one supplier, including the cleaner, penetrant, and developer. Application of dye penetrants takes the following sequence when using aerosol cans.

1. Clean the surface. Surface soil will absorb the penetrant and thus mask any defects; grease and oils will prevent the penetrant from entering the flaws. Preliminary ultrasonic cleaning is very useful if equipment for it is available. The cleaner is sprayed over the surface, allowed to remain in place for a short time to dissolve any film or soil, and then wiped off with a clean cloth. This operation can be repeated if necessary. After cleaning, the surface is allowed a brief interval in which to dry off. Scratch brushing or buffing are not suitable cleaning methods, as these processes tend to close up small flaws.

2. Apply the penetrant. The penetrant is then sprayed. If it does not wet the surface, the cleaning must be repeated. The penetrant is pulled into the flaws by capillary action. Warming the surface assists this action, but warming the penetrant is not always recommended since some penetrants have low flash points. The penetrant is allowed to remain on the surface for a short time to ensure penetration. For the very best sensitivity, the penetrant is sometimes applied more than once to the surface. The penetrant is then wiped or washed from the surface in accord with the manufacturer's instructions, leaving penetrant only in the flaws. Typical penetration times are 2 to 5 min, though longer times may be needed at low temperatures. Complete removal of the penetrant from the surface is necessary to prevent false indications.

3. Apply the developer. Finally a thin coat of developer is sprayed on the surface. This coat must be uniform and even, without heavy laps or runs to mask flaw indications. The developer, which is white, has a blotting-paper action on the penetrant left in the flaws, drawing it out by capillary action so that a red blush appears in the area of the

defect. Warming of the part will assist in withdrawing the penetrant into the developer.

The proper method of spraying from an aerosol can is to hold the nozzle of the can about 10 in. from the surface and spray at right angles to the surface, laying down a thin uniform deposit. Before spraying, the can should be shaken thoroughly to ensure uniform mixing of the contents. Clogging of the aerosol nozzle is a rather common trouble. A clogged nozzle may be cleared by spraying a short burst on an available surface. If this does not clear the nozzle, it must be removed and the passages cleaned from both ends with a wire.

Aerosol cans should not be stored in hot areas. The empty cans should not be incinerated, because they may explode.

Leak testing Dye penetrants make excellent leak testers for tanks with wall thicknesses not more than approximately ¼ in. No pressure is required. Leak testing is begun by cleaning the outside surface of the tank. The penetrant is sprayed on the inside surface. Then the developer is applied to the outside. The penetrant can pass through a leak in metal ¼ in. thick in about 1 min. This leak test must not be performed after a hydrostatic leak test, because water from the hydrostatic test will block small leaks in the metal, thus making penetrant action impossible. Even an air pressure test may blow moisture into a flaw and prevent dye penetration.

Dye penetrants may also be used for testing the completeness of bonding in brazed joints.

The ASTM procedure E165-60T contains an excellent discussion of liquid penetrant methods.

20.4 *fluorescent penetrants*

Fluorescent penetrants are generally used for the same purposes as dye penetrants. A fluorescent dye is used instead of a red dye. The method of applying a fluorescent penetrant is much the same as that used for dye penetrants. Cleaner is first applied as previously described, then the penetrant, and finally the developer. Disclosure of flaws is made by illuminating the surface with a special mercury bulb producing ultraviolet "black light" with a wavelength in the range of 3400 to 3800 A. This shortwave illumination causes fluorescence of the penetrant, usually yellow green. Viewing is best done in a darkened area, although the fluorescence is visible in daylight.

Figure 143 is a photograph of the Zyglo brand penetrant spray cans with the mercury lamp and its transformer.

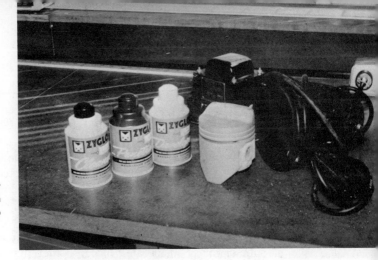

Fig. 143 Set of fluorescent penetrant spray cans, with "black light" mercury lamp and transformer.

20.5 magnetic particle inspection

The magnetic particle inspection method is limited to ferromagnetic materials, which means in effect that it is chiefly confined to steels and cast irons. The basic operation consists first of magnetization of the workpiece with a powerful magnetic field of more than a thousand amp-turns. Then the surface is covered with a thin layer of magnetic powder, either black iron or red iron oxide, or fluorescent. The powder may be applied dry or suspended in a low-viscosity liquid. If there is a small crack, the powerful magnetic field in the workpiece establishes a north magnetic pole on one side of the crack and a south pole on the other. The magnetic powder is attracted to these poles and thereby marks the crack. The layer of powder may be blown off the surface in an area where there are no cracks, but will be held to the surface at the crack. For a permanent record, a piece of Scotch tape may be laid over the powder and the powder thus picked up on the tape.

The surface must be clean and reasonably smooth, especially if subsurface cracks are to be detected, although the method is not reliable if defects are any great distance below the surface. Defects deeper than half an inch below the surface are hardly likely to be found at all. The workpiece may have to be magnetized in two directions at right angles to each other in order to ensure that a magnetic field is produced approximately at right angles to a possible crack. Tapping of the workpiece will help to disclose the particle pattern.

The powerful magnetic field required is produced by a low-voltage transformer that can produce 600 to 1000 amp or more. A typical magnetic particle machine is the Magnaflux machine shown in Fig. 144. The current output from this machine can be controlled by a three-position switch, maximum current being 900 amp. But like an electric

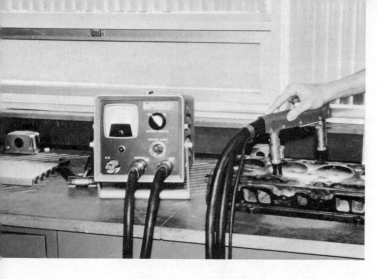

Fig. 144 Magnafluxing an engine block with a prod attachment and direct current.

stove with a five-heat switch, this machine is not often used at less than maximum current. Heavy #0000 cables connect to the front of the machine, and at the other end connect to the two-contact prod shown in the photograph. The workpiece is actually a short circuit across the output of the Magnaflux machine. A contact switch to operate the machine is mounted on the prod. Both a.c. and d.c. are available, the direct current being produced by a half-wave rectifier. Direct current is used for the detection of subsurface cracks, and alternating current is used to find surface cracks, since the skin effect of 60-cycle current concentrates more of the current at the surface. The Magnaflux machine may be likened to a high-current, low open-circuit voltage, short duty cycle welding transformer. Indeed, welding machines are often used as current sources for magnetic particle inspection, so that in effect the welding machine can inspect its own work, a practice that we do not wisely entrust to human operators.

When magnafluxing a workpiece, the prods must contact the work before the current is turned on, because any arcing of the high current to the work will cause burns or heat treating. Another precaution in this type of inspection concerns the short duty cycle of the machine, only about 25%.

An alternate method of magnetizing the workpiece is to wind one of the cables around it or even to bring one cable close to it. Cable-produced magnetic fields are often used when a welding machine is used as a power source. A typical welding machine may have an output of only 300 amp, which may be insufficient for magnetic particle inspection. By winding four turns of a cable about the workpiece, a magnetic field of 1200 amp-turns can be produced.

Occasionally false indications are given by this inspection method. If there are variations of magnetic permeability in the workpiece or differences in carbon content, a magnetic particle indication may be given at the boundary between these variations. A line indication may also be produced at the point where a metallic object has been dragged across the workpiece, or at a flash-butt weld.

A magnetic particle test leaves the workpiece magnetized. In some cases such residual magnetism cannot be tolerated. Engine blocks must not be permanently magnetized, for if they are, they will attract any small magnetic particles in the lubricating oil, and the consequences will be scoring and wear of the block. Residual magnetism in aircraft structures may cause compass error or upset sensitive electrical instruments. The best method of demagnetizing a workpiece is to subject it to a 60-cycle magnetic field that is slowly decreased in strength. The actual procedure is to connect the cable to the a-c connections of the machine and wind two turns of one cable around the workpiece. The prod contacts may be shorted on any convenient piece of metal. The workpiece is then slowly withdrawn out of this solenoid coil, or the coils slowly moved off the workpiece.

The magnetic particle method may be used for the disclosure of a variety of defects in welds, such as incomplete fusion, porosity, slag inclusions, and others. Probably its most important use is in the testing of fillet welds. The ASTM Standards E109-57T, Dry Particle Inspection, and E138-58T, Wet Magnetic Particle Inspection, together with E125-56T, Reference Photographs for Magnetic Particle Indications, present an excellent review of this inspection method.

20.6 eddy current testing

Just as the electron beam and ultrasonic devices may be used both for welding and for the testing of welds, so may eddy currents be used both for induction welding and weld testing. Eddy current testing, however, is as yet largely confined to the production line testing of such materials as tubing and pipe, although small portable units are available for purposes other than weld testing. The method is not yet in use for field testing of weldments as standard practice.

When a coil carrying alternating current at high frequency is brought close to an electrically conductive material, eddy currents are produced in the material by induction. The magnitude of the induced eddy currents will be influenced by many factors:

1. The magnetizing current
2. The number of energizing turns
3. The frequency
4. The electrical conductivity of the material
5. The magnetic permeability of the material

6. The shape of the material
7. The relative position of the coil and the material
8. The cross section of the material
9. Any cold working or heat treating given to the material (affecting its conductivity and permeability to the magnetic field)
10. The grain size of the material
11. Flaws in the material

Suppose the butt welds of welded tubing must be inspected by the eddy current method. One arrangement is to pass the tubing through an energizing coil to induce an a-c eddy current in the tube. In addition to the energizing coil, a search coil (also called a pickup coil, reading coil, etc.) circles the tubing. The eddy currents induced in the tubing will themselves induce eddy currents in the search coil, which can then be connected to a sensitive current meter or voltmeter to indicate the induced current or voltage in the coil. If the butt weld throughout a length of welded tubing is sound, a certain level of current or voltage is induced in the search coil. Suppose, however, that there is a small flaw at one point in the butt weld. This flaw will slightly distort the magnetic field induced in the tubing by the energizing coil. When this flaw passes within range of the search coil, the needle on the search meter will move.

It has already been suggested that the search coil may report many factors other than flaws, such as differences in diameter and cross-sectional area, relative position of coil and tubing, etc. The actual eddy current tester must therefore be adjusted to report only those conditions that are of interest to the inspector, since a generalized report covering a score of conditions might be so powerful as to mask the very defects he is looking for.

One method of restricting the number of variables that the eddy current tester will detect is to vary the frequency in the energizing coil. The higher the frequency, the greater will be the skin effect, and thus surface conditions can be detected. Conditions well below the surface will not be reported by the eddy current tester, whereas surface defects will be exaggerated by the increased reactance produced by the higher frequency. Eddy current testers use frequencies in the range of about 1 to 300 kc per sec.

In addition to flaw detection, eddy current testers are used to detect variations in grain size, hardness, ductility, heat treatment, electrical conductivity, alloy composition, and eccentricity and wall thickness in tubing. These instruments will also measure the thicknesses of paint coatings, anodizing, porcelain enameling, or chromium plating, to accuracies as high as 0.000001 in. in some instances. On production line work, pipe and tubing can be examined at rates up to perhaps 3000 ft per min. Flaws as closely spaced as 0.1 in. can be detected at slower rates of 50 ft per min or more.

Ultrasonics is the science or the use of acoustic energy at or above 20,000 cycles per sec. For testing purposes, frequencies from 1 to 10 megacycles are employed, 2¼ megacycles being a commonly used frequency. Generally the smallest defect that can be discovered by ultrasonic testing has roughly the same order of magnitude as the length of the sound wave used. Hence the use of very high acoustic frequencies with their corresponding short wavelengths, as in this example.

What is the approximate size of the smallest defect that can be detected in a stainless steel plate by ultrasonic testing at 2¼ megacycles? We must make the convenient assumption that the minimum detectable defect is the length of the acoustic wave in stainless steel. The velocity of sound in stainless steel must be looked up in a handbook.

frequency × wavelength = velocity of sound in stainless steel

$$2{,}250{,}000 \times L = 226{,}000 \text{ in./sec}$$

$$L = \frac{1}{10} \text{ in.}$$

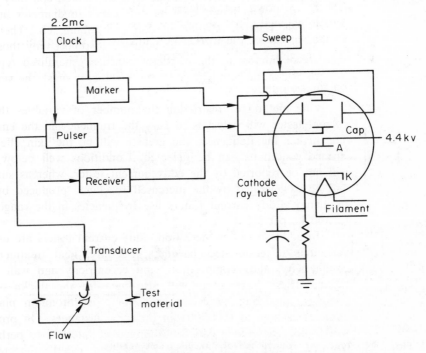

Fig. 145 Schematic diagram of an ultrasonic flaw detector. (Branson Instruments Sonoray 5)

nondestructive testing of welds
401

and the smallest detectable defect is assumed to be this size. This, however, is only a "ball-park" figure. Very often defects as small as $\frac{1}{32}$ in. can be detected at this frequency.

Figure 145 is a block diagram of an ultrasonic flaw detection instrument, actually the Branson Instruments Sonoray 5. The "clock" circuit is a $2\frac{1}{4}$ megacycle electronic oscillator. This sends out $2\frac{1}{4}$-megacycle alternating current to the piezoelectric search crystal, which converts the electric energy to $2\frac{1}{4}$-megacycle acoustic energy. This acoustic wave is fired into the material to be tested. If there is a flaw such as a crack within the material, the acoustic wave reflects off the surface of the crack and returns to the search crystal as an echo. The echo comes from the *near* side of the crack, not the far side. The transmitter wave by this time is shut off in the ultrasonic generator so that the crystal can "listen" for echoes. The returning echo cyclically strains the crystal, which then responds by generating alternating current in the same frequency that it receives from the echo pulse. This crystal-generated a-c voltage is then amplified and applied to the horizontal plates of a cathode ray oscilloscope. A small defect returns a small echo, which appears as a short vertical pip on the scope, whereas a large defect will appear as a large pip.

Several types of acoustic waves are used for ultrasonic testing. These are shown in the diagrams of Fig. 146. The *straight beam* of Fig. 146 is a longitudinal or straight wave sent into the work perpendicular to the surface of the work. With this wave, the transmitting crystal and the receiving crystal can be one and the same, unless the transmitting crystal is placed on the top surface of the work and the receiving crystal on the bottom surface. In the latter two-crystal method, the presence of

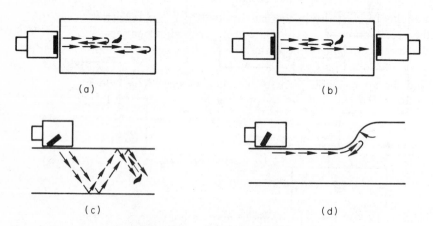

Fig. 146 Types of acoustic waves for ultrasonic testing.
(a) Longitudinal wave with reflection, (b) through transmission,
(c) shear wave, (d) surface wave.

nondestructive testing of welds

a flaw must be detected by a loss of acoustic power due to the interruption of a defect in the path of the acoustic wave. Under the stimulus of the acoustic wave, the vibrating particles of the metal move back and forth parallel to the path of the beam.

The *angle beam* or shear-wave method sends an acoustic wave into the work at an angle of about 45°. This wave bounces back and forth off the top and bottom surfaces of the workpiece searching for flaws. The echo will return by the same method of shear waves. In the shear-wave method, the vibrating particles of the metal vibrate at right angles to the path of the acoustic beam.

If the acoustic beam is sent out at a small angle to the surface of the workpiece, then *surface waves* are propagated over the surface of the material. Such waves behave somewhat like waves on the surface of a liquid, and the motion of the particles of the metal, like those in water waves, is both parallel and perpendicular to the wave. Two types of surface waves are used for ultrasonic flaw detection: Rayleigh waves and Lamb waves. If the thickness of the material is large with respect to the acoustic wavelength, the wave will be a Rayleigh wave, but if the material thickness is of the order of the wavelength, then the wave is a Lamb wave. Rayleigh waves travel at a velocity that is about 90% of the shear wave velocity in the material, and Lamb wave velocities depend on the material thickness and the frequency.

The velocity of a longitudinal acoustic wave in a solid material is given approximately by the following formula:

$$v = \sqrt{\frac{144\,Eg}{w}}$$

where v = acoustic velocity in feet per second
E = modulus of elasticity in the usual pounds per square inch
g = the acceleration of gravity, 32.2 feet per second per sec
w = the specific weight of the material in pounds per cubic foot

Example Find the approximate velocity of sound in steel. The modulus of elasticity is 30×10^6 psi, and the specific weight is closely 500 lb per cu ft.

$$v = \sqrt{\frac{144 \times 30 \times 10^6 \times 32}{500}} = 12 \times 1000 \sqrt{\frac{30 \times 32}{500}}$$
$$= 16{,}800$$

The actual value is 18,800 fps. This formula may be considered accurate only if a straight beam is sent down the length of a bar with a diameter not greater than the acoustic wavelength. Note that the formula applies only to a straight beam. Shear waves have velocities of about 40% of the straight beam velocity.

ULTRASONIC VELOCITY

Material	Straight Beam Velocity, ips	Angle Beam Velocity, ips	Surface Wave Velocity, ips	E	Specific Gravity
air	13,000				1.3×10^{-3}
lube oil	55,000				0.92
water	59,000				1.00
carbon tetra-chloride	37,000				1.6
glass	222,000	129,000	116,000	9×10^6	2.3
polystyrene	92,000	44,000	40,000	0.75×10^6	0.90
polyethylene	77,000	21,000	19,000	0.1×10^6	0.92
plexiglass	105,000	43,000	39,000	0.5×10^6	1.2
nylon	103,000	42,000	38,000	0.5×10^6	1.1
aluminum, pure	240,000	120,000	110,000	10×10^6	2.6
yellow brass	185,000	85,000	76,000	15×10^6	8.45
copper	182,000	84,000	76,000	16×10^6	8.9
lead	77,000	25,000	23,000	2.4×10^6	11.3
magnesium	227,000	120,000	108,000	6.5×10^6	1.75
monel	210,000	107,000	97,000	26×10^6	8.9
nickel	237,000	118,000	105,000	30×10^6	8.9
steels	225,000	120,000	110,000	29×10^6	7.9
tungsten	205,000	113,000	105,000	60×10^6	19.25
zirconium	180,000	102,000	96,000	15×10^6	6.5

20.8 interface behavior
of acoustic waves

If the ultrasonic probe is simply laid against the surface of a metal, even in the event of a flaw it is possible that no echoes will appear on the scope. If, however, the surface of the metal is coated with a film of water or oil, then an echo will disclose the flaw. This film of fluid is termed a *couplant*: it couples the probe and the metal together so that the sound pulse can pass into the material with sufficient power to return an echo. The explanation for the requirement of a couplant is as follows.

When the acoustic beam strikes the metal surface, it behaves like a beam of light: some of the acoustic energy is reflected away by the surface, and some is transmitted into the surface. The amount of energy reflected off the surface is determined by the acoustic impedance of the two materials, couplant and metal, and it is desirable to reduce the amount of reflected energy to the practical minimum. The acoustic impedance of a material is the product of the acoustic velocity v in the material and the density of the material. The ratio of the reflected energy to the supplied energy is given by

$$\frac{E_{ref}}{E_{supp}} = \left(\frac{d_1 v_1 - d_2 v_2}{d_1 v_1 + d_2 v_2}\right)^2$$

where d = density and v = velocity. Of the supplied energy, what is not reflected will be transmitted into the material being tested.

Without any other couplant, a thin layer of air will couple the probe to the work. To see what amount of energy is transmitted to a steel plate without a couplant (other than air), use d_1 and v_1 for air and d_2 and v_2 for steel. To obtain an order-of-magnitude or "ball-park" notion of how much energy is reflected and lost, we shall simply use specific gravity for density, from the ultrasonic velocity table.

$$\frac{E_{ref}}{E_{supp}} = \left(\frac{1.3 \times 10^{-3} \times 13,000 - 7.9 \times 225,000}{1.3 \times 10^3 \times 13,000 + 7.9 \times 225,000}\right)^2$$
$$= \left(\frac{1.3 \times 13 - 1,777,500}{1.3 \times 13 + 1,777,500}\right)^2$$

In both numerator and denominator, the first number, compared with the second number, is so small that it can be ignored. Therefore

$$\frac{E_{ref}}{E_{supp}} = \frac{1,777,500^2}{1,777,500^2} = -1$$

indicating that virtually all the energy is reflected off the near surface and almost no energy enters the steel to find defects. The minus sign simply means that the reflected acoustic energy is traveling in the opposite direction to that of the incident supplied energy, a minus sign always indicating a 180° phase difference.

To improve these unfavorable conditions, we shall use a couplant with a density heavier than air, such as water. For water, $v = 59,000$ (from the table) and specific gravity is 1.0.

Repeating the calculation with water discloses that about 95% of the energy is reflected, leaving 5% to enter the steel. This is a small fraction to transmit but is a considerable improvement over air. The heavier the couplant, the greater the energy transmitted in search of flaws. The calculations made above are of course only order-of-magnitude estimates.

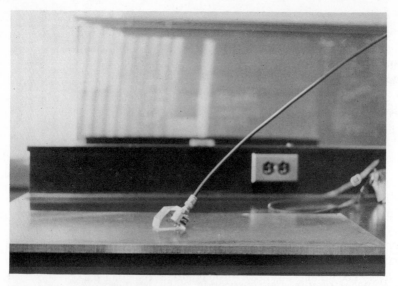

Fig. 147 An ultrasonic shear wave transducer on a piece of 1/2-inch thick nickel plate.

For the production of shear waves, the transducer probe is mounted on a plastic wedge cut to an angle such that the acoustic wave will enter the workpiece obliquely. Figure 147 is a photograph of a shear wave transducer. The velocity of sound in the plastic wedge is not the same as that in the material to be examined. Since the two velocities are different, the wave will undergo a change in direction in crossing from one material into the other. This change of direction is called "refraction," and is exactly the same as that shown by light beams. A spoon in a tumbler appears to be bent because the beam of light bends as it enters the water medium from the air medium. The angle of refraction is given by the following expression (see Fig. 148):

$$\frac{\sin i}{\sin r} = \frac{v_1}{v_2}$$

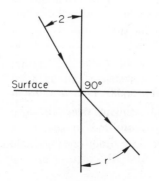

Surface   90°

Fig. 148 Refraction of acoustic waves.

where $i =$ the angle of incidence
$\qquad r =$ the angle of refraction
$\qquad v_1 =$ the velocity in the first medium
$\qquad v_2 =$ the velocity in the second medium

This expression holds for both longitudinal and shear waves. The formula is used in determining the angle of the plastic shoe if the shear wave is to enter the test material at a certain angle. It is possible to have a 90° angle of refraction, but no acoustic energy would enter the second medium.

20.9 ultrasonic techniques

One of the disadvantages of ultrasonic inspection compared with other NDT techniques is that it calls for considerable skill, both in its techniques and in the interpretation of the echoes that appear on the cathode ray screen. In the ultrasonic-testing of welds, especially fillet welds, it is always possible to pick up echoes. If these are interpreted as flaws, all the welds might have to be gouged and rewelded, but this is most unlikely. If a double-V butt joint is to be welded from both sides, it is foolish to ultrasonic-test until the joint is completed on both top and bottom. If welded on one side and then ultrasonic-tested, variations in penetration, fit-up, etc. may well be read as flaws. Since so much of the interpretation and resulting decisions on weld quality depend on the skill and experience of the operator, the best procedure is to ultrasonic-test first and then to radiograph those areas that the ultrasonic test has declared to be doubtful. This greatly reduces the amount of radiography, the more expensive test method.

Figure 149 is a photograph of the Branson Sonoray 5 instrument operating with a straight-beam transducer. Figure 150 shows the controls on the front panel of the instrument, Fig. 151 the controls on the top panel, and Fig. 152 the controls on the rear panel. Although all these add up to a great many knobs and adjustments, most adjustments are made during tune-up of the instrument and before testing is begun. All are not necessarily used.

The instrument is basically a high fidelity amplifier that has greater fidelity than is built into record players because the accuracy of interpretation of the showings on the scope depends on the fidelity with which the instrument reproduces the echoes that come back to the transducer.

Suppose that the instrument is to examine a butt weld in 1-in. plate by the straight-beam method (see Fig. 149). This requires only one transducer for both transmission and reception. After the instrument has

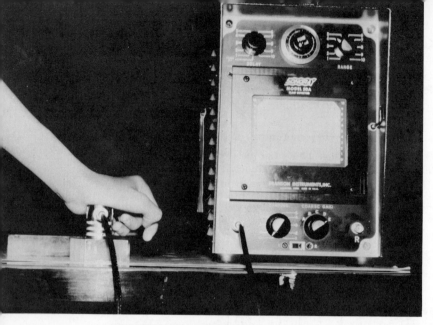

Fig. 149 Photograph of a Branson Sonoray 5 Ultrasonic Flaw Detector with straight beam transducer.

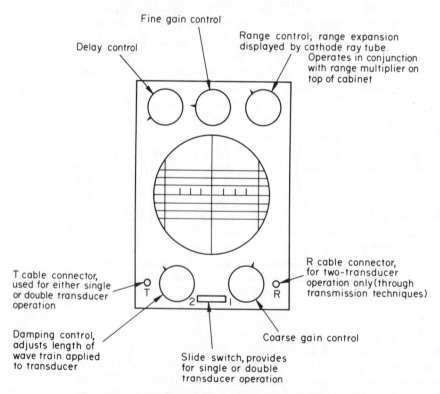

Fine gain control

Delay control

Range control; range expansion displayed by cathode ray tube. Operates in conjunction with range multiplier on top of cabinet

T cable connector, used for either single or double transducer operation

R cable connector, for two-transducer operation only (through transmission techniques)

Damping control, adjusts length of wave train applied to transducer

Coarse gain control

Slide switch, provides for single or double transducer operation

Fig. 150 Controls on the front of the Branson Sonoray 5.

nondestructive testing of welds
408

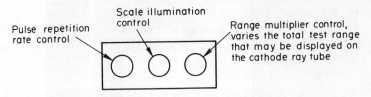

Pulse repetition rate control

Scale illumination control

Range multiplier control, varies the total test range that may be displayed on the cathode ray tube

Fig. 151 **Top panel controls of Sonoray 5.**

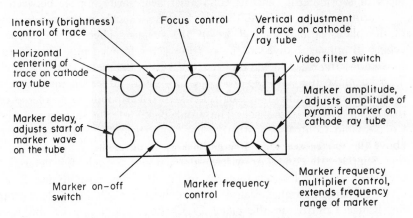

Intensity (brightness) control of trace

Focus control

Vertical adjustment of trace on cathode ray tube

Horizontal centering of trace on cathode ray tube

Video filter switch

Marker amplitude, adjusts amplitude of pyramid marker on cathode ray tube

Marker delay, adjusts start of marker wave on the tube

Marker on–off switch

Marker frequency control

Marker frequency multiplier control, extends frequency range of marker

Fig. 152 **Rear panel controls of Sonoray 5.**

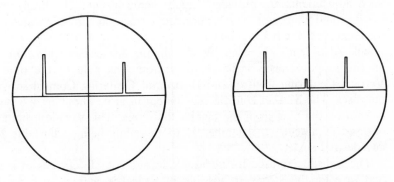

Fig. 153 (a) **Ultrasonic reference pip (left side) and echo from bottom surface of a plate 1 inch thick.** (b) **Same plate, with a flaw echo at the half-depth of the plate.**

warmed up and is adjusted, a reference pip appears on the scope and remains there for as long as the transducer is held to the steel plate. This reference pip is actually the echo from the surface contacted by the transducer. An echo will also be returned by the opposite or bottom surface of the material, as in Fig. 153. A scale is marked on the face of the scope. Suppose for convenience that the echo pip from the bottom surface of the plate is 4 scale divisions away from the reference pipe. Then 4 scale divisions represent a thickness in this material of 1 in., or 1 scale division represents $\frac{1}{4}$ in.

The transducer is then moved over the weld area, searching for flaw echoes. The two echoes from the two surfaces of the plate will remain on the scope. Suppose that a flaw is picked up. The flaw will produce a third pip. The flaw must necessarily lie between the top and bottom surfaces of the material, and its echo must necessarily appear between the two surface echoes. Suppose that the flaw lies exactly at the mid-thickness of the plate, or half an inch below the surface. Then on the scope its echo will appear 2 divisions away from the reference pip. The operator thus knows the exact location of the flaw within the metal (see Fig. 153b).

To make the echo pip from the flaw show larger on the scope, the operator turns up the Gain Control, which corresponds to a volume control on a TV or radio set. The front panel of the instrument has a Coarse Gain Control beneath the scope screen and a Fine Gain Control above the scope (see Figs. 149 and 150).

Suppose the operator wishes to enlarge the scale for determining the depth of any flaws within the metal. He may wish to use 8 scale divisions per inch rather than 4. To expand the operating scale, he turns the Range Control on the panel front above the scope or the Range Multiplier on the top panel, or both.

TV sets have adjustments for brightness and contrast of the picture. Such adjustments are provided on ultrasonic testers. The brightness (intensity) and sharpness of the fluorescent trace on the scope are adjusted by means of the two knobs on the rear panel marked Intensity and Focus. Also, it may be desirable to shift the fluorescent trace up or down on the scope screen, or horizontally from one side to the other. The Vertical Centering Control and Horizontal Centering Control serve these purposes. The Marker controls may be cut in also. These draw a sawtooth pattern on the bottom of the face of the scope. This sawtooth pattern can be used as a scale, the number of tooth points being adjustable to give any desired scale.

The transducers used for ultrasonic testing contain crystals of materials that provide the strongest possible piezoelectric action, such as quartz, barium titanate, lead zirconate, lithium sulfate, and others. The thickness of the crystal is made to equal about half of the acoustic wavelength produced. The crystal is mounted in a supporting plastic mount and faced with material such as aluminum oxide that will protect it from the abrasion of the metal surfaces being searched. Various shapes of shoes may be used to make the transducer conform to the shape of the part to be tested.

For calibration and checking, various test block arrangements embodying prepared flaws can be made up. One type of check apparatus uses a set of test blocks of 2 by 2-in. aluminum alloy bar with flat-bottomed holes drilled in one end to the same depth. A $\frac{1}{64}$-in. hole is drilled in one block, a $\frac{2}{64}$-in. hole in a second block, and so on, the eighth block containing an $\frac{8}{64}$-in. hole. Alternately the same size hole may be drilled to different depths in different blocks. The test blocks are read by placing the transducer on the end of the block opposite to the hole.

In addition to flaw detection, the ultrasonic instrument is used to check on the progress of corrosion and abrasion by making periodic measurements of metal thickness. Suppose that the maintenance department of a manufacturing plant wishes to know when to replace a pipe carrying corrosive liquid. The thickness of the pipe wall can be measured over a period of time at regular intervals. As the pipe wall corrodes, the echo pulse from the inside wall of the pipe moves closer to the reference pip on the scope. The actual rate of corrosion can thus be watched and measured without removing the pipe from service. However, thickness cannot be measured in material thinner than about 12 gauge. In thin material the echo pulse returns so soon that it is almost superimposed on the reference pulse, so that the two cannot then be differentiated on the scope screen. An acoustic wave travels about $\frac{1}{4}$ in. in 1 millionth of a second in metal.

The various ultrasonic testing methods may be summed up as follows:

1. *Straight beam.* The commonest and easiest method. The same crystal serves as transmitter and receiver.

2. *Through transmission.* A transducer is used on both top and bottom surfaces of the work, the receiving crystal picking up the sound energy from the transmitting crystal.

3. *Angle beam.* Usually a shear wave. With this method it is possible to search for flaws all the way around the periphery of a pipe or tube as the acoustic energy echoes and re-echoes off the outside and inside wall surfaces.

4. *Surface wave.* Surface waves are projected over the surface of the workpiece for the detection of surface or shallow flaws, especially in thin materials.

5. *Immersion.* The workpiece is immersed in a bath of oil or water. The acoustic wave is projected through the liquid into workpiece. A strong echo is always received from the near surface of the workpiece.

6. *Transducer wheel.* A liquid-filled wheel containing the transducer is rolled along the workpiece.

7. *Resonance.* A tunable variable-frequency oscillator is used. The frequency is adjusted to provide the maximum response from the work specimen. At this frequency the material of the workpiece between the surface and the flaw vibrates in resonance at its natural frequency.

20.10 industrial radiography

The most reliable and trusted nondestructive method for weld testing is radiography. This is actually a photographic method that follows the general principles of photography except that instead of visible light, extremely penetrating and short-wave radiation in the X-ray range is used. The first use of X rays for weld inspection took place in the United States in 1925; at about the same time gamma ray inspection using natural radium as the source of gamma rays was first tried. Radium is no longer used for this purpose.

The basic method of radiography is shown in the simulated setup of Fig. 154. The photograph shows a small section of a steel butt weld that is to be X-rayed for defects. The photographic film is laid underneath the metal to be photographed. X-rays or gamma rays from some source penetrate the metal and reach the film, developing an image of the metal on the film. Every material absorbs radiation at a different rate. Suppose the weld has a slag inclusion. Slag absorbs radiation to a lesser degree than steel does and therefore will transmit more radiation to the film than the steel will. The area of the film directly underneath the slag will receive more radiation than the rest of the film under the steel will and will show up as a darker area on the negative, indicating a weld flaw. The same effect is shown in the blowholes in Fig. 138. Following the same principle, a steel insert in magnesium in Fig. 138 is disclosed as the light, undeveloped part of the film in the middle of the casting, since steel transmits less than a tenth as much radiation as magnesium at the kilovoltage used.

The resulting photographic record is called a *radiograph*. In photo-

Fig. 154 Simulated arrangement for radiographing a weld, showing film in cassette, penetrameter beside the welded plate, and lead foil under cassette.

nondestructive testing of welds
412

graphy with visible light, a negative is produced from which a positive contact print is made. In radiography, only the negative is produced, although it is possible to produce a positive. Figure 55 is a contact print made from a radiograph negative. The other differences in technique between visible camera work and radiography will be discussed at a later stage. A difference in the construction of the film may be noted here. Since the X rays can pass through the film, there is a photographic emulsion on *both* sides of X-ray film. In effect, this makes the required exposure only half as long, a significant saving in time, since most radiographic exposures require several minutes or longer.

20.11 licensing of industrial radiographers

The use of isotopes and X-ray tubes represents a potential hazard to personnel unless the radiation is controlled. In both the United States and Canada, persons or companies desiring to possess and use radioisotopes must first apply for a license to do so, in the United States from the Atomic Energy Commission, Division of Licensing and Regulation, and in Canada from the Atomic Energy Control Board. The production, import, export, possession, buying, selling, leasing, hiring, loaning, exchanging, acquiring, storing, operating, shipping, consumption, use, and disposal of radioisotopes are all governed by regulations under the appropriate statute. Since X-ray tubes can be turned off and radioisotopes cannot be so controlled, regulations on the use of X-ray tubes are not yet so rigorous as those governing the use of isotopes.

In Canada, certification of industrial radiographic personnel is handled by the Physical Metallurgy Division, Department of Mines and Technical Surveys, under the requirements of the Canadian Government Specifications Board Standard 48-GP-4. The certification applies to the use of both X-ray and gamma radiation. Two grades of radiographer are certified: junior industrial radiographer and senior industrial radiographer. A senior industrial radiographer is responsible for deciding the radiographic technique, establishment of safety regulations, interpretation of the films, and general supervision. A junior industrial radiographer manipulates the devices and processes the films under the general supervision of the senior radiographer. Certification in the junior grade requires high school education, one year of experience in the field, and the passing of written examinations in three subjects: general radiography, radiation safety, and film processing. Certification as senior radiographer requires at least two years of experience in the certified junior grade and the passing of both written and practical tests.

In the United States, two similar grades are licensed under the Atomic Energy Commission: radiographer and radiographer's assistant. Such licensing, however, applies only to the use of isotopes and not to the operation of X-ray tubes. In the United States such isotopes are referred to as "by-product material," the word meaning that such material is made in nuclear reactors as a by-product of the nuclear reaction.

20.12 radioactive isotopes

Radioactive isotopes, or radioisotopes, are either found in the natural state or manufactured in nuclear reactors. The natural radioisotopes, such as uranium, thorium, polonium, and radon, are very heavy elements of high atomic number that are unstable and break up into smaller particles. Such elements had limited use in radiography before the advent of the nuclear reactor. The majority of these natural radioisotopes emit large alpha particles, the nuclei of helium atoms. The atom of uranium, the fuel used in nuclear reactors, divides into large fragments and releases neutrons, heat, and gamma radiation. On the other hand, artificial radio-isotopes, now used for radiography, emit beta particles, the high-speed negative electrons, and gamma radiation. Since artificial radioisotopes are made in nuclear reactors, the reactor had to be invented for such radio-isotopes to be available.

Most of the world's radioisotopes are manufactured by atomic energy commissions in the United States, Canada, Russia, and England. In 1964 Canada distributed 1,400,000 curies of radioisotopes, a larger commercial production than that of any other country. A very great variety of artificial radioisotopes is available, though industry and science use only a restricted number of these. Isotopes with particular characteristics are required for special purposes. For leak testing, isotopes that have a rapid rate of decay (that is, short half-life) are used, so that the isotope will be radioactive for the short time that the leak testing is in progress and will be harmless afterward. But isotopes employed for the thickness gauging of steel sheet, paper, or plastic film must have a reasonably constant level of radiation over a relatively long period of time, which means a long half-life. Chlorine-38 has a half-life of only 37 minutes, sodium-24 (used for leak testing) of 15 hours, iridium-192 (radiography) of 74 days, cobalt-60 (radiography) of 5.3 years, cesium-137 of 30 years, and carbon-14 of 5700 years. These elements are available in elemental form or as solid, liquid, or gaseous compounds. Dangerous quantities are not necessarily employed in radiation work: as little as one thousand billionth of a gram (and a gram is $\frac{1}{453}$ of a pound) of sodium-24 may be detected and therefore may be sufficient for leak testing or similar purposes.

The production of artificial radioisotopes is simple in principle.

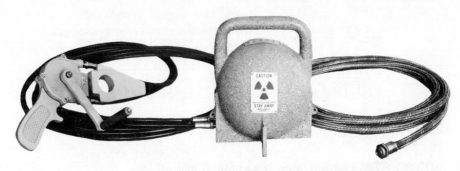

Fig. 155 Gamma camera. The radioactive source is pushed to the end of the source tube (on the right-hand side) by cranking the handle. (Courtesy Radionics, Inc.)

Cobalt-60 may be used as an example. Natural cobalt, Co-59, is encased in an aluminum capsule. The capsule is pushed into one of the irradiation channels in a reactor. The natural cobalt is left in the reactor for a considerable period of time to become irradiated with neutrons. As time passes, more and more cobalt nuclei capture an extra neutron, thus converting to cobalt-60. The quantity of cobalt-59 cannot be left in the reactor until every atom has captured an extra neutron for these reasons. First, to convert every atom of cobalt would require an infinite time. Second, while waiting for the last million nuclei to acquire an extra neutron, the first million to be converted would be already radioactive and would be decaying to a nonradioactive condition, so that nothing would be gained.

The following radioisotopes are used for the testing of welds. Cobalt-60 and iridium-192 are used most, the others finding less frequent employment. Xenon-133 is a gas used for leak testing.

INDUSTRIAL RADIOISOTOPES

Isotope	Radiation, Mev	Half-life
radium (no longer used)	12 rays, 0.24–2.20	1620 years
cobalt-60	1.33 and 1.17	5.3 years
iridium-192	0.61, 0.58, 0.468, 0.316 and 0.308	74 days
xenon-133	0.081	5.3 days
ytterbium-169	0.052	32 days
thulium-170	0.084	129 days

For the gammagraphing of welds, these isotopes are enclosed in a lead-lined steel container called a *gamma camera* (Fig. 155). The radioactive source is used by being pushed from the container to the end of the long source tube shown by means of the remote control cable also shown. The camera must be locked when not in use. The source within the camera may range in capacity from 1 to 100 curies. (The curie is explained in Sec. 20.14.)

20.13 half-life

The radioisotopes, both natural and artificial, decay by emission of alpha and beta particles and gamma rays to an ultimately stable condition. As observed above, the artificial radioisotopes used in industry decay by beta and gamma emission. The loss of a beta particle—a negative electron—must leave the atom with a net positive charge increased by one. This electron did not come from the electron energy levels outside the nucleus of the atom, as with X radiation, but from the nucleus. It is known and can be proved however, that no nucleus contains electrons, and in any case, an electron is far larger than a nucleus. What has happened in radioactive decay is that a neutron in the nucleus as it releases the beta electron, has converted into a proton. But a change in the count of protons in the nucleus means that the element has been changed to another element by a gain of one atomic number (the atomic number is the count of protons). Cobalt-60 thus decays to nickel, iridium-192 to platinum, and cesium-137 to barium. The emission of the beta electron is accompanied by the simultaneous emission of a gamma photon, which is the radiation used for radiography with gamma cameras.

It is impossible to predict when any specific atom will thus disintegrate. For any large number of atoms, the *half-life* is the time period in which half of the atoms will have disintegrated. Thus iridium-192 has a half-life of 74 days. This means that in 74 days half of the atomic nuclei will be disintegrated to a stable condition (platinum). In the next 74 days half of the remaining atoms will have disintegrated, which means that in this second half-life one-quarter of the atoms will disintegrate. In the third half-life of 74 days, half of the remaining atoms will disintegrate, or one-eighth. After 3×74 days only one-eighth of the atoms will be radioactive.

Mathematically, this disintegration follows the formula for the decay of the voltage charge on a capacitor. (This mathematical function, it seems, is one of the most important in industrial science.)

$$N = N_0 e^{-kt}$$

where N = number of atoms not yet decayed
N_0 = number of atoms originally present
$e = 2.718$ = base of the natural logarithms
t = elapsed time
k = decay constant = $0.693/T$, where T = half-life of the isotope

The radioactivity of a radioactive source is always quoted in curies (c). The curie is also the unit in which sources are purchased, instead of pounds, ounces, or grams. A curie is that quantity of radioactive material in which 3.7×10^{10} atoms are disintegrating every second. The use of the unusual unit was established at the time radium was the only useful radioisotope. In 1 g of radium there are 3.7×10^{10} atomic disintegrations every second. Although 1 g of radium produces 1 c of radioactivity, a curie of some other source could be less or more than a gram. As many as 120 c or more may be used for industrial radiography, but for such purposes as leak testing a few millicuries or even microcuries might suffice. A microcurie means 3.7×10^4 disintegrations every second.

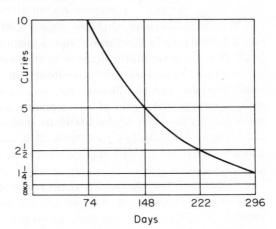

Fig. 156 Decay curve for iridium-192.

Since the number of disintegrations decreases by half in each half-life of the material, the number of curies likewise decreases by half in the same time period. In 74 days 1 c of iridium-192 is reduced to ½ c. Figure 156 shows the decay curve for iridium-192.

The *specific activity* is the measure of physical concentration of a radioactive source and is expressed as curies per gram or curies per cubic centimeter.

20.15 radiation hazard

Everyone is aware that gamma (X-ray) radiation is potentially dangerous to health. The nature of this potential hazard, however, is not well understood. In particular, the remarkable safety record of the radiation industry

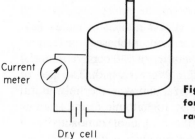

Current meter

Dry cell

Fig. 157 Simple apparatus for demonstrating the effects of radiation.

has not been made known to the general public. Safety does not make news, but accidents do. The radiation industry is the safest of all industries in terms of lost-time accidents; it has only half the accidents of the next safest industry and has achieved its excellent safety record, not by being frightened of radiation, but by being intelligent about it.

Figure 157 is a sketch of a simple apparatus often used to demonstrate the effects of radiation. A dry cell is connected through a current meter to a cylinder made of sheet metal. A concentric wire within the sheet metal cylinder is connected to the positive terminal of the dry cell. Since the circuit is definitely an open circuit, no current will flow, and the meter will give no indication. The air between the cylinder and the wire is an insulator.

Suppose, however, that the air between cylinder and wire is exposed to X or gamma radiation. A weak current will then be indicated on the meter.

This simple apparatus illustrates perhaps the most basic characteristic of radiation: *radiation ionizes atoms*. Radiation passing through the insulating air frees electrons from their energy levels within the atom. These ionized electrons and the positive air ions are attracted to the cylinder and wire acting as electrodes, and thus a current is produced. This apparatus can be considered a *radiation meter*, for increased radiation dosage of the air will produce a heavier current through the meter. Ionization of the air can be produced by any type of radiation: alpha, beta, gamma, or neutrons, but not lower-energy sound, radio, infrared, visible light, or ultraviolet radiation.

The amount of radiation is measured in *roentgens* (r). If 2080 million ion pairs (that is, electron plus positive ion) are produced in a cubic centimeter of air at 0C (32F) and atmospheric pressure as a result of radiation, then the radiation dose is 1 roentgen. One roentgen is far more than a radiation worker is permitted to receive in any reasonable period of time, though this dose presumably would do him no harm whatever. Lethal doses are in the range of 500 or more. Smaller doses are measured in milliroentgens (mr), or thousandths of a roentgen. To put the roentgen in terms of electric current in the apparatus discussed above, it would require about 3 million r to make the meter indicate 1 ma.

Ionization requires the expenditure of energy. One roentgen represents the expenditure of a minute amount of energy, 87 ergs. The erg is a small energy unit in the metric system. If a 1 g force is accelerated at a rate of 1 cm per sec per sec for a distance of 1 cm, an erg of energy has been consumed. Also, 1 joule $= 10^7$ ergs, and 1 joule per sec $= 1$ w.

From the point of view of health hazard we are more concerned with damage done to the human body by a dose of 1 r than to its effect on air. The human body is not air but is composed largely of soft tissue, heavier than air, and the amount of ionization or radiation damage from 1 r is greater in the human body than in air. An *exposure* dose of 1 r results in an *absorbed* dose or damage of almost 95 ergs per g of soft tissue, which would probably ionize 1 molecule in every 20 billion in the human body.

The medical aspects of accidental radiation injury are concerned chiefly with somatic (whole body) and genetic injuries. Very large roentgen doses are required for either type of injury. If the whole body is exposed, a dose of 50 r will cause transient changes in the blood, such as temporary destruction of white or red blood cells, followed by rapid recovery from this condition. Severe doses of 100 r or more produce the characteristic radiation syndrome ("syndrome" is a medical term for a group of symptoms that may or may not be named as a specific disease). The symptoms that appear with small doses are nausea, vomiting, and lowered blood-cell count. Still higher doses produce radiation burns, which never completely heal. Lethal doses are in the range of 500 r or higher, but as with most diseases, some persons are more resistant to radiation than others are. Long-term effects of radiation may be an increased incidence of skin cancer, leukemia, and perhaps other diseases among persons who have in the past allowed themselves to be exposed repeatedly to unnecessarily high doses. As for genetic injuries, there is apparently no conclusive evidence of significant genetic damage, such as sterility, for dosages below a lethal dose.

The statutory regulations in any country that control exposure of individuals to ionizing radiation permit maximum exposures far below 1 r. Permitted doses are about one ten-thousandth of the dose that would produce any medical symptoms.

The measure of the radiation dose given to body tissues is measured in *rads*. A rad is a dose corresponding to the absorption of 100 ergs of energy per gram of tissue. Since 1 r represents 87 ergs of energy, 1 r $= 0.87$ rad. The difference between a curie, a roentgen, and a rad need not be confusing. The curie measures the amount of radioactive material: the roentgen measures the amount of radiation produced by such material: the rad measures the absorbed dose from this radiation.

ABSORBED DOSE PER ROENTGEN EXPOSURE

Radiation Energy, Kev	Rads Muscle	Rads Bone
50	0.926	3.58
100	0.948	1.45
200	0.963	0.979
500	0.957	0.925
1000	0.956	0.922

The above table shows that the absorbed dose in rads per roentgen of exposure is greater for bone than for muscle. The reason for this follows the usual principle that materials of higher atomic weight absorb X rays better than materials of lower atomic weight do. In the higher photon energy ranges the difference in the X-ray absorption of various materials (whether tissue or metals) is much less, so that the absorption dose in bone is not greatly different from that in muscle.

Two other terms are used in measuring radiation dose. The relative biological effectiveness, abbreviated RBE, for any type of radiation is the relative amount of damage done by that type of radiation as compared with X rays:

Radiation	RBE
X-rays (gamma rays)	1
beta rays	1
protons	5
slow neutrons	about 3
fast neutrons	about 10
alpha particles	20

The rad dose is multiplied by the RBE to obtain the dose in *rems*. Equal rem doses produce the same biological damage. For X-ray and gamma radiation, it is roughly true for soft tissue that

$$1 \text{ r} = 1 \text{ rad} = 1 \text{ rem}$$

Regulatory agencies specify allowable exposures for personnel in terms of rems. The following table is the estimated dose received in North America generally (not in Arctic areas) from unavoidable background radiation. However, these figures vary somewhat according to geography, altitude, type of work, type of building, and other factors. The soil in your own backyard has a few grams of uranium per ton, and even the healthy human body contains small amounts of radioactive material.

It has been estimated that for every rem of exposure received during his lifetime, an individual's life is reduced by 2 ½ days. This may or may or may not be true. The reader can estimate the shortening of his lifespan

BACKGROUND RADIATION

Source	Reproductive Organs mrem/yr	Bones, mrem/yr
cosmic rays (at sea level)	28	28
radium in water	5	38
gamma rays from uranium in soil	47	47
carbon-14 and potassium-40 in the human body	21	13
radioactive material in buildings	20	20
atmospheric fallout	3	5
total background radiation	124	151

as a result of background radiation from the background radiation table.

For work in industrial radiography, three general methods are available for the protection of personnel from ionizing radiation:

1. Reduction of the time of exposure
2. Removal of personnel as far from the source of radiation as possible
3. Protection of personnel by such shielding materials as lead and concrete.

The effects of distance and shielding will be discussed presently.

20.16 regulations governing exposure of personnel to ionizing radiation

There are small and unimportant differences between the United States and Canada in the allowable exposures of personnel to ionizing radiation.

The Atomic Energy Commission in the United States sets out the following permitted maxima for gamma or gamma plus X ray:

REMS PER CALENDAR QUARTER

whole body, blood-forming organs, eyes, reproductive organs	$1\frac{1}{4}$
hands and forearms, feet and ankles	$18\frac{3}{4}$
skin of whole body	$7\frac{1}{2}$

Canadian limits are very similar:

MAXIMUM PERMISSIBLE DOSES FOR RADIATION WORKERS, CANADA

	mrem/yr	mrem/quarter	mrem/hr
for the whole body, blood-forming organs, eyes, reproductive organs	5,000	3,000	2.5
hands, forearms, feet, ankles	75,000	20,000	37.5
skin of whole body	30,000	8,000	15.0

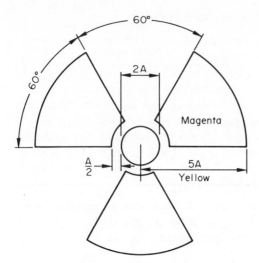

Fig. 158 Radiation warning symbol.

The millirem per hour figures are not regulatory but are based on an assumed 2000 working hours in a year, by calculation. For nonradiation workers in Canada, the permitted doses are a tenth of the values cited.

The total cumulative dose permitted to radiation workers has been established by international agreement as $D = 5(N - 18)$, where D is the total received dose in rads and N is the age of the worker in years. Persons under eighteen years of age and pregnant women are not hired to undertake work that involves exposure to ionizing radiation. Both in Canada and United States, periodic medical examination of radiation workers and the keeping of certain medical and other records is a requirement. Radiation monitoring instruments such as film badges and Geiger-Muller counters must be available at all times, and radiation warning signs must be posted in radiation areas. Figure 158 shows the radiation symbol required to be posted by both countries.

No radiographic exposure device may have a radiation level in excess of 200 mr at any exterior surface of the device nor in excess of 10 mr per hr at 1 m from any exterior surface.

20.17 radiation monitoring

instruments

The simple apparatus of Fig. 157 could be used as a radiation meter if the current meter used in the circuit had a dial scale graduated in roentgens or milliroentgens. Most radiation meters measure radiation levels either by thus measuring current or by measuring the strength of an electric charge produced by ionization.

The *pocket dosimeter* is a modification of Fig. 157 but uses only the cylinder and the wire electrode. Pocket dosimeters, which may be clipped to any pocket of the operator's clothing like a pen or pencil, are shown in Fig. 159. The wall of the instrument is one electrode. The other electrode is a pivoting electrode. The dosimeter is charged up on a little battery-charger by means of dry cells. When fully charged, the dosimeter reads zero roentgens. As ionizing radiation passes through the dosimeter, the electric charge slowly leaks off and the movable electrode moves

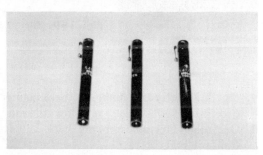

Fig. 159   Pocket dosimeters.

across the scale of the dosimeter. The scale is graduated from 0 to 200 mr. The wall of the dosimeter must be so designed as to give the least possible shielding from radiation.

The advantages of this device are its convenient size and the fact that a person may read his exposure at any time. Usually the exposure is read at the end of each day's work and recorded. Sometimes these instruments give too high a reading owing to leakage of the charge across the insulation of the chamber—they may sometimes even record increasing exposures in the absence of radiation. Because of these occasional eccentricities, it is best to wear two dosimeters. If the two readings do not agree, the *lower* reading is taken as the correct one.

Dosimeters should be worn on the part of the body most likely to be exposed. For example, if a shielded source is being carried by hand, the best position for the dosimeter is on the hip pocket on the carrying side.

The *film badge* (Fig. 160) is also used for personal monitoring. Such badges are usually worn for a week and the film then developed. The darkening of the film records the amount of the exposure received by the wearer. Like the dosimeter, film badges should be worn in a place where the maximum possible exposure will be recorded. However, the film badge does not inform the wearer of this exposure until the film is developed.

Each film badge carries the wearer's name and serial number. The top of the badge has an open window to allow entry of beta rays (which are completely shielded by metal barriers except very thin foils) and three areas of different metal shielding.

Fig. 160   Film badge.

1. One millimeter of aluminum, back and front, to transmit all radiation except the softest (i.e., very low kilovolt) X rays.
2. One millimeter of cadmium, back and front, to stop soft X rays and transmit hard X rays.
3. One quarter millimeter of copper, back and front, to separate hard (i.e., fast) electrons from soft X rays. By this rather elaborate construction, the type of radiation can be known as well as the relative exposure.

Control film badges, not worn by radiographic personnel, are maintained on the badge rack. These control badges are periodically developed to ensure that the badge rack areas are free of radiation.

Both the pocket dosimeter and the film badge have a probable accuracy of ±10%.

The *Geiger-Muller counter* (Fig. 161) is used as a survey meter to indicate instantaneous levels of radiation but not to indicate an accumulated personal dose. This counter has a gas-filled diode connected to the instrument by a flexible electric cable. The diode has a metal shield built around it with a window in it. If the window is open, all types of radiation can enter the diode through the window. If the window is closed, any alpha or beta radiation is shielded from the diode, and only gamma radiation can reach it. The diode itself is a hollow cylinder of stainless steel, copper, or brass. This cylinder is the cathode. The anode is a tungsten wire concentric with the cathode. A high voltage is placed across the diode, but it not high enough to ionize the gas in the tube.

If an alpha, beta, or gamma (X-ray) particle passes through the diode, it will collide with a gas molecule and ionize it. The freed electron is attracted to the anode, and the positive ion to the cathode. As the free electron moves toward the anode, it will collide with another gas molecule and release another electron. Since each electron may collide with gas

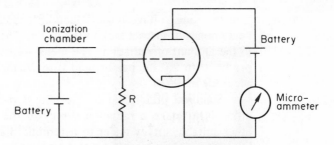

Fig. 161 (a) Schematic Geiger counter circuit.

Fig. 161 (b) Geiger-Muller radiation detector.

molecules before reaching the anode, many electrons are released, enough to produce a minute current. This small current passes through the extremely high resistance R in the circuit of Fig. 162, producing a voltage drop. This causes the upper end of the resistor to rise in voltage, so that the vacuum tube grid becomes more positive, allowing the tube to conduct. (In modern G-M counters, transistors are substituted for vacuum tubes.)

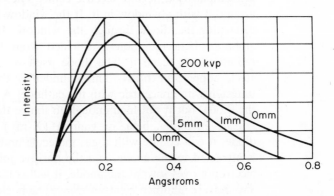

Fig. 162 Effect of filtering 200 kvp X rays through aluminum filters of varying thickness.

The resulting voltage pulse is amplified and produces a click in a set of headphones or gives a kick to the meter. The meter reading is proportional to the amount of radiation. The meter itself has three ranges: 0 to 0.2 mr per hr, 0 to 2.0 mr per hr, and 0 to 20 mr per hr. Such meters have an accuracy of $\pm 20\%$.

Standard practice after returning a radioisotope to its shielded condition is to make a radiation survey of the area with a G-M counter or other suitable survey meter to determine that the whole of the source has been returned to its container.

20.18 the inverse square law

X and gamma radiation travel in straight lines from the point of origin, like other electromagnetic radiation. Radiation of lower frequencies, such as ultraviolet or visible light, may be reflected, refracted, or focused by various devices such as mirrors, lenses, or dish antennas. Because of their extremely short wavelength, gamma rays cannot be reflected or focused. On meeting a reflecting surface, such radiation travels straight through into the material. All radiography therefore is simply the production of shadow patterns of the material photographed by means of the radiation that penetrates through the metal to the film.

Like all radiation, X rays diverge when they are emitted and cover an increasingly larger area with an intensity that decreases as the distance from their source increases. If the X-ray beam covers 1 sq ft of area at 1 ft from the source, it would cover 4 sq ft at 2 ft from the source, 9 sq ft at 3 ft from the source, and so on. Further, if at 1 ft from the source the exposure was 1 r, at 2 ft the exposure would be $\frac{1}{4}$ r, at 3 ft $\frac{1}{9}$ r, etc. This simple relationship between intensity and distance is called the *inverse-square law*.

The inverse-square law governs the exposure time of X and gamma ray photography. If an exposure of 10 min is required when the film is 1 ft from the tube, the required exposure will be 40 min at 2 ft from the tube or source, or 90 min at 3 ft.

$$\frac{I_1}{I_2} = \frac{d_2^2}{d_1^2}$$

I_1 and I_2 are the X- or gamma ray intensities in roentgens at distances d_1 and d_2 respectively. For photographic exposure times

$$\frac{t_1}{t_2} = \frac{d_1^2}{d_2^2}$$

where t_1, t_2 are required exposure times at their respective distances.

All materials, even air to a slight degree, absorb gamma rays. The amount of this absorption depends chiefly on the gamma ray wavelength, the absorbing material, and its thickness. Very hard gamma rays are absorbed less than soft gamma rays are. Heavy materials of high atomic number such as lead or uranium are better absorbers than light materials of low atomic number such as beryllium or aluminum, which are reasonably transparent to radiation. Greater thicknesses of material absorb larger proportions of this radiation. Doubling the thickness, however, does not double the absorption. The transmission of gamma rays through any substance follows a mathematical rate similar to that of radioactive decay. Radioactive decay was expressed as a half-life, the time for half the remaining number of radioactive atoms to disintegrate. In the same way, the half-value layer (HVL) of a material is that thickness of a material that reduces the exposure to one-half. Two half-value layers reduce the exposure to one-quarter and three to one-eighth. Occasionally the tenth-value layer is used: this thickness reduces the exposure to one-tenth.

For calculating the required thickness of shielding to reduce radiation to any given level in roentgens, the radiation level of the exposed source must be known. Such radiation levels are given in milliroentgens per hour per curie at one meter.

Material	Mr/Hr at 1 M, unshielded	Steel	Lead	Water	Concrete	Aluminum
				Half-value Thickness, in.		
cobalt-60	1300	0.87	0.5	5.3	2.7	2.2
iridium-192	550	0.44	0.2	3.2	1.9	1.2
cesium-137	390	0.68	0.25	3.6	2.1	1.6

An example of shielding calculation For an unshielded 20-c source of iridium-192, what is the exposure in roentgens at 2 ½ m if two half-value layers are used for protection?

Solution. 20 c of Ir-192 unshielded will produce an exposure of 11,000 mr per hr at 1 m.

At 2 ½ m the same source, unshielded, will give an exposure rate of $\frac{1}{6.25} \times 11{,}000$ or 1770 mr per hr.

Two HVL's will reduce the exposure to one-quarter, or ¼ × 1770, which is 442½ mr per hr.

Linear absorption coefficient Since transmission of gamma or X rays follows the mathematical relationship for decay of capacitor charge or for radioactive decay, it can be expressed as

$$I = I_0 e^{-\mu t}$$

where I = intensity of gamma rays after transmission
I_0 = intensity before transmission
t = thickness of transmitting material, in inches (or centimeters)
$e = 2.718$ = base of the natural logarithms
μ = linear absorption coefficient = the fractional decrease in intensity per inch of absorbing material

For monochromatic radiation (that is, radiation of uniform wavelength) such as is approximately produced from isotopes, but only in rare instances from X-ray tubes

$$\mu = \frac{0.693}{\text{HVL}}$$

Both the linear absorption coefficient and the half-value layer depend on the wavelength of the radiation as well as the absorbing material. The more penetrating character of the harder radiation is shown in the table of half-value layers. The radiation from Co-60 is more than 1 Mev, with a HVL in steel of 0.87 in., while Ir-192, radiating at about 0.5 Mev, has a HVL in steel of 0.44 in. There is no significance to the fact that 0.44 is half of 0.87.

The radiation from an X-ray tube is not monochromatic but is spread over a range of wavelengths. Absorption of radiation from tubes does not strictly follow the half-value relationship. The first half-value thickness will actually absorb a somewhat larger fraction than half the radiation, and the following HVL's will absorb somewhat less than half the received radiation. This is because the very soft components of the radiation have little penetrating power and may all be absorbed in the first half-value layer: the first half-value layer may be virtually a full-value layer for the softest fraction of the radiation.

The absorption of radiation is less if the half-value layer is greater. This fact should suggest that in the radiographing of welds, the contrasts in the radiographic picture will be *less* for very short-wave radiation than for softer radiation, the former having the smaller absorption coefficient. For highest radiographic contrast, radiation with the highest possible absorption coefficient is required. Radiography requires that radiation be *absorbed* before reaching the film; hence the more the absorption, the better the photography. Light metals such as aluminum are X-rayed at voltages of about 100 kvp. Such light metals do not have very great absorptivities for radiation other than soft radiation, and to obtain contrast, the tube voltage must be lowered. The use of 1 million X-ray volts on $\frac{1}{8}$-in. aluminum would show absolutely nothing except the outline of the workpiece.

Another radiographic technique based on absorption principles is that of *filtering*. Filters are used in ordinary visible-light cameras to reduce the range of wavelengths (colors) received by the camera. Filters have the same purpose in radiography: they make the heterogeneous X radiation somewhat more monochromatic. Radiation filters are simply sheets of metal to intercept the radiation before it reaches the workpiece and the film. Such filters absorb the softer components to a greater degree than the hard components, concentrating the radiation toward the hard end. Figure 162 shows the effect of filtering 220-kvp X rays through aluminum filters with thicknesses of 0, 1, 5, and 10 mm.

20.20 radiographic equivalence factors

The different absorption characteristics of metals of course affect the exposure times for gamma and X-ray photography. If it requires 10 min of exposure to obtain an exograph of 1 in. of steel, then less than 10 min will radiograph the same thickness of aluminum or magnesium if other conditions remain the same. What exactly should the exposure time be to photograph the aluminum? Such problems of converting from one metal to another are handled by means of tables of equivalence factors for metals. The following equivalence factors are from Eastman Kodak Company's book *Radiography in Modern Industry*.

EQUIVALENCE FACTORS

Metal	50 kv	100 kv	150 kv	400 kv	1000 kv	Ir-192	Co-60
magnesium	0.6	0.6	0.05				
aluminum 1060	1.0	1.0	0.12			0.35	0.35
aluminum 2024	1.4	1.2	0.13			0.35	0.35
carbon steel		12	1.0	1.0	1.0	1.0	1.0
stainless 304		12	1.0	1.0	1.0	1.0	1.0
copper		18	1.6	1.4		1.1	1.1
brass (Cu-Zn)			1.4	1.3	1.2	1.1	1.1
zinc			1.4	1.3		1.1	1.0
zirconium			2.3	1.55	1.0		

At low kvp's, aluminum is taken as the standard metal and is assigned an equivalence factor of 1.0. For higher kvp's and for sources, steel is the standard, again with the equivalence factor of 1.0. Other metals are rated against these standard metals. The use of the table can be understood from an example:

Two inches of pure aluminum is radiographically equivalent to what thickness of steel (a) at 150 kvp, (b) with Ir-192?

At 150 kvp, the factor for pure aluminum 1060 is 0.12, or $\frac{1}{8}$. The actual thickness of the aluminum, 2 in., is multiplied by the factor to obtain an equivalent thickness of steel of $\frac{1}{8} \times 2 = \frac{1}{4}$ in. steel. The exposure in minutes required to radiograph $\frac{1}{4}$ in. of steel is used for radiographing 2 in. of aluminum at 50 kvp.

When using Ir-192, the exposure in minutes required to radiograph 0.70 in. of steel is used to radiograph 2 in. of aluminum 1060.

The equivalence factor table shows up the effect already noted—as the photon energy of the radiation increases, the absorption differences between materials decrease. This can be seen by a comparison of copper and steel throughout the table. Therefore to show up a slag inclusion or other defect most prominently in a radiograph, the lowest possible kilovoltage should be used.

20.21 absorption and backscatter

In the radiographing of welds, the photographic film is laid against the weld, and radiation from the source is supplied to the other side of the metal. Some fraction of the radiation is absorbed by the metal being radiographed. Ideally, the fraction of the radiation transmitted through the metal makes a shadowgraph of defects on the film. No radiation is reflected. However, because radiation does not behave in this ideal manner, problems arise. It is necessary first to examine the behavior of the absorbed fraction of the radiation.

Three important processes occur when radiation in the gamma ray range is absorbed by a material:

1. photoelectric absorption
2. scattering
3. electron pair production

The absorption coefficient is the sum of these three effects:

$\mu =$ (photoelectric absorption fraction) + (scattering fraction)
+ (pair production fraction)

and of the received radiation from the source

(fraction transmitted) + (fraction absorbed) $= 100\%$

In *photoelectric absorption,* the energy of the incident photon is used to eject an electron from an atom. The electron thus ionized is termed a photoelectron. This is exactly the same process that occurs in the cathode of a photoelectric cell, hence the term photoelectric absorption. The probability of photoelectric absorption is greatest if the photon has enough energy to eject an electron from a K shell. Since all the photon energy is absorbed by the electron, the first demand on this energy is for ionization, any remaining energy being used for kinetic energy to accelerate the electron in some direction. The electron will quickly lose this kinetic energy in collisions with adjacent atoms, which will thereby be ionized also.

The vacancy thus created in the K shell will be filled by an electron moving into it from an outer shell, resulting in the emission of a photon of softer (lower Kev) radiation than that which caused the vacancy. In effect then, the material absorbing radiation from a source or an X-ray tube also becomes a radiation-emitter, producing secondary radiation. Since this secondary radiation is fired off in all directions, it will act merely to fog the photographic film without adding to the useful photographic effect.

A use may be made of photoelectrons in radiography, however. Heavy elements such as lead produce many times more photoelectrons than lighter metals do. It is common practice to utilize the effect by placing lead foil on the side of the film opposite to the X-ray tube. When X radiation enters this lead foil, photoelectrons are produced in large quantities. Collisions between these electrons and the atoms of the film emulsion produce an intensifying effect that reduces the required length of exposure. Fluorescent screens may also be used at the back of the film but are not preferred in industrial photography because of the poor definition (fogging) given to the radiograph by this visible-light radiation.

Photoelectric absorption decreases with higher-energy radiation, but of the three absorption processes, it is the predominant one for long-wave radiation. The use of lead intensifying screens is less effective with Co-60, for example.

Since photoemission involves secondary emission, one important implication should be noted: materials used to shield against radiation may themselves give off radiation, though to a much lesser degree.

Scattering Two types of scattering are possible. One type (unmodified scattering, which involves no loss of energy by the photon) occurs only for X rays too soft to be used in industrial photography. Modified scattering, also called the *Compton process,* results from collisions between photons and electrons in which the direction of photon is deflected. The photon also loses energy to the collision electron, so that the deflected photon becomes softer, or longer-wave, and has lower Kev. Compton scattering is not influenced by the atomic number of the material and decreases with increasing photon energy. Compton scattering is the predominant absorption effect in the middle range of radiation energies, that is, below 1 Mev, just as photoelectric absorption predominates for lower-energy radiation. Such scattering is yet another of the effects producing fogging of the film, thus lowering the quality of industrial radiography.

Electron pair production According to the Einstein relativity equation, $E = mc^2$, there is a direct relationship between mass and energy. Energy may convert into mass, or mass into energy. Pair production is the production of mass from energy.

The mass of an electron is the equivalent of 0.51 Mev. Now a photon with an energy of 0.51 Mev cannot create an electron, even though it has the required amount of energy, for the photon has no charge, and a negative charge is required for an electron. A photon with an energy of at least 2×0.51 Mev, or 1.02 Mev, however, can be converted into mass in the following process. Two electrons will be produced by annihilation of the photon, one being a negative electron and the other a positron, or positive electron. The sum of 1 negative charge and 1 positive charge equals the charge on the photon, which is zero. From the point of view of radiation safety or photographic quality, this is an ideal absorption method, since there is no random scattering such as is created by the other two processes. All ionizing radiation disappears when matter is created.

The positron very quickly disappears by combining with a negative electron. Both particles are annihilated to produce two photons of 0.51 Mev, which travel in opposite directions.

Pair production is not a likely process unless the radiation is at energy levels somewhat above 1.02 Mev. The process contributes significantly to the total absorption process only in high-energy radiography at levels of 10 Mev or higher. Any energy in the annihilated photon above 1.02 Mev is used as kinetic energy to accelerate the two electrons produced.

Industrial radiography is intended to be done by *primary radiation,* or radiation emitted directly and in straight lines from a source or tube. This ideal photographic process is interfered with by secondary and scattered radiation. *Secondary radiation* arises from material exposed to the primary radiation. *Scattered radiation* is radiation in which direction has been deviated. Scattered radiation must be minimized since it does not contribute to the formation of the image on the film but instead reduces the contrasts and masks the details. X-ray scattering increases with thickness of material and is greater with dense materials such as zirconium or lead. Scatter can be reduced by increased X-ray voltage or change to a source with harder radiation, such as the substitution of Co-60 for Ir-192, when radiographing thick steel sections. The use of a lead filter between the metal and the film is often a good method of reducing backscatter from the metal being radiographed.

20.22 other applications of primary and
secondary radiation in nondestructive testing

The absorption of X rays, gamma rays, and beta particles as they pass through matter is used as a method for measuring the thickness of materials. If primary radiation is used for thickness gauging, a radiation source is located on one side of the material and a radiation detector on the other. The thickness of the material can be determined by the intensity of the radiation transmitted by the material. Gamma radiation sources for thickness gauging must be selected for long half-life and must be corrected for radioactive decay.

In gauging thickness, it is not necessary to locate the radiation source and the radiation detector on opposite sides of the material. They may both be located on the same side. In the latter arrangement, the detector must measure backscatter radiation instead of primary radiation. Beta gauging is particularly effective for backscatter thickness gauging. The amount of backscatter is very nearly proportional to the material thickness when beta radiation is used.

The ability of a material to backscatter beta rays increases with the atomic number (density) of the material. If a coating material, such as chrome plating or paint, has a different density from the base material, beta backscatter gauging can be used to determine the coating thickness. Coating-thickness measurements as fine as one-millionth of an inch are possible by such backscatter method.

20.23 very high energy
X radiation

Special X-ray machines, either betatrons or linear accelerators (sometimes called linacs) must be used for the radiography of steel thicknesses of 12 in. or more. Such machines have outputs in the range of 4 to 35 Mev. The betatron produces high-speed electrons by spinning them in a circle. A fluctuating magnetic field is used to accelerate the electron around its circular path. In a typical betatron, the electron gains about 70 v per revolution from the fluctuating field, which is pulsed in synchronization with the rotation of the electron. After about a third of a million revolutions, the electron has gained 24 Mev of energy and is then deflected to strike a target, which then produces the X radiation. Such machines are in use with manufacturers of heavy-walled pressure vessels for nuclear and coal-fired power plants.

20.24 unsharpness

For absolute sharpness of photographic reproduction, the focal spot of a source or an X-ray tube must be a point source of radiation. But since the focal spot of a tube will measure about one millimeter and that of an isotope source about an eighth of an inch, there must be a small amount of blurring or unsharpness around the edges of a test specimen, its holes, and defects. From Fig. 163

$$U = \frac{Ft}{d}$$

where U = unsharpness
$\quad\quad F$ = size of focal spot
$\quad\quad t$ = specimen-to-film distance
$\quad\quad d$ = source to specimen distance

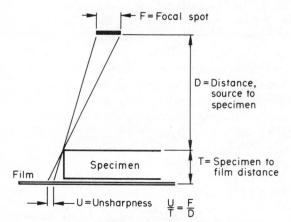

Fig. 163 Geometry of unsharpness.

The formula indicates that the smaller the focal spot, the less the unsharpness. To further reduce unsharpness, the longest possible target-to-film distance should be used consistent with a reasonable exposure time (too long an exposure time will increase fogging effects), the film should be as close to the specimen as possible, and the film should be at right angles to the radiation. Unsharpness is usually limited to 0.01 in. in most specifications.

20.25 the photographic effect
of gamma radiation

X-ray film (it is apparently never called gamma ray film) consists of a transparent cellulose acetate material uniformly coated on both sides with a silver bromide emulsion. Manufacture of photographic film must surely be a serious contender for the title of the World's Most Fascinating Industry. The film must be produced in utter darkness, and any accidental illumination is disastrous. Any reader unfamiliar with this industry might care to speculate on how photographic film can be inspected for scratches and blemishes in the absence of illumination—it is not every hundredth sheet of film that is inspected, but *every* sheet of film.

Irradiation of the film in the course of taking the picture deposits black metallic silver from the emulsion, this activity being proportional to the amount of radiation received on the film. The exposure received by the film can be expressed as an *exposure factor*, a quantity that combines source strength, time, and distance of source from film. The exposure factor for X rays is

$$\frac{\text{milliamps} \times \text{time}}{(\text{distance})^2}$$

Thus if the time of exposure is doubled, the milliamps can be reduced to half. For gamma radiation,

$$\frac{\text{curies} \times \text{time}}{(\text{distance})^2}$$

If the time of exposure is doubled, the curies (or roentgens) can be reduced to half. The exposure factor thus combines source strength, time, and the inverse-square law.

The silver bromide emulsion occurs as grains, visible under a microscope. These give the visual impression called graininess. The slower films have less graininess and give better quality of photography than the faster films do. Graininess increases if the kilovoltage is increased, or if fluorescent intensifying screens are used. If quality of radiography is the critical factor, a slow film will therefore be used, but if short exposure times are necessary, a fast film is the choice.

Normal developing time for X-ray film is 5 min at a temperature of 68 F. Reduced development time is required at higher temperatures of the developer solution. The developing chemicals generally contain metol and hydroquinone and have the chemical action of reducing the silver bromide and removing the bromide from the exposed silver. The developer has little effect on the bromide that has received no exposure. An alkali solution is required for development, the alkali allowing the developing chemicals to enter the pores of the emulsion. Sodium sulfate and potassium bromide are added for preservative and to suppress fogging.

To stop the development of the film, it is immersed in an acid stop bath for half a minute to a minute. This bath consists of a dilute acetic acid solution to neutralize the alkali of the developer.

Fig. 164 4 1/2 by 17 X-ray film hung on film hangers for processing.

The last step in the finishing process is fixing. This removes the undeveloped silver from the emulsion by means of sodium thiosulfate (hypo) or ammonium thiosulfate. A weak acid is also added to the fixer to neutralize any alkaline developer adhering to the film. Finally, a hardening agent such as aluminum chloride is added to the fixer to harden the emulsion.

The film is washed in running water after fixing to remove any adhering chemicals. Washing time is at least 20 min. The last step in the film-processing sequence is to dry the film in a drying cabinet with hot air. Small drying cabinets for the purpose are often improvised with some aluminum sheet and a portable hair dryer of the kind used in beauty parlors. Film processed through these stages will give a permanent record unless constantly exposed to direct sunlight. Figure 164 shows an X-ray film hung on a film hanger for processing. Figure 165 is a photograph of the processing tanks in a small X-ray dark room.

Fig. 165 X-ray film processing tank in a darkroom.

As the developer solution processes more and more film, its effectiveness decreases. To restore the developer, replenishers are added to the tank. The developer chemicals will be exhausted more rapidly with highly exposed film than with film less exposed or less dark. The film is always agitated during developing and fixing. Failure to do this will result in streaks in the film.

The low-illumination red lights used in darkrooms are called *safelights*. These use a bulb of 10 w or less. Red light is used because the photon energy of red light is the lowest in the visible range of radiation. X-ray film is not especially sensitive to such light, since the X-ray emulsion is blue-sensitive. However, the film is exposed to the safelights only for loading and unloading the film and for film processing. The amount of fogging produced by such exposure is not detectable.

20.26 photographic density

The amount of film blackening is called photographic density, or density for short. Figure 166 is a radiograph of a step wedge of varying thicknesses of metal, showing several degrees of density. A density of 1.0 is very light, 2.0 is gray, and 3.0 or higher is black. Maximum densities of about 4.5 are sometimes used, but such high densities require high-intensity illuminators if the film is to be read. Density is quantitatively defined as the logarithm to the base 10 of the ratio of the visible-light intensity incident on the film to the light transmitted by the film:

$$D = \log_{10} \frac{I_0}{I_t}$$

where $I_0 =$ intensity of light received and $I_t =$ intensity of light transmitted by the film. The darker the film, the less light it will transmit and the higher the density.

Suppose the density is 1.0 (very limited blackening). Then 1.0 is the

Fig. 166 Radiograph of a step wedge showing various densities, from 1.9 to 0.6.

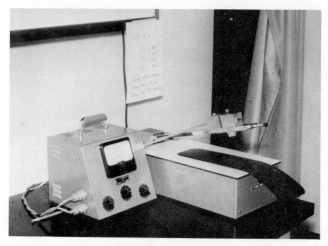

Fig. 167 A densitometer with a sheet of X-ray film in position.

logarithm of 10 or $^{10}\!/_1$. A film of this density transmits only 10% of the light received by it. Suppose the density is 2.0. Then since $10^2 = {}^{100}\!/_1$, the film transmits only 1% of the light that falls on it. For a density of 3.0, the film will transmit only $\frac{1}{10}$% of incident light. If a sheet of white bond paper is held up to the light, it will transmit a certain amount of light. Such paper has a density of 0.4. Since $10^{0.4} = 2.5$, such paper transmits 40% of the light it receives. Such medical X rays as a chest X ray or an X ray for a fracture, use a density of 1.5. Since $10^{1.5} = 31.6$, the medical X-ray film transmits about 3% of any light received.

Density is measured on an instrument called a *densitometer*, one type of which is shown in Fig. 167. This instrument uses a light source on one side of the film and a photoelectric cell on the other. The current produced in the photoelectric cell is read out on a microammeter with a scale graduated in density units. Actually, with only a little experience, any person can become reasonably proficient in estimating densities by eye.

It is differences in density in the radiograph that reveal flaws in the weld.

20.27 X-ray film

Manufacturers supply film in several speeds, types, and sizes. Standard sizes of X-ray film, in packages of 25, 50, 75, or 100 sheets, are as follows:

$3\frac{1}{2} \times 17$	8×10
$4\frac{1}{2} \times 10$	10×12

$4\frac{1}{2} \times 17$		11×14
5×7		14×17
7×17		

or are available in rolls 200 ft long or longer, 16, 35, 52, and 70 mm and 5 in. wide. Equivalent films in three brands are shown in the following table, the fastest film at the top and the slowest film at the bottom:

Kodak	Dupont	Ansco Superay
F	504	D
KK		C
AA	506	A
M	510	B

The list is not a complete list for any manufacturer.

For each type of film, the manufacturer can supply a film *characteristic curve*. Figure 168 gives the characteristic curves for Kodak grades with lead backing screens. These curves give densities against relative exposure expressed as log relative exposure. As this is slightly confusing, the following examples may be helpful:

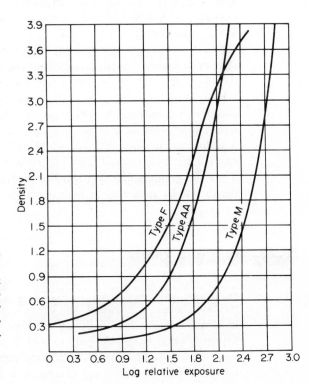

Fig. 168 Characteristic curves of Kodak Industrial X-ray Film, Types F, AA and M. Developed 5 minutes at 68F in Kodak Rapid X-ray Developer or Kodak Liquid X-ray Developer and Replenisher. (Courtesy Radiography Markets Division, Eastman Kodak Company)

Example 1

Using Kodak M, an exposure of 50 mam (milliamp-minutes) gives a density of 1.5. A density of 2.5 is desired. What exposure should be used?

For $D = 1.5$ and Kodak M, log relative exposure is 2.4. For $D = 2.5$, log relative exposure is 2.64. The logarithm 2.4 means $10^{2.4}$, and $10^{2.4} = 250$. Similarly log 2.64 means $10^{2.64}$, which is 435.

The required exposure is $^{435}\!/_{250} \times 50$ mam $= 87$ mam.

Example 2

Using Kodak AA, an exposure of 30 mam gives a density of 1.4. Find the exposure for a density of 2.4.

For $D = 1.4$, log relative exposure is 1.74, a relative exposure of 55. For $D = 2.4$, log relative exposure is 2.0, a relative exposure of 100. The required exposure $= ^{100}\!/_{55} \times 30$ mam $= 55$ mam.

The characteristic curves also provide information on relative speeds of the grades of film. As an example, compare at a density of 1.5 Kodak AA and M. At this density, log relative exposure of AA is 1.65, corresponding to a relative exposure of $10^{1.65}$ or $44\frac{1}{2}$, whereas log relative exposure of film M is 2.2, a relative exposure of $10^{2.2}$ or 158. The relative speeds of these two films are as $44\frac{1}{2}$ is to 158. For every $44\frac{1}{2}$ mam of exposure with AA, 158 mam are required with type M to do the same job at the same density.

For most industrial X-ray film, the characteristic curve becomes steeper at higher densities. Industrial radiography uses the highest possible densities that can be examined on the X-ray illuminator. Consider two slightly different thicknesses in a radiographed weld, due perhaps to incomplete penetration. The two thicknesses will produce two slightly different exposures. For this small difference in exposure there will be a difference in film density, which will depend on the portion of the characteristic curve used. This difference is greatest for the higher densities. Thus the greatest film contrast between weld defect and absence of weld defect will be indicated at high densities.

20.28 exposure charts

A typical exposure chart is shown in Fig. 169. This graph shows the relation between material thickness and kilovoltage (or curies) and milliamp-minutes for an X-ray tube or minutes for a source. Such an exposure chart is specific only to a certain X-ray tube, a definite development time (usually 5 min), a definite density, a specific film, and a fixed source-to-film distance, and of course a specific metal or alloy.

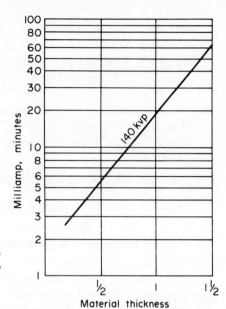

To prepare an exposure chart, a pile of plates is built up to produce a stepped wedge, like the one photographed in Fig. 166. Such wedges may also be purchased in various metals. The photographic procedure for making an exposure chart is as follows:

1. At the desired kilovoltage a series of exposures of the wedge is made. A geometric progression is used, such as 1, 2, 4, 8, 16 min.
2. For each exposure time, measure the film density at a number of wedge thicknesses.
3. Record these densities in a table similar to the following:

Thickness, in.	Film Density			
	1 min	2 min	4 min	8 min
0.1				
0.2				
0.3				
etc.				

4. From this tabulation, plot a series of density-thickness curves on a single graph sheet. Use one curve for each time period used in the tabulation.
5. From these curves, interpolate the thickness at which the required film density is obtained in each separate exposure.
6. On semilog paper (Fig. 169) plot the thickness and exposure values. This is the exposure chart. The points on the chart may tend to form a slight curve instead of a straight line. This will happen if the thicker

portions of the wedge act as a filter for the softer components of the radiation.

The exposure chart may also be used for certain changes in the photographic conditions:

1. Change in source-to-film distance: correct by using the inverse square law.
2. Change to a different film: correct by comparing the film speeds of the two films.
3. Change in density: correct by using the characteristic curve of the film.
4. Change in the metal to be radiographed: use the equivalence factor table.

The exposure chart is sometimes referred to as a "technique" chart.

20.29 penetrameters

Most specifications require that the radiographic technique disclose defects as small as 2% of the thickness of the material to be radiographed. Proof must therefore be furnished that this sensitivity has been met in the radiograph. The method of proof is to add an artificial defect that is 2% of the thickness.

This artificial defect is called a *penetrameter* and a typical one is shown in Fig. 170. This penetrameter is identified as 50FE, signifying that

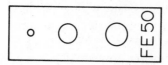 Fig. 170 Penetrameter.

it is used in the radiography of steel alloys 0.50 in. thick or greater.

Before radiographing a weld, the penetrameter is placed on the workpiece on the source side at one end of the weld but not above any possible defect area. If the finished radiograph discloses the penetrameter and its three holes, this is acceptable proof that any 2% defect is disclosed also.

20.30 the production
of a radiograph

In the production of a radiograph, a film type is first selected. The required kilovoltage or source is decided, as well as the source-to-film distance and the required film density. Then from an exposure chart the exposure is determined, milliamp-minutes for a tube or minutes for a source.

In the darkroom a sheet of film of the required size is placed in the film cassette. Redipack film, already packed and ready for radiography, may be used. The cassette or redipack is then attached to the weldment. Lead letters are attached to the weldment to identify the job number and location of the photograph on the weldment. Personnel are then cleared from the area, which is then marked as a radiation area, and the photograph is taken.

As thus established, the sequence of operations in making a radiograph is a simple and routine. But the mere acts of fastening the film and taking the picture do not guarantee that defects will be disclosed, or if disclosed, that they will be properly interpreted. A flat closed crack of less than 2% of the workpiece thickness may be missed, especially if the radiation is at right angles to the crack.

Butt welds are customarily shot at right angles to the plane of the weld, for reasons of economy. In circumferential butt welds in pipe, this is not effective, since the top of the pipe weld will be superimposed on the bottom of the pipe weld in the radiograph. On small diameter pipe, what is called the double-wall technique, using a small aspect angle to the radiation, is employed, as indicated in Fig. 171. The image of the weld will be an oval pattern. Circumferential butt welds on tanks may be shot by fastening roll film around the weld area on the outside of the tank and placing the radiation source at the center of the tank.

Fillet welds are most usually examined by directing the radiation at an angle that roughly bisects the angle of the joint. Unlike butt welds, fillet welds have a considerable variation in the thickness of metal to be penetrated. This condition may produce either underexposure of thick sections or overexposure of thin sections of metal. Either effect produces a loss of flaw sensitivity.

Even more difficult radiographic conditions are presented by a solid round bar that must be examined by a beam of radiation at right angles to its length. Here the section thickness varies from a maximum at the middle to zero at the two sides. On solution to the problem is the double-film technique, which simultaneously shoots superimposed fast and slow film

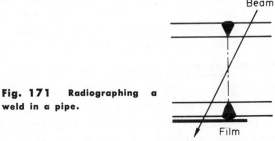

Fig. 171 **Radiographing a weld in a pipe.**

placed under the specimen. The fast film will supply a satisfactory radiograph of the thicker sections and the slow film of the thinner sections. Alternately, a section-equalizing technique may be used. The outer and thinner part of the specimen may be built up with a material of density similar to that of the specimen, either with thin strips or a cradle. The same effect is produced by immersing the workpiece in a bath of liquid with approximately the same absorption as the specimen. There are of course no liquids with the density of steel, except molten steel, but such liquids can be formulated by dissolving lead acetate or other heavy compounds in water. A round bar would be immersed in such a liquid up to the level of its horizontal diameter. There must be no air bubbles in the liquid, since these will be interpreted as blowholes in the workpiece.

Radiographs are examined by illuminators made for this purpose. Under examination, the images disclosed on the processed film may be any of the following:

1. Internal defects in the weld
2. Accidental markings on the metal surface due to undercut, hammer marks, weld spatter, and others
3. Film markings arising from mishandling of the film, such as undue pressure on the film

20.31 technique for radiographic examination of welded joints

Perhaps no authority explains radiographic procedure better than specification UW-51 of Section VIII of the *Boiler and Pressure Vessel Code,* "Technique for Radiographic Examination of Welded Joints." The following procedure is abstracted from the Code, UW-51:

(b) The weld ripples or weld surface irregularities, on both the inside and the outside, shall be removed by any suitable mechanical process to a degree such that the resulting radiographic contrast due to any remaining irregularities cannot mask or be confused with that of any objectionable defect. Also the weld surface shall merge smoothly into the plate surface. The finished surface of the reinforcement may be flush with the plate or have a reasonably uniform crown not to exceed the following thickness:

Plate Thickness	Thickness of Reinforcement, inches
up to ½″ incl.	$\frac{1}{16}$
over ½″ to 1″	$\frac{3}{32}$
over 1 to 2	$\frac{1}{8}$
over 2	$\frac{5}{32}$

(d) The weld shall be radiographed with a technique which will indicate the size of defects having a thickness equal to and greater than 2% of the base metal thickness.

(e) Penetrameters shall be placed on the side nearest the radiation source. At least one penetrameter shall be used for each exposure, to be placed at one end of the exposed length, parallel and adjacent to the weld seam, with the small holes at the outer end. Material of the penetrameter shall be substantially the same as that of the plate under examination. Thickness of the penetrameter shall not be more than 2 per cent of the thickness of the plate being radiographed.

(j) Identification markers, the images of which will appear on the film, shall be placed adjacent to the weld, and their locations shall be accurately and permanently marked on the outside surface near the weld, so that a defect appearing on the radiograph may be accurately located.

(k) The job number, the vessel, the seam, and the manufacturer's identification symbol or name shall be plainly indicated on each film.

(m) Sections of weld that are shown by radiography to have any of the following types of imperfections shall be judged unacceptable and shall be repaired.

(1) Any type of crack or zone of incomplete fusion or penetration.

(2) Any elongated slag inclusion which has a length greater than
$\frac{1}{4}''$ for T up to $\frac{3}{4}''$
$\frac{1}{3}$ T for T from $\frac{3}{4}''$ to $2\frac{1}{4}''$
$\frac{3}{4}''$ for T over $2\frac{1}{4}''$
where T is the thickness of the thinner plate being welded.

(3) Any group of slag inclusions in line that have an aggregate length greater than T in a length of 12T, except that the distance between the successive imperfections may exceed 6L where L is the length of the longest imperfection in the group.

(4) Porosity in excess of that shown as acceptable by the standards given in Appendix IV. [This appendix consists of six pages of porosity charts.]

PROBLEMS

1 How would you distinguish between the following on a radiograph:
(a) a blowhole and a slag inclusion
(b) a crack and lack of penetration

2 What are the basic requirements imposed on a liquid to be used for penetrant inspection?

3 Why is a clean surface required for penetrant inspection?

4 Why must dye penetrant leak testing be performed before any hydrostatic test is executed?

5 What is the basic principle behind the magnetic particle test?

6 How is a part demagnetized after magnetic particle inspection?

7 Why is high frequency necessary for ultrasonic flaw detection?

8 Calculate the approximate velocity of sound in an aluminum alloy weighing 169 lb per cu ft with an E value of 10×10^6.

9 Explain why a couplant may be needed in ultrasonic flaw detection.

10 Why are safelights in radiographic darkrooms red?

11 Why are sources bought by the curie instead of by the pound weight? Suppose sources could be bought by the roentgen. Would this be better for the user and why?

12 Why are radioisotopes often shipped by air freight despite the weight of their containers?

13 (a) What is the approximate curie strength of 32 curies of iridium-192 after 1 year?
(b) What is the approximate curie strength of 100 curies of cobalt-60 in 1964 if it was bought in 1948?

14 This problem requires more than high school mathematics. Determine the age of the earth, given the following information:
Uranium-238, with a half-life of 4½ billion years, decays to lead-206, which is stable (infinite half-life). U-238 always contains Pb-206 because this lead is the end element of uranium disintegration. For every 100 atoms in the uranium-lead mixture, 46 are lead and 54 are uranium.
The answer to this problem can be conjectured with an error of about 30 million years without doing any mathematics at all. Try it.

15 Define a curie and a roentgen.

16 Why is ionizing radiation more dangerous to bone than to soft tissue?

17 What three methods are available for the protection of personnel from ionizing radiation?

18 (a) Supposing that the statistics in the background radiation table of Sec. 20.15 are true, which exposes you to more background radiation, atmospheric fallout or the hobby of gardening?
(b) Do you have any reasons for being somewhat skeptical about this background radiation table?

19 Probably the greatest hazard to your life is highway driving. Could the general methods employed in programs of radiation safety be applied to highway driving? How? Would highway driving then be as safe as radiation work is?

20 What advantages does the pocket dosimeter have over the film badge and the film badge over the pocket dosimeter?

21 Explain the operation of the Geiger-Muller counter.

22 An exposure of 10 min is required for radiographing with a focus-to-film distance of 3 ft. What is the required exposure (a) at 5 ft   (b) at 2 ft?

23 For an unshielded 10-c source of cobalt-60, what is the exposure in roentgens per hour at 3 m if two half-value layers of concrete are interposed?

24 For an unshielded 10-c source of cobalt-60, what is the exposure in milliroentgens per hour at 10 m if the protection of three half-value layers is employed?

25 (a) According to the equivalence factor table in Sec. 20.20, how many inches of magnesium is equivalent to 1 in. of aluminum at 100 kv?
(b) How many inches of copper is equivalent to 2 in. of steel at 150 kv?
(c) Why is there little difference in equivalence factors for Co-60?
(d) According to the equivalence factor table, aluminum 2024 (containing about 4% copper) absorbs more radiation than pure aluminum. Why?

26 Why is lead foil sometimes placed on the back of the photographic film?

27 Which is the principal absorption process
(a) at lower kilovoltages
(b) medium ranges of kilovoltages
(c) high-energy radiation

28 What is unsharpness? What factors influence the degree of unsharpness?

29 What is an exposure factor?

30 What percentage of light will be transmitted for the following densities: (a) 0.6, (b) 1.8, (c) 2.2?

31 Suppose that an exposure of 20 mam gives a density of 2.0 with Kodak M film. What exposure is required to produce a density of 3.0?

32 (a) An exposure of 30 min gives a density of 3.0 with Kodak AA film. What exposure will produce a density of 1.8?
(b) A density of 2.5?

33 What is a penetrameter?

FABRICATION

METHODS

Part **V**

Materials may be stressed in tension (pull), compression (crushing), or shear (cutting), or in a combination of any of these. A constantly applied stress, such as the load carried by a foundation pile under a building, is termed a *static stress*. Suddenly applied stress, as from a pile driver or a forging hammer, or repeatedly applied stress, such as received by vehicle springs, is called a *dynamic stress*. Dynamic stresses are much more difficult to design for and are the cause of most unpredictable stress failures. *Residual stresses* are stresses built into a structure as a result of fabrication and are always present in weldment because of weld shrinkage and distortion.

Figure 172 shows a cantilever beam carrying an end load. The beam must strain or deflect under the load, and this deflection takes the form of a bend that may or may not be visible, depending on the magnitude of the stress, the modulus of elasticity of the beam material, and the stiffness of the beam cross section. The amount of beam deflection is usually proportional to the load applied to the end of the beam, until the point is reached at which plastic strain replaces elastic strain. All three types of stress are present in the beam—tension, compression, and shear. The top surface of the beam is under tension, the bottom surface under compression. In addition, there are shear stresses in the beam. The wall that supports the beam must exert an upward force on the beam, whereas the load exerts a downward force. These two forces exert a scissors effect that if great enough would shear through the beam just as though the beam were placed in a shear and cut through. Any machine member that is bent or flexed is subject to all three types of basic stress.

STRESSES

IN

WELDS

21

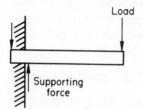

Load

Supporting
force

Fig. 172 Cantilever beam
under an end load.

It is not customary to load structures to stresses as high as the yield strength of the material. At the yield load, control is lost over the dimensions and deflections of the material, which at that point begins to develop strains of indefinite magnitude. The yield stress itself is known by actual destructive tests performed on samples of the material. Stresses are held well below the yield stress by applying *factors of safety*. If a structural steel has a yield stress of 33,000 psi, most building codes will limit the allowable stress to 20,000 psi (or even less). The factor of safety, based on the yield stress, is then 33,000/20,000 or 1.65. Thus there is a margin for uncertainty, error, material variation, and downright mistakes of 65%, which has been found by experience to be sufficient for such structures as steel building frames and warehouse racking.

21.2 stresses in fillet welds

The smallest cross section of a fillet weld is the throat, or the section at 45° to either leg. Stresses will be highest on the throat area of a fillet weld because this area is the smallest that must carry the stresses for the fillet weld. The area of a fillet throat is 0.707 × leg length. It is assumed that a fillet weld can fail only in shear. The following example illustrates the calculation of throat stresses.

Example A certain construction code limits shear stresses in fillet welds to 11,000 psi in low-carbon structural steels with a yield stress in tension of 33,000 psi. What is the maximum load that a fillet weld can support per inch of weld if the two legs of the weld are $\frac{3}{8}$ in.?

The length of weld is 1 in. The width of the weld sustaining the shear stresses is the throat dimension, 0.707 × leg, or 0.265 in. The total cross-sectional area supporting the load of 11,000 psi is 0.265 × 1, or 0.265 sq in.

$$\text{stress in psi} = \frac{\text{load}}{\text{area}}$$

$$11,000 \text{ psi} = \text{load}/0.265$$

Allowable load $= 11,000 \times 0.265 = 2920$ lb per in. of fillet weld.

For another application of shear stress in fillet welds, consider the following case. A 60,000-gal overhead tank is supported on four legs. The steel of the empty tank weighs 20,000 lb (tank only, not including the supporting legs). How many inches of fillet weld with ⅜ in. leg are needed to joint the legs to the tank, if the tank specification allows 11,250 psi in shear?

The fillet welds joining the tank to the four legs must support the overhead tank and its water contents by means of shear stresses. To determine the weight of the water, recall that 1 U.S. gal = 8.33 lb. Total weight of tank and contents = (8⅓ × 60,000) + 20,000 = 520,-000 lb. Allowable load per inch of ⅜ in. fillet weld = 0.707 × 0.375 × 11250 = 3000 lb. Required minimum number of inches of fillet weld on four legs = 520,000/3000 = 174 in., or 44 in. per leg.

21.3 hydrostatic stresses

If a flat-bottomed storage tank is filled with water, there is a hydrostatic pressure over the flat bottom of the tank due to the dead weight of the water. Consider a head of 1 ft of water supported by 1 sq ft of bottom, which is a cubic foot of water. What is the pressure in pounds per square inch on the tank bottom due to 1 ft of head?

One cubic foot of water weighs 62.4 lb at room temperature. This 62.4 lb is supported by 144 sq in. of bottom surface. The pressure on the bottom in psi

$$= s = \frac{P}{A}$$

$$= {}^{62.4}/_{144} = 0.434 \text{ psi}$$

Therefore 1 ft of water produces a load or stress of 0.434 psi, or 2.3 ft of water head equals 1 psi.

Example 1
What is the compressive stress on a tank bottom for a head of 40 ft of water?

$$40 \times 0.434 = 17.5 \text{ psi}$$

Example 2
As you drive through a certain town, you estimate the height of the town's overhead tank as 120 ft. What is maximum town water pressure?

$$120 \times 0.434 = 52 \text{ psi pressure}$$

21.4 the electric resistance strain gauge

The above simple stress situations are easy to calculate, but in a great many instances it is simply impossible to determine stress by calculation. It is then necessary to have practical methods of determining stress: Although there is no such thing as a stress meter, many strain-measuring instruments are available, and if the strain can be found, the stress is obtained by multiplying by the E value of the material.

One of the best devices for obtaining the strain (and stress) at a point in a structure is the electric resistance strain gauge. This is a tiny gauge that can be cemented to the surface of a metal to indicate the strain in the material. Figure 173 shows a strain gauge testing of a warehouse rack. The small gauges are cemented to the legs of the rack and are reading out compression stresses and shear stresses in the legs.

The little strain gauge contains a grid of fine wire about 0.001 in. in diameter of copper-nickel alloy. If this grid of wire is cemented to the test specimen and the specimen is loaded, the wire grid must strain the same amount as the surface to which it is cemented. Suppose that the specimen is loaded in tension. Then the strain gauge wire grid will be stretched. This stretching will lengthen the grid wires and reduce their cross section. Both these effects will increase the electrical resistance of the wire by perhaps several millionths of an ohm. There is a direct correlation between change in electric resistance and change in strain (or stress). The small gauge is connected to an instrument called a strain indicator, which reads out the change in resistance as a change in strain

Fig. 173 Strain gauge testing of welded warehouse racking. The tiny white patches on the legs of the racking are resistance strain gauges. The concrete blocks subject the rack to a known load, and the stress and strain in the rack are read out on the two rectangular panel instruments in front of the rack. A concrete block may be seen being weighed on a scale behind the rack.

in millionths of an inch. Since temperature changes will also change the electrical resistance, the instrument must have temperature compensation.

Another less accurate but simpler method of finding stresses is the Stresscoat method. The structure is painted with a brittle paint which cracks when the structure is strained (stressed). The pattern of the cracks in the Stresscoat can be analyzed to determine the stresses.

21.5 stresses in thin-walled cylinders

Here we consider a thin-walled cylinder, such as a piece of tubing, with an internal pressure. The stresses in the wall of the tubing are to be determined. We must first make the following assumptions:

1. There are no thermal stresses.
2. The cylinder material is elastic and not plastic. (This analysis does not apply to polyethylene pipe, for example).
3. There are no bending stresses, only bursting stresses (that is, the cylinder is not supported on two cradles).
4. The thickness of the cylinder wall divided by the diameter is $\frac{1}{10}$ or less, that is, the cylinder must be thin-walled with respect to its diameter.

To determine first the stress in a longitudinal butt joint in the cylinder (full penetration assumed), we use Fig. 174 and the following notation:

p = internal pressure, psi
D = diameter, inches
t = wall thickness, inches

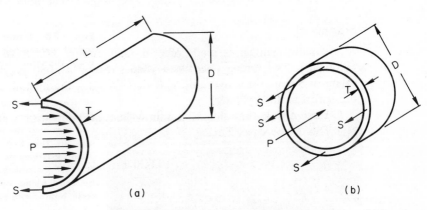

(a) (b)

Fig. 174 Stresses in the wall of a thin cylinder. (a) Longitudinal stress, (b) circumferential stress.

The force tending to separate the two halves of the cylinder is pDL, where $L =$ cylinder length. For convenience take L as 1. This bursting force is resisted by the tension forces in the material of the cylinder. These tension forces $= s \times t \times 2$, where $s =$ the tension stress.

Then
$$pD = 2st$$

and
$$s = pD/2t$$

For the stress in a circumferential or girth weld, full penetration only, consider that the force tending to blow off the cylinder end is $p\pi R^2$, where πR^2 is the cylinder end area. Substitute as follows:

$$\pi R^2 = \frac{\pi}{4} D^2$$

The force $p\pi R^2 = p \left(\frac{\pi}{4}\right) D^2$ is resisted by the stress in the circumferential butt weld. The resisting force in the butt weld $= (\pi Dt)s$

$$\pi Dts = \frac{\pi}{4} D^2 p$$

$$ts = \frac{pD}{4}$$

and
$$s = \frac{pD}{4t}$$

which is half the longitudinal stress. The longitudinal weld will fail first.

Example

A hydraulic cylinder is made of 6-in.-O.D. tubing with a 16-gauge wall (0.06 in.). The tubing steel has a yield stress of 42,000 psi. A factor of safety of 3 is used for hydraulic cylinders. What is the maximum allowable pressure for this cylinder?

First check that this is a thin-walled cylinder with t/D less than $\frac{1}{10}$. This is the case. Then

$$s = {}^{42,000}\!/_{3} = 14,000 \text{ psi allowable}$$

and
$$p = \text{unknown}$$
$$D = 6$$
$$t = 0.06$$

Then $\qquad p = \dfrac{2ts}{D}$

$$= \dfrac{2 \times 0.06 \times 14{,}000}{6} = 280 \text{ psi}$$

21.6 unfired pressure vessels

For the design of cylindrical pressure vessels, unfired, the boiler code does not allow the use of the following formula for longitudinal stresses; $s = pD/2t$. This formula assumes that the welded longitudinal butt joints in the cylinder are as strong as the plate itself: for a pressure vessel, such an assumption must first be proved correct. If all welded butt joints are welded from both sides of the joint and fully radiographed, then the joint may be assumed to be as strong as the parent plate, that is, joint efficiency is 100%. If all joints are double-butt-welded and only spot-radiographed with at least one radiograph every 50 ft of welding, then joint efficiency E must be taken at only 85% of the strength of the parent plate. If there is no radiography, then joint efficiency E must be taken at 70% for double butt welding. Tables of allowable stress are given in the code. In general, the allowable stress for any steel plate is about one-quarter of the ultimate tensile strength, provided the temperature of the vessel does not exceed 650F.

Design formulas for unfired pressure vessels are either

$$t = \dfrac{PR}{SE - 0.6P} \quad \text{OR} \quad P = \dfrac{SEt}{R + 0.6t}$$

where $\quad t =$ thickness of shell plate
$\qquad P =$ internal pressure, psi

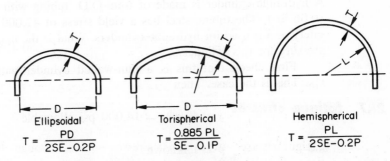

Fig. 175   Pressure vessel heads and design formulas. (ASME Boiler and Pressure Vessel Code)

R = inside radius, in.
S = allowable stress
E = efficiency of the welded joints
 = 1.00 for full radiography
 = 0.85 for spot radiography
 = 0.70 for no radiography

The cylindrical pressure vessel must be equipped with two formed heads. Standard heads and their design formulas are shown in Fig. 175.

The following are the dimensions of a commonly seen propane tank:

maximum working pressure	250 psi
inside radius of cylindrical shell	20 in.
hemispherical heads, inside radius L	20 in.
allowable stress	17,250 psi

To find the plate thickness for the hemispherical heads

$$t = \frac{PL}{2SE - 0.2P} = \frac{250 \times 20}{2 \times 17250 \times 0.85 - 0.2P} = 0.17 \text{ in. for } E = 0.85$$

The thickness of the cylindrical shell depends on the radiography. For 100% radiography, $E = 1.00$

$$t = \frac{250 \times 20}{17250 \times 1 - 0.6 \times 250} = 0.292$$

For spot radiography, $E = 0.85$

$$t = \frac{250 \times 20}{17250 \times 0.85 - 0.6 \times 250} = 0.344$$

For no radiography, $E = 0.70$

$$t = \frac{250 \times 20}{17250 \times 0.7 - 0.6 \times 250} = 0.416$$

21.7 fatigue stresses

Fatigue stresses are dynamic stresses applied through thousands or millions of cycles. Such machine parts as springs, axles, exhaust valve stems, truck frames, aircraft propellors, and aircraft wings rarely fail from static stresses but from fatigue stresses of much lower intensity than the static stresses they can withstand.

Consider the following case: A welding shop has built hundreds of steel truck dump boxes, but one day turns out its first aluminum dump body. The aluminum sections of the body are heavy, and the aluminum welds are skillfully made with experienced operators and proper equipment. Tension tests show that the welds meet the required strength levels, more than 30,000 psi. After the customer has tried out his aluminum dump body for a month, perhaps he phones the fabricating shop to express his satisfaction.

Then a crack develops, not in one of the welds, but just at the edge of the weld. The body is returned to the shop for repairs. A week later perhaps, more cracks may appear. Since the cracks are not in the weld but in the adjacent plate, the welds are not suspect but the aluminum plate is.

What was wrong with the aluminum plate? Nothing.

Perhaps the weld shop was not aware that nonferrous metals are more sensitive to fatigue than steels are. In order to ensure that their first aluminum body would not fail, the welders reinforced their welds above the plate surface. However well-intentioned, this was a serious mistake. Changes in section, even a slight weld reinforcement, promote fatigue failure. The best joint for fatigue resistance is a smooth double-welded butt joint. By reinforcing the joint, the operator ensured that the weld would not fail, but he also ensured fatigue failure at the edge of the joint, where the stress is raised by reason of the weld reinforcement. This is not a matter of the damaging heat effects in the heat-affected zone but a matter of *stress concentration*.

A fatigue failure is always a tension failure. The crack always commences at the surface at some change of section such as a scratch or surface roughness, a crater crack, or even an arc burn, and through continued working and cycling the crack slowly deepens until there is no longer sufficient metal section to carry the load. Since fatigue is a tension failure, it follows that materials of higher tensile strength should have higher fatigue strengths. Steels have ultimate tensile strengths of 60,000 psi or greater. Aluminum alloys suitable for welding do not have ultimate tensile strengths in excess of 40,000 psi and thus will not match the steels for fatigue resistance.

Since a fillet weld involves a change of contour in the weld section, fillet welds promote fatigue failure. As in a butt weld, the failure will not likely take place in the weld but at the edge of the weld. Weld concavity or convexity will make fatigue failure more likely, because shape factors increase the concentration of stress. If fatigue is to be expected, double fillet welds and double lap welds must be used where possible, and the fillet weld should be continuous, not intermittent. Butt welds expected to sustain fatigue loadings should be welded from both sides. Backing strips and backing rings should not be used.

PROBLEMS

1 How much shear load in pounds can be carried by a 1-in.-long fillet weld, ¼ in. leg length, if the allowable stress is 11,500 psi?

2 A building beam carrying a floor load of 50 tons is supported at each end of the beam by a vertical column. The beam-to-column connection is made by means of fillet welds. If the allowable shear stress is 13,000 psi, how many inches of ⅜-in. leg fillet weld are required at each connection?

3 A certain nickel alloy has an ultimate tensile strength of 80,000 psi. The boiler code permits an allowable stress for this material of 7300 psi. What is the factor of safety?

4 What is the total force required to punch a ⅞-in.-diameter hole in ¾-in. thick material with an ultimate shear strength of 30,000 psi?

5 You estimate the height of the overhead tank in a certain town as 92 ft. What is maximum water pressure in the town at street level?

6 What is the pressure on a submarine at a depth of 600 ft?

7 The feedwater pump for a certain high-pressure boiler supplies water to the boiler at a pressure of 2000 psi. How high a column of water could this pump support?

8 A certain grade of 4-in. pipe has an inside diameter of 4.00 in. and a wall thickness of 0.250 in. If the allowable stress in the pipe wall is 15,000 psi, how much pressure may the pipe support
(a) if the pipe is considered to be a thin-walled cylinder
(b) if the pipe is considered to be a cylindrical unfired pressure vessel (no radiography)?

9 A 1-in. Schedule 40 pipe has an inside diameter of 1.097 in. and a wall thickness of 0.109 in. If this pipe meets the assumptions for the formula for thin-walled cylinders, find the allowable pressure for an allowable stress of 15,000 psi. If not, apply the boiler code formula using the same stress and assuming no radiography.

10 A water storage tank has a diameter of 30 ft and a plate thickness of ¼ in. If this tank is considered to be a thin-walled cylinder (not a pressure vessel) with an allowable stress of 15,000 psi, what is the maximum height of water that can be allowed in the tank?

11 (a) Find the wall thickness of a propane storage tank, given the following information: tank inside diameter 50 in., maximum allowable pressure 250 psi, allowable stress 18,000 psi, 100% radiography.

(b) What will be the wall thickness if radiography is not done?

12 Find the wall thickness for a propane storage tank, given the following information: tank inside diameter 40 in., material aluminum 6061-T6 with allowable stress 6000 psi, 100% radiography, maximum working pressure 250 psi.

22.1 pipe and tubing

It is not easy to explain the difference between pipe and tubing. There are a number of differences, the chief ones being those of raw material, manufacturing process, tolerances, finish, price, and dimensions (although tubing can be ordered to pipe dimensions). Pipe uses for raw material a sheet material called *skelp*, a hot-rolled mill edge sheet supplied in coils. The coil of skelp is unwound, heated in a continuous furnace, rolled into circular form, and then forge-welded by heat and pressure. This is the most common method of manufacturing pipe, though not the only method. Most tubing is resistance-welded, although seamless tubing is also produced. Tubing is made from hot or cold rolled sheet or strip that has been rolled to closer tolerances than skelp. Welded tubing is cold-roll-formed and the edges butt-welded electrically. Whereas pipe is normally furnished without removal of mill scale, tubing is free of scale.

The machines used for butt-welding pipe and tubing include some of the most expensive in use, costing $100,000 or more, and have welding speeds up to about 500 ft per min. Some of the pipe and tube welding methods were discussed under Resistance Welding. The Yoder Company, a familiar firm name in this business, can supply for pipe and tube production arc welders, radiofrequency induction welders, radio frequency resistance welders (called Thermatool welders), a-c–d-c resistance welders, and a-c welders in frequencies from 60 to 360 cycles.

Tolerances are rather loose for pipe and more rigid for tubing. The lower grades of pipe are allowed tolerances on wall thickness of 12½% under nominal thickness and 1% on outside diameter. Much pipe is

FABRICATION
PRACTICES

22

intended for threaded ends, whereas tubing is not threaded. If pipe is to be connected to threaded pipe fittings, then for all wall thicknesses the outside diameter must be held constant. The most common wall thicknesses are designated Standard or Schedule 40, and Extra Heavy (XH) or Schedule 80. Other Schedule wall thicknesses are also in use, from the thin-wall Sched 5 to the heavy-wall Sched 160.

DIMENSIONS OF SCHEDULE 40 AND SCHEDULE 80 PIPE
(In Inches)

Nominal Pipe Size	O.D.	Schedule 40					Schedule 80	
		I.D.	Wall Thickness	Weight/ Ft., lb.	Area of Metal, in.^{2}		I.D.	Wall Thickness
⅛	0.405	0.269	0.068	0.244	0.072		0.215	0.095
¼	0.540	0.364	0.088	0.424	0.125		0.302	0.119
⅜	0.675	0.493	0.091	0.567	0.167		0.423	0.126
½	0.840	0.622	0.109	0.850	0.25		0.546	0.147
¾	1.050	0.824	0.113	1.130	0.33		0.742	0.154
1	1.315	1.049	0.133	1.678	0.49		0.957	0.179
1¼	1.660	0.380	0.140	2.272	0.67		1.28	0.191
1½	1.900	1.610	0.145	2.717	0.80		1.50	0.200
2	2.375	2.067	0.154	3.65	1.075		1.94	0.22
2½	2.875	2.469	0.203	5.8	1.70		2.32	0.276
3	3.500	3.068	0.216	7.57	2.23		2.90	0.30
4	4.500	4.026	0.237	10.8	3.17		3.83	0.337
5	5.563	5.047	0.258	14.6	4.30		4.81	0.375
6	6.625	6.065	0.280	19.0	5.6		5.76	0.43
8	8.625	7.891	0.322	28.55	8.4		7.625	0.50
10	10.750	10.020	0.365	40.5	11.9		9.59	0.59
12	12.750	11.938	0.375	53.6	15.75		11.38	0.69

The pipe table indicates that Sched 80 pipe has about 50% more wall thickness than Sched 40. Pipe manufactured to ASTM A-120 standard is perhaps used the most. This standard includes black and galvanized welded and seamless pipe for ordinary uses with steam, water, gas, and air. It is not intended for close coiling or bending nor for high-temperature service. This is the lowest grade of pipe for which there is an ASTM standard. ASTM A-53 covers black and galvanized pipe for coiling and bending, and A-106 is the standard for seamless carbon steel pipe for high-temperature service and suitable for bending.

Wrought-iron pipe is sometimes used for corrosive service. Wrought iron contains about 2½% of silicate slag stringers. Corrosion of the pipe is generally stopped by these slag stringers, which are unaffected by all except the most aggressive chemicals. The slag stringers do not cause difficulty if the pipe is to be welded, but if the pipe must be cut with the oxyacetylene torch, an occasional large slag stringer may resist the heat of the torch.

For temperatures above 750 F and for power plant work, low-alloy piping, containing small amounts of chromium and molybdenum and manufactured to ASTM Standard A-335, must be used. Such pipe has special welding requirements determined by the alloy ingredients, including the use of low-alloy rods E7010, E8011, or those of higher strength.

Schedule pipe in stainless steel is designated 40S, 80S, etc. Most stainless pipe is produced in austenitic grades. Such piping is selected for high- and low-temperature work and for chemical and process piping. If such pipe must resist corrosive chemicals, stabilized stainless steels must be used, and welds must be ground smooth to leave no crevices.

Aluminum piping has been gaining in popularity. It is light in weight and resists corrosion by a variety of mild chemicals. Aluminum does not form toxic chemicals with most foods and drugs. Most other nonferrous metals are also used as piping materials. Lead piping has excellent resistance to aggressive chemicals but must be supported against its tendency to sag. Copper, nickel, and their alloys are selected for resistance to specific chemical attack, especially fresh and salt water.

Plastic pipe may be used for its light weight, ease of installation, or corrosion resistance. Thermoplastic piping materials are usually joinable either by adhesive bonding or by plastic welding. Most plastic pipe is produced to iron pipe sizes and in Schedules 40 and 80.

Brazed copper tubing is frequently substituted for pipe in plumbing systems. This tubing does not have standard pipe dimensions and is not intended for threading. Made of commercially pure copper, it is available in four types:

1. Type K: either hard or soft temper, for water, steam, and hot water service
2. Type L: hard or soft temper, for less severe service than type K
3. Type M: hard temper only, for interior heat and low pressure
4. Type DWV (drainage waste vent): hard temper only, for drain and vent lines

Tube is made in two principal grades; mechanical and pressure tubing. Mechanical tubing is the type that the welder usually fabricates. Most tubing is supplied in the cold-formed condition, either welded or seamless. Tubing is supplied to closer tolerances than pipe is, and its dimensions are almost always different from pipe dimensions.

Tubing has three dimensions: outside diameter, inside diameter, and wall thickness. Mechanical tubing ordinarily is ordered to outside diameter and wall thickness. If inside diameter is more important, then inside diameter and outside diameter will be specified. Whichever two of the three dimensions are specified, the tolerance error will fall on the dimen-

Fig. 176 Rollers for supporting belt conveyors used in conveying bulk materials. Such rollers are made of short lengths of tubing with MIG welded ends.

sion not specified. Standard sizes for round seamless cold-finished carbon steel mechanical tubing range from outside diameters of ⅜ to 1¾ in. by 1/16-in. increments and up to 3½ in. by ⅛-in. increments. Gauge thickness for the tube wall uses the Birmingham Wire Gauge (BWG) system, which is slightly different from the sheet steel gauge system:

Tubing Wall Thicknesses

BWG	Thickness
20	0.035
18	0.049
17	0.058
16	0.065
14	0.083
13	0.095
12	0.109
11	0.120
10	0.134
5/32″	0.156
3/16″	0.188
7/32″	0.219
1/4″	0.250

Like almost all products, tubing is sold by the pound. The weight of carbon steel tubing can be determined by the formula

$$W = 10.68 \ (D\text{-}t)t \ \text{lb/lineal ft}$$

where $D =$ outside diameter of tubing in inches and $t =$ wall thickness in inches.

Figure 176 is a photograph of welded steel tubing as used in belt conveyors for material handling. The ends of the tubes are usually MIG-welded. Later photographs in this chapter show welded tubing for boilers and steam generators. On a less dramatic scale, the wristbars of your wrist watch, by which the wrist strap is attached to the watch, are made of very small diameter tubing.

22.2 welding fittings for welded pipe

Welding fittings, such as weldells, T's, reducers, and others, are produced to high-quality standards, are stress-relieved, and are usually radiographed. Pipe ends for welding are beveled either 30 or 37½°, with a ¹⁄₁₆-in. nose for wall thicknesses up to ¾ in. Figure 177 shows the more commonly used welded pipe fittings, which are available in wall thicknesses from the light Sched 5 up to Sched 160 or even heavier and in a range of materials both ferrous and nonferrous. Socket welding fittings use a somewhat different joining method. Such fittings are so designed that the pipe length can be inserted into a socket in the fitting and welded to it. These fittings are usually forged carbon steel for pressures of 2000 psi or higher.

Valves are not made with beveled ends for welding, except for special valves such as high-pressure high-temperature steam valves rated at 900 psi and higher. These severe-duty valves are made of cast or forged steel and can be welded without harm to the valve. Valves for lower pressures usually have cast-iron bodies (except for corrosion service) unsuitable for welding. Such valves are usually flanged, though small valves may have screwed ends. Small bronze valves for use with copper

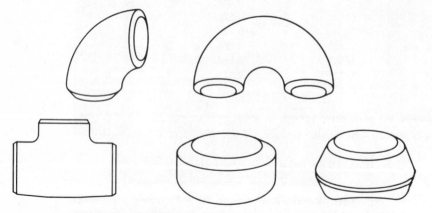

Fig. 177 Fittings for welded pipe: weldell, 180° return bend, cap, and weldolet.

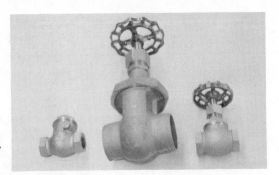

Fig. 178 Valves: swing, check, gate, and globe.

Fig. 179 OS&Y valves (outside screw and yoke valves). The rear valve with the screw projecting above the handwheel is open. The near valve is closed.

Fig. 180 Various pipe flanges. (a) A 12-inch slip-on flange and blind flange, (b) welded pipe showing seven weld-neck flanges.

tubing in plumbing lines have "solder ends" suitable for brazing to pipe. The common globe, gate, and check valves are shown in Fig. 178. The outside screw & yoke (OS & Y) valve (Fig. 179) has a stem that rises through the handle of the valve and indicates by its position whether the valve is open or closed.

The common pipe *flanges* (Fig. 180) are the weld neck, slip-on, and blind flange. Such flanges are of forged steel and rated for pressures of 150, 300, 400, 600, 900, 1500, and 2500 psi. The pipe is inserted into the flange and lap-welded at both ends of the flange. Pairs of flanges are bolted together with a rubber, Durabla, or other type of gasket between the pair.

22.3 piping layouts and takeoffs

The length of straight pipe required to form into a pipe bend is called the *developed length* of the pipe. Calculations for pipe bends are based on the radius of the bend measured to the centerline of the pipe.

Forming a complete circle with a radius R (to the centerline of the pipe) requires a developed length of $2\pi R$, or $6.283R$. Since there are 360° to a circle, a 45° bend has a developed length of $\frac{45}{360} \times 6.283R = \frac{1}{8} \times 6.283R = 0.785R$.

Example

Find the developed length of a double offset expansion bend with a radius of 8 ft if the tangent length on the ends is 3 ft.

Double offset expansion bends are used to take up the expansion in pipelines. They are laid out as shown in Fig. 181. The top of the bend includes 270°, and then the curve reverses, bending in the opposite direction through 135° on each side, followed by 3 ft of tangent. There is a total of 540° of bend, or a circle and a half. The developed length in the bends is therefore $1\frac{1}{2} \times 6.283 \times 8 = 75.40$ ft. Add 6 ft for tangents. Total developed length is 81.40 ft.

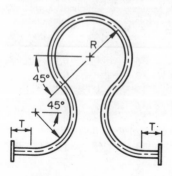

Fig. 181 Double offset expansion bend.

A *piping takeoff* is a list of required fittings and pipe, taken off a drawing or blueprint. Some knowledge of blueprint reading is necessary to do this type of estimate. To show the procedure, a takeoff will be made from the drawing of Fig. 182, which shows a part of the piping in a pumphouse. Here we shall take off piping quantities for the suction and discharge piping for the 1000 U.S. gal per min diesel-driven firepump. First find the firepump. The suction line from this pump goes through a Victaulic coupling and an 8-in. OS & Y valve (the cross symbol identifies a valve) to a welded 10-in. header pipe. The discharge line goes from the pump through a 6 × 8 increaser, an 8 × 8 × 4 tee, Victaulic coupling, check valve, and gate valve, to a flanged elbow. Notice that all fittings are flanged. Now if we take off the fittings from the 10-in. header through the pump to the flanged elbow on the discharge line, the quantities should be

2 8-in. OS & Y gate valves, flanged ends
2 8-in. Victaulic couplings
1 6 by 8-in. increaser, flanged ends
1 8 by 8 by 4-in. tee, flanged ends
1 8-in. check valve, flanged ends
1 8-in. 90° ell, flanged

and a few short lengths of pipe. The slip-on flanges remain to be counted. All fittings are flanged and the pump is flanged, but 150-lb slip-on flanges are required on the ends of all pieces of straight pipe, except those with Victaulic ends. A total of 5 150-lb slip-on flanges are required, in 8- and 10-in. diameters.

The following table gives estimating data for general pipe welding. The usual choice of rods for such noncritical pipe work is E6010, sometime E6011.

GENERAL PIPE WELDING, SCHED 40 PIPE

Manual Shielded Arc

Pipe Diameter, in.	Electrode Diameter, in.	Current, amp	Minutes/ Joint	Pounds Rod/ Joint
1	3⁄32	70	5	0.12
2	3⁄32	70	8	0.2
3	3⁄32	70	12	0.4
4	1⁄8	85	16	0.6
5	1⁄8	85	20	0.75
6	1⁄8	85	26	1.1
8	1⁄8	85	33	1.7
10	1⁄8	85	42	2.7

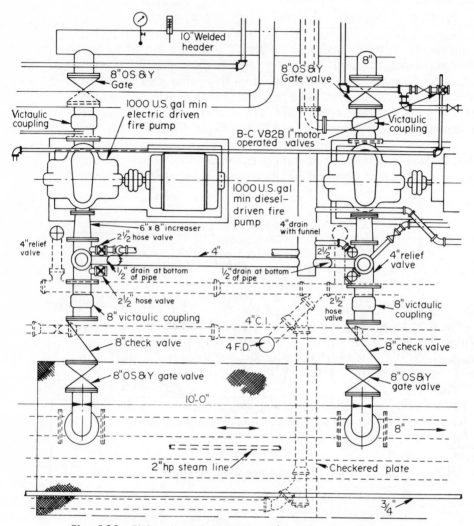

Fig. 182 Piping in a pumphouse, plan view (above) and elevation (right). A 10-inch welded header is supplied from a large storage tank (not shown) and in turn supplies two fire-pumps in parallel, one being driven by an electric motor and the other by a diesel engine. The two pumps supply water to an 8-inch water main.

fabrication practices
470

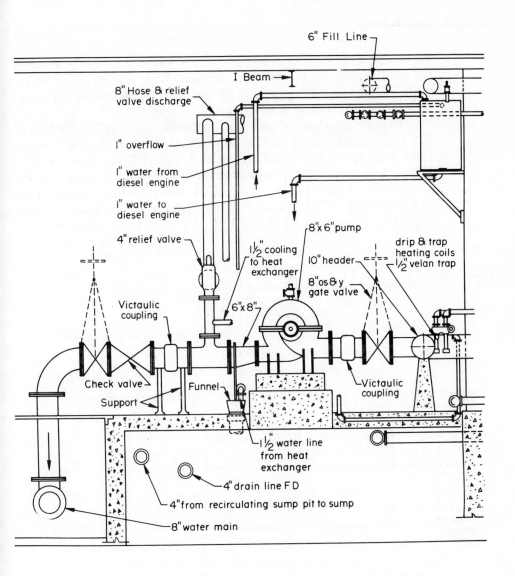

6" Fill Line

I Beam →

8" Hose & relief valve discharge

I" overflow

I" water from diesel engine

I" water to diesel engine

4" relief valve

$1\frac{1}{2}$" cooling to heat exchanger

8"x 6" pump

10" header

drip & trap heating coils
$1\frac{1}{2}$" velan trap

8" os & y gate valve

Victaulic coupling

6"x 8"

Check valve

Funnel

Victaulic coupling

Support

$1\frac{1}{2}$" water line from heat exchanger

4" drain line F D

4" from recirculating sump pit to sump

8" water main

22.4 welded T connections
in pipe and tubing

To connect one pipe at right angles to another pipe of the same diameter, the tee connection of Fig. 183 must be used. Each pipe must first be cut to the proper shape of opening if the two parts of the connection are to fit. The layout procedure is as follows.

The circumference of each pipe is divided into twelve segments of 30° each, or some other number of segments. Point 1 on pipe A meets point 1 on pipe B at 1'. Similarly points 2 meet at 2' and points 3 at 3'. If pipe A is opened flat, it will have the shape shown in the flat in the figure. With a little experience it is possible to lay out these curves on the two pipes freehand with welder's chalk, without this preliminary layout work. It is the mark of a competent pipe welder to be able to do so.

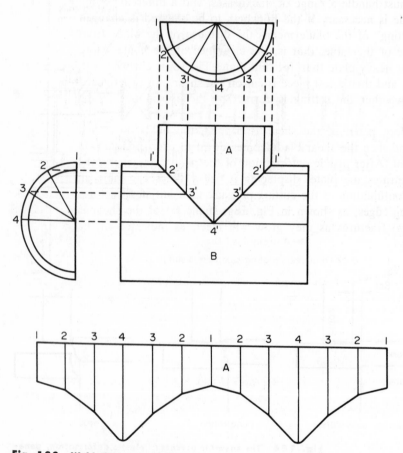

Fig. 183 Welded tee connection.

Basic fabricating equipment for weldments includes shears for cutting plate, brakes for bending plate, punches for punching holes, and rolls for bending plate to various curvatures. In addition to these fabricating items, positioning equipment is used to hold and position the weldment during welding.

Shears are supplied in plate width capacities of 4, 6, 8, 10 ft, and up and in plate thickness capacities from about 16 gauge up. The thickness capacity applies to mild steel only. A shear with a ¼-in. capacity must be derated for higher-strength steels. Since stainless steels have about double the shear strength of mild steels, such a shear would have a capacity of about ⅛-in. thickness in stainless steel. As so many experimenters in shops have discovered, only a relatively small overload is sufficient to wreck a shear, and the repair bill that follows the experiment is not small. A shear must handle a range of thicknesses, and a different setting of the shear blade is necessary if the thickness to be sheared is changed greatly. The "setting" of the blade means the distance of the blade from the shearing edge of the table, that is, the clearance of the blade. More set is required for heavy plate than for thin plate. The set is checked with thickness gauges, and then a test piece is cut on the shear. An experienced man can judge whether the setting is correct by the appearance of the cut edge.

When the foot pedal of the shear is tripped, the hold-downs first grip the plate, and then the shear blade comes down to exert pressure on the plate to be cut. After plastic deformation of the plate commences, the shear blade penetrates the plate, displacing it below the shear table an equal amount. Continuation of the cutting pressure then initiates fractures at the two cutting edges, as shown in Fig. 184. If the set of the shear is correct, these two fractures as they grow will meet, as indicated in the

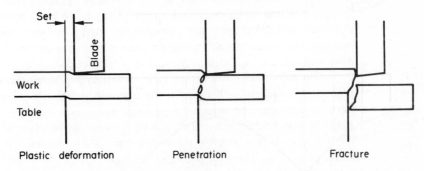

Plastic deformation   Penetration   Fracture

Fig. 184 **The shearing process: plastic deformation, penetration, and fracture.**

Fig. 185 A plate roll bender. (Webb 9L roll)

figure. If the set is incorrect, they cannot meet, and the result will be a ragged edge.

Sometimes the squaring bar of a shear is not accurate. To find out whether a shear will shear square, shear a square of plate material by making a cut on each adjacent side in succession, and then measure the two diagonals of the plate.

Plate bending rolls are used to roll plate and sheet into cylinders. These machines have three horizontal rolls that bend the plate plastically as it is rolled between them at about 20 ft per min. The thickness of plate that can be rolled depends on the diameter of the rolls. A set of rolls 5 in. in diameter will roll a maximum plate thickness of $\frac{3}{16}$ in., and 6-in. rolls will roll plate perhaps as thick as $\frac{5}{16}$ in. Hand-operated rolls as small as 2 in. are found in sheet metal shops. Very large rolls up to 24 in. in diameter and 20 ft long are occasionally found in large shops, but for bending very heavy plate hydraulic presses and dies are used to form the plate into an arc of a circle by making single bends one at a time.

The rolls may be of either type shown in Fig. 186, the initial pinch type or the pyramid roll type. In the pyramid roll the two lower rolls are fixed in position and driven by gearing. The top roll, larger in diameter than the two bottom rolls, is driven by friction as the plate is fed through the machine. It is adjustable up or down to set the diameter of the cylinder to be produced. The first part and the last part of the plate through the rolls will be flat, but these portions can be first formed on a brake before rolling the rest of the plate.

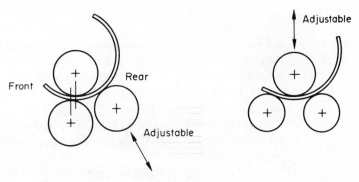

Fig. 186   Initial pinch and pyramid type plate roll benders.

The pyramid roll is not suitable for thin-gauge material. The initial pinch type is therefore more common. In this type all three rolls have the same diameter. The top roll is fixed in position. The lower front roll is adjusted to pass the thickness of the plate, and the rear roll adjusts for cylinder diameter.

To roll a cylinder, the rolls are adjusted and a plate passed through. The diameter of the curve is then checked and the rolls adjusted until the proper diameter is obtained. Different roll settings will be required to roll the same diameter out of different materials of the same thickness. The plate material must be bent plastically, and this requires different stress levels in different materials. Then too, different materials have different springback characteristics. It occasionally happens that the roll operator will misjudge the setting for rolling material of a very high yield-strength, so that after rolling, the plate recovers to the flat position again by elastic springback.

Fig. 187   A plate-lifting clamp with friction jaw.

Other types of bending rolls are used to form angles, channels, and other shapes into arcs of circles by means of three appropriately shaped roll wheels. General-purpose metal-working machines are popular because they can shear, slot, nibble, punch, flange, bead, fold, dish, and cut curves merely by changing the dies in the machine.

For handling and transporting heavy plate, *plate clamps* are a necessity. Such clamps are shown in Fig. 187. This clamp can be dropped over the edge of a plate, but when traction is applied to the clamp, the movable jaw of the clamp grips the plate. The clamp is loosed simply by slacking off the cable.

A variety of *welding jigs and positioners* contribute to the ease and speed of welding. For the shop welding of tanks and cylinders, turning rolls such as those of Fig. 188 are used and enable the operator to weld girth seams in the flat position. The rolls are driven at a speed to correspond with the welding speed; this imposes the requirement of an expensive infinitely variable speed drive. The drive rolls are usually equipped with polyurethane rubber tires, in which the center-to-center distance is adjustable for various diameters of welded vessel. Such turning rolls have been built with capacities exceeding 600 tons and have been used for the girth welding of submarines, nuclear reactors, and rocket shells. Very thin-walled vessels with easily distorted shells require special designs of turning rolls to minimize such distortion.

A general-purpose welding positioner is shown in Fig. 189. Such positioners can rotate the workpiece about either two or three axes. For exact matching to welding speeds, such positioners must be driven by

Fig. 188 Turning rolls for the welding of cylinders. (Webb Corporation Model U-12 W/R500)

fabrication practices
476

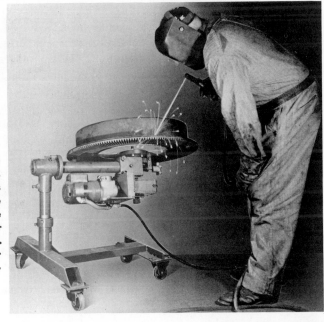

Fig. 189 (a) Special welding fixture by Webb Corporation. The face plate to the left is used to hold the workpiece during welding, and can rotate the workpiece about either or both of two horizontal axes. (b) A small welding positioner in use. (Aronson Machine Company AW 300 positioner)

Fig. 190 Airline welding and engineering C 20416 circumferential welding machine with two welding heads.

infinitely variable speed drives. They may be operated by means of a foot pedal, or the drive may be automatically controlled by the welding controls and synchronized with the other welding operations such as wire feed and gas flow.

Welding lathes, also called circumferential welding machines, can rotate the workpiece about one axis for the welding of girth welds in smaller sizes of cylinders, although even aerospace rocket cases are welded on such equipment. Figure 190 is a photograph of such a positioner, on which the welding equipment is mounted. This machine can handle diameters up to 60 in. The tailstock is equipped with an air cylinder to apply end pressure to compensate for weld shrinkage and to provide upsetting of the welded joint. The track along the top of the machine allows the welding head to be positioned at any point along the main axis of the machine.

For longitudinal welding of flat material or the longitudinal seams of cylinders, equipment operating on the principle of Fig. 191 is employed. The top shoes which clamp the work may be fixed or may pivot for clamping. The backup bar is clamped against the top shoes by means of air pressure in the pneumatic hose. The backup bar is often made of copper, so that it may also serve as a chill plate. For welding such reactive metals as titanium, the backup bar is drilled with holes to permit argon shielding of the bottom side of the joint.

Other types of welding jigs frequently used are shown in Fig. 192.

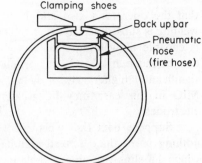

Fig. 191 Longitudinal seam welder in use on a rolled cylinder.

These are often used in field erection as well as in the production shop.

Probably the greatest advantage of MIG welding over manual shielded arc welding is the remarkable reduction in welding time made possible by wire feed. What is sometimes overlooked by buyers of MIG equipment, however, is that these potential savings are usually not realized if welding positioners are not employed. To illustrate, consider the following case. At a certain work station in the shop, the operator has been joining short lengths of 1-in. pipe to flanges by means of a single fillet weld. Using stick electrodes without a positioner, the operator needs perhaps 30 sec to make such a joint. This is a welding speed of about 8 in. per min. This slow welding speed is explained by the small diameter circle

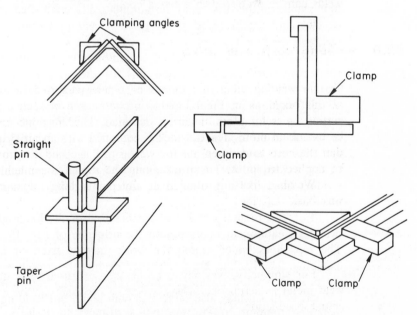

Fig. 192 A selection of welding jigs which are in common use: for corner welding, fillet welding, butt welding, and miter welding.

fabrication practices

that the operator's arm and hand must follow. Suppose now that MIG welding is substituted in order to speed up the operation. The MIG method is capable of welding speeds of many feet per minute, but the operator cannot move his MIG gun around the same circular fillet weld at any significantly higher rate of speed. It is possible that the over-all cost of MIG in this case may be greater than the cost of welding with stick electrodes.

Suppose next that we furnish the operator with a simple positioner, nothing more than a fixed spindle sloping up at an angle of 45°, over which he slips the pipe and flange. He will rotate the pipe with his left hand while he MIG-welds with the right hand, always welding in the flat position downhand as the work is rotated under the MIG gun. The use of this simple fixture will reduce his time for the fillet weld to about 15 sec, resulting in a welding speed of 16 in. per min.

This speed still does not exploit the potential time savings of the MIG method, however. Sixteen inches per minute is slow, and at this slow speed the operator will probably pile up an unnecessarily heavy fillet section, thus consuming an excessive weight of wire. The final solution is to rotate the work with a suitable motor with variable speed control, so that the required welding speed can be obtained. The MIG gun would be mounted in a fixture allowing it to lie always on the fillet weld circle without the need for constant manipulation. By this means, fillet welds can be produced in a few seconds.

22.6 welding costs and times

Certain welding times and speeds have been reported in earlier sections of this book, as in the tables giving resistance welding data or flame-cutting times for plate of various thicknesses. Here costs and times must be examined more closely. At the outset we must be realistic and admit that the costs and times that prevail in one shop or circumstance cannot be applied to another. Any data can serve only as guidelines.

Welding, like any other manufacturing process, consists of the two very basic activities of

1. preparation and cleaning up
2. actual welding production

For simplicity, we may consider all operations that do not deposit weld metal as setup operations, whereas arc time can be considered the actual production. Often exceeding arc time, setup time includes such operations as fitting, clamping, positioning, tack welding, cleaning slag, changing electrodes, cleaning torches, connecting ground clamps, and a diversity of other necessary operations. We would expect the setup time to become longer as the production run becomes longer because long production runs can justify more elaborate setups, such as those employed in subarc welding. The complex setup operation is justified by the savings made in reduced production time. By means of almost fantastically complex setups and jigs that may cost hundreds of thousands of dollars, automobile workers can weld in a few seconds such components as rear-axle housings and seat frames that otherwise might require almost an hour to weld. Such complex setting up is done by tooling engineers.

In field work, mostly a one-of-a-kind operation, setting up occupies much more of the operator's time than it does in the shop. Operations cannot be controlled in the field to the degree that they are in the shop. Convenient access to the work is not usually possible; neither is good positioning. The welder or welding crew may have to set up scaffolding and planks and then reposition the scaffolding frequently. The welder may have to wait for material, or he may be delayed by other subtrades working on the same contract. In the end, the percentage of actual arc time is much less on the jobsite than it is in the shop. Shop arc time may be as high as 80%, even with manual shielded arc welding. Arc time in the field does not usually exceed 30% of working time and can be much less.

By and large, the total cost of a weldment includes the cost of estimating and preparing the bid (often substantial), the cost of any design and drafting required, rental cost of equipment and cost of material, including the filler rod, the labor, inspection, and transportation. In submitting a bid, these costs must be marked up to cover contingencies (the job may take longer than the estimated time), overhead costs, and profit. Overhead costs include the very real costs of the office— rent, light, stationery, bank charges, and the hundred other expenses of simply being open for business. Many small welding shops fail through a too optimistic estimate of their actual overhead costs. Frequently the overhead cost can be considered as a certain percentage of the labor cost. For many products, it is approximately 100% of labor cost. Basing overhead on shop labor is reasonable. Many overhead costs, such as rent, light, cost of keeping the books, and even machine rental, vary directly with the amount of labor employed. The final markup on the bid estimate is the markup for profit. Profit must be maintained at a sufficiently high level, otherwise the bank manager may call in his loan to the weld shop, which will mean the end of the business.

22.7 estimating the consumption of welding rods

If welding wire is used as filler metal, then every pound of wire will produce almost a pound of filler metal in the welding bead. But if stick electrodes are used, then the estimating becomes more complicated. There are, first of all, stub losses, which seem to average 13 to 14% of electrode weight for 14-in. rods. In addition to spatter loss, which may range from 5 to 12% of electrode weight, there is also some strange and unaccountable wastage of stick electrodes. Some rods are merely strewn over the floor if supervision is poor, others make coat hangers, tie wire, or hangers for trouble lamps. In general, stick electrodes are too versatile and available compared with reels of MIG wire. Finally, the flux coating on the rod does not usually contribute to the filler metal.

The actual amount of filler metal that can be deposited from 100 lb of welding rods is subject to many variables besides those just mentioned. Those variables that depend on rod characteristics are as follows:

1. type of rod
2. type of flux coating
3. diameter of rod
4. current density

Deposition efficiency is higher with large-diameter rods. It is also better with such flux coatings as E6024. Although experience will vary, 100 lb of rods in the box should deliver 50 to 70 lb of deposited metal in the weld. The actual ratio must be determined by investigating a few jobs to find out the approximate deposition efficiency. The following tables will give approximate consumption of stick electrodes per 100 ft of weld seam for mild steel. They are based on the figure of 1 cu in. of mild steel = 0.28 lb.

DEPOSITED METAL PER 50 LB OF BOXED RODS

| AWS Class | Rod Diameter, in. | | | | |
	$\frac{1}{8}$	$\frac{5}{32}$	$\frac{3}{16}$	$\frac{7}{32}$	$\frac{1}{4}$
6010	30–32	30–32	32–33	33–34	33–34
6011	30–32	31–32	32–33	33–34	33–34
6012	30	31	31	32	33–34
6013	30	31	31	31	31
6024	27	27	29	30	30
7018	30–32	31–32	31–32	32	32–33

WELD METAL PER 100 FT OF DOUBLE-WELDED CLOSE-BUTT JOINTS, FLAT POSITION

Material, in.	Deposited Metal/ 100 Ft of Joint, lb	Add for Each $\frac{1}{32}$ in. of Gap
$\frac{1}{8}$	11.9	1.3
$\frac{3}{16}$	17.8	1.9
$\frac{1}{4}$	21.5	2.7
$\frac{5}{16}$	23.8	3.3

WELD METAL PER 100 FT OF JOINT FOR CLOSE-BUTT WELDS, 100 % PENETRATION, FLAT POSITION

Material, Gauge	Rod Size, in.	Deposited Metal/100 Ft of Joint, lb	Add for Each $1/32$ in. of Gap
20	$3/32$	1.3	
18	$3/32$	1.4	
16	$1/8$	2.0	
14	$1/8$	2.6	
12	$5/32$	4.2	1.0
$1/8''$	$5/32$	5.9	1.33
10	$5/32$	6.0	1.5

DEPOSITED METAL PER 100 FT OF FILLET WELD, EQUAL LEG SIZES

Fillet Leg, in.	Deposited Metal/ 100 Ft of Joint, lb
$1/16$	0.7
$1/8$	2.65
$3/16$	6.0
$1/4$	10.6
$5/16$	17.0
$3/8$	25.0

DEPOSITED METAL PER 100 FT OF WELD, SINGLE 60°V WITH $1/16$-IN. NOSE

Material, in.	Deposited Metal/ 100 Ft of Joint, lb	Add for Each $1/32$ In. of Gap
$3/8$	30.4	5.0
$1/2$	53.0	6.5
$5/8$	82.0	7.8
$3/4$	116.0	9.0
$7/8$	158	11
1	205	12

DEPOSITED METAL IN POUNDS PER HOUR OF ARC TIME

Class of Rod	Rod Diameter, in.				
	$1/8$	$5/32$	$3/16$	$7/32$	$1/4$
6010	1.8	2.7	3.7	5.1	6.1
6011	2.0	2.8	3.8	4.6	5.7
6012	1.9	2.8	4.0	4.7	6.0
6013	1.7	2.7	3.4	4.3	5.4
6024	2.8	4.0	5.5	6.5	7.5
7018	2.1	3.1	4.2	5.4	6.6

The high deposition rate of 6024 rods is apparent from the table.

Example 1

A butt weld must be made in 150 ft of $\frac{1}{8}$-in. sheet. The fit-up is poor. Assume that the operator will be using the arc for 45 min in every hour. Full penetration is required, welding from one side only.

(a) Find the required number of pounds of rods for the work.
(b) How much time will be needed to complete this job?

(a) For $\frac{1}{8}$-in. sheet, close butt, 5.9 lb of weld metal are required in every 100 ft of joint. Since the fit-up is poor, assume a $\frac{1}{32}$-in average gap, for which $1\frac{1}{3}$ lb of weld metal must be added per 100 ft. Total deposited metal per 100 ft $= 5.9 + 1.3 = 7.2$ lb.

Suppose that 6011 rods are selected, in $\frac{5}{32}$-in. diameter. Then 31 to 32 lb of weld metal are deposited from every 50 lb of rods. Assume 30 lb, to be on the safe side.

required weight of rods per 100 ft $= 7.2 \times \frac{50}{30} = 12$ lb
required weight of rods for 150 ft $= 18$ lb

(b) From the last of the tables, 2.8 lb of metal will be deposited per hour of arc time for 5/32-in. E6011 rods. Arc time is $\frac{3}{4}$ hr in every hour. Therefore in 1 clock-hour, the operator will deposit $\frac{3}{4} \times 2.8$, or 2.1 lb of deposited metal.

The total is 7.2 lb of deposited metal per 100 ft, or 10.8 lb in 150 ft. The job time will be $\frac{10.8}{2.1}$, or about $5\frac{1}{4}$ hr.

Example 2

Fillet welds are to be run on each side of a $\frac{5}{16}$-in. plate 60 ft long. Leg length of the fillet weld is specified as $\frac{3}{16}$-in. Arc time is estimated at 40 min in each hour.

(a) Find the weight of rods required.
(b) Find the time required to complete this welding.

(a) From the tables, a $\frac{3}{16}$-in leg fillet weld requires 6 lb of deposited metal per 100 ft. A total of 120 ft of fillet is to be welded, requiring 6×1.2, or 7.2 lb of deposited metal.

Suppose that 6024 rods are selected because of the high deposition rate of this class of rod. We can then expect 27 lb of deposited metal from 50 lb of rods in a $\frac{5}{32}$-in. diameter. The required weight of rods $= 7.2 \times \frac{50}{27} = 13\frac{1}{3}$ lb.

(b) With 6024 rods there will be 4 lb of deposited metal per hour of arc time. At 40 min of arc in every hour, the deposited metal per clock hour will be $2\frac{2}{3}$ lb. The total job hours $= \frac{7.2}{2.67} = 2.7$ hr.

As an example of a simple weldment, the design and costing of a small steel smokestack will be determined.

The stack will be fabricated of mild steel, 14 gauge, with a diameter of 16 in., distance from concrete foundation to centerline of breeching 4 ft, and a height of 32 ft above the breeching centerline to the top of the stack. The stack must be equipped with 3 ft of breeching of the same diameter as the stack, a birdscreen, and a rain cap. The stack drawings are given in Fig. 193.

The circumferential joints in the stack may be either butt or lap. If lap-jointed, the upper course of the joint must be inside the lower course of the joint, so that any ledges are placed outside the stack and not inside. Any plate ledges inside the stack will support condensed moisture, which will rapidly corrode the stack. Flue gases contain a great deal of moisture —10% of what goes up the chimney is water vapor if natural gas is burned—and when the boiler is shut down, this moisture condenses in the stack, slowly corroding it. Corrosion will first appear in the upper part of the stack, because the flue gas loses heat as it travels up the stack. This stack is made of heavy 14 gauge steel in order to give it a little longer life against the ravages of corrosion.

The stack used in this example is butt-jointed. Suppose the stack is to be fabricated by a small shop, which has a set of 5-in. rolls only 4 ft long. The stack must therefore be made in 4-ft lengths butt-welded together.

The layout for the tee-breeching cuts has been detailed previously in Sec. 22.4. The stack also requires a bird screen and a rain cap. The opening around the top of the stack, between it and the rain cap, must offer a smoke area at least equal to the diameter of the stack. The material of the screen will reduce this area somewhat. The area of a 16-in. stack is approximately 192 sq in. in cross section. The circumference of the stack is 50.25 in. If the rain cap is placed 5 in. above the top of the stack, there will be ample area for escape of the flue gases between it and the top of the stack. This smoke area will be closed up with 18-gauge expanded metal mesh (Fig. 194) with diamond openings $\frac{1}{2} \times 1\frac{1}{4}$ in. This mesh is too light to be arc-welded, but may be gas-welded or brazed to both the stack and the rain cap. Such mesh weighs 65 lb per 100 sq ft.

The rain cap must be cone-shaped. It will be assigned a diameter of 18 in., or slightly greater than the stack diameter. It is rather difficult for rain or snow to get into a stack, even without a rain cap, because there is normally an updraft in a stack whether the stack is hot or cold.

Suppose the rain cap is to have a height of 5 in. Then the slant height of the stack is 10.3 in. This 10.3 in. is the radius of the circle of metal cut out for the rain cap. To make a conical rain cap, a segment must be cut out of the circle. The actual circumference of the rain-cap

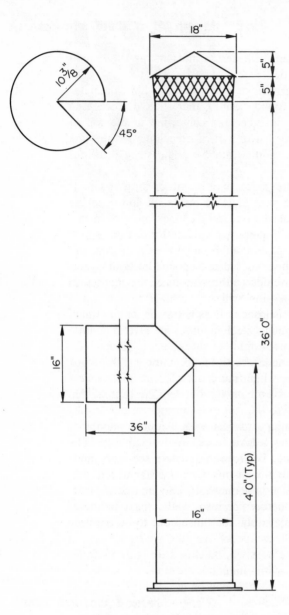

Fig. 193 Drawings for a steel smokestack.

circle for a radius of 10.3 in. is 64.7 in. But the actual diameter of the finished rain cap should be 18 in., giving a circumference of 56.5 in. The segment cut out must measure 64.7 − 56.5, or 8.2 in. on the circumference. This is $8.2/64.7$ of the sheet circumference. The segment to be cut out must have a central angle of $8.2/64.7 \times 360°$, or 45°. The rain cap may be made of 20-gauge material.

This stack will be completely shop-fabricated. It must be fastened

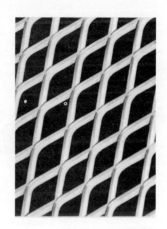

Fig. 194 Expanded metal mesh.

to its foundation by anchor bolts. These should not be smaller than ½ in. A rolled 2 × 2 × ³⁄₁₆ angle will be welded to the bottom of the stack and drilled for 6 anchor bolts.

This completes the design of the stack. Depending on competitive conditions, it should sell for about 20 cents a pound. To determine the weight of the stack, consult the table of weights of sheet steel in Chapter 6.

The first step in fabricating this stack is to prepare a *shear list* for the shear operator. The shear list is simply a list of sizes and gauges of squared sheet and the number of each size required. The sheets for the stack are sheared and then taken to the roll to be formed to the 16-in. circle. The circle of metal for the raincap is cut with a nibbler, and the base angle is drilled and rolled. The stack pieces are welded together, and the breeching tube is also welded. With welder's chalk the stack and the breeching are marked for cutting with the torch, after which the breeching is joined to the stack. The base angle, expanded metal, and rain cap are attached. The last step before shipment is the spray painting of the stack. This may be a prime coat only, the finish coat to be applied after erection.

22.9 welded storage tanks

The welded storage tank is a major product of the welding industry. Small tanks include compressed air tanks for paint spray systems, domestic hot water tanks, fire extinguisher bottles, domestic oil storage tanks, and a wide variety of others. Larger shop-fabricated tanks include propane storage tanks and the underground gasoline storage tanks used by service stations to supply gasoline to the pumps. Mobile tankage includes milk trucks of stainless steel, beer trucks, petroleum products trucks, and the

Fig. 195 Welded stainless steel tank trailer for the bulk transport of beer.

Fig. 196 Tank form for liquified petroleum gas (LPG) products. All tanks are welded. The long horizontal tanks with hemispherical ends are propane storage tanks. The spherical tanks store butane.

various types of tank cars used by the railroads (Fig. 195). Figure 196 is a photograph of a group of petroleum products tanks, which can be identified by their shape: the bullet shape identifies a propane tank and the sphere a butane storage tank.

Overhead tanks for municipal water storage are another familiar landmark. These are built in standard sizes from about 50,000 gal up to 5 million gal. Even larger tanks have been built for the storage of water or petroleum products—up to 150 million gal.

Tankage requires some or all of the following list of fixtures and attachments: fill connection, vent connection, draw-off connection, overflow connection, ladders, lifting lugs, and roof. These must be supplied to the requirements of the applicable code: American Petroleum Institute, American Water Works Association, or other.

A tank has a certain diameter and axial length in feet and volume in cubic feet. The liquid to be stored in the tank, however, is metered in gallons. The relationship between the cubic foot and the gallon (U.S. gallon in the United States and both the U.S. and the Imperial gallon in Canada) is covered by the following constants, based on fresh water at 60 F:

$$1 \text{ cu ft} = 2.64 \text{ lb}$$
$$= 7\tfrac{1}{2} \text{ U.S. gal}$$

$$
\begin{array}{rcl}
 & = & 6\tfrac{1}{4} \text{ Imperial gal} \\
1 \text{ U.S. gal} & = & 8.33 \text{ lb water} \\
 & = & \text{about } 6^2/_3 \text{ lb petroleum} \\
 & = & {}^5/_9 \text{ Imperial gal} \\
 & = & 0.133 \text{ cu ft} \\
1 \text{ Imperial gal} & = & 10 \text{ lb of water} \\
 & = & \text{about 8 lb of petroleum} \\
 & = & 1.2 \text{ U.S. gal} \\
 & = & 0.16 \text{ cu ft} \\
1 \text{ barrel} & = & 55 \text{ U.S. gal}
\end{array}
$$

Example

Find the storage capacity in gallons of a ground storage tank 100 ft I.D. and 40 ft high to the overflow pipe.

The enclosed volume is 314,000 cu ft. This corresponds to a capacity of 2,355,000 U.S. gal.

22.10 boilers and steam generators

Small packaged boilers, completely shop-fabricated, are used for the heating of small and large buildings at low steam pressures of less than 15 psi. A typical section through such a boiler is shown in Fig. 197(a). The burner fires into the large-diameter tube, called a furnace pass or first pass. The hot gases then reverse at the back of the boiler and flow back to the front of the boiler through the bank of 3-in. tubes, then being discharged up the stack. Such a boiler is called a two-pass firetube boiler, since the hot gases make two passes of the length of the boiler. The "firetube" designation means that the hot gases are inside the tubes and the water outside the tubes. Three-pass and four-pass boilers are also built. The tubes are supported by tube sheets at the front and back of the boiler. This general design of packaged boiler is called a Scotch Marine boiler, despite the fact that it has little if anything to do with the Scotch and is not used to generate steam for ship's turbines.

Larger boilers, used to generate steam for electric power in large central generating stations, are always water-tube boilers. These large steam-producers are not called boilers but *steam generators*, for good and sufficient reasons that do not concern us here. Together with the large manned space vehicles the larger steam generators are without doubt the proudest monuments to the welder's art and technology. These enormous steam generators are weldments as much as 200 ft tall (not including the chimney), producing up to 6 million lb of steam every hour at perhaps 2500 psi and burning 400 tons of coal per hour to produce this steam. The cost of such generators is in the millions. Such a unit supplies steam

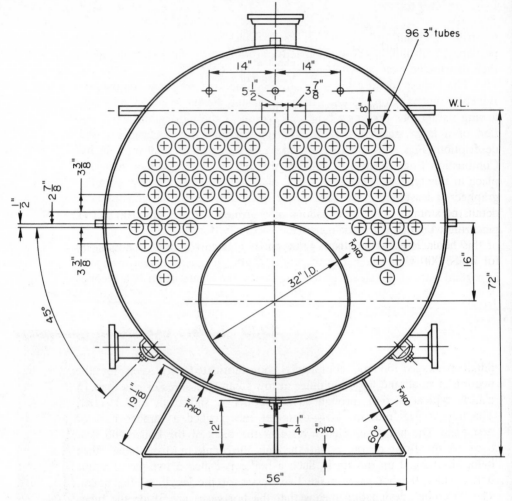

Fig. 197 (a) Section through welded scotch marine heating boiler.

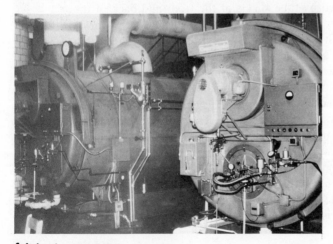

Fig. 197 (b) Typical scotch marine low-pressure (12 psi) heating boiler installation. This pair of welded boilers are cleaverbrooks 300 boiler horse-power four-pass boilers.

fabrication practices
490

to drive a steam turbine, which itself drives an electric generator of perhaps a half-million kilowatt capacity, producing the final electric power then distributed from a switchyard over a whole state.

The largest steam generators are manufactured by three companies: Babcock-Wilcox, Combustion Engineering, and Foster Wheeler. The following paragraphs present a brief description of the fabrication and erection of a large steam generator. The photographs that accompany the description (Figs. 198 and 199) are views of the erection of steam units by Combustion Engineering Ltd and suggest that mediocre welders have no place in this type of work. Every inch of pressure vessel welding is radiographed at least once. Figure 198 is a general view of the construction details of a small steam generator, the VU-60 design of Combustion Engineering. A large generator cannot be successfully reproduced on a page of this book. Briefly, the steam generator is a huge box with water tubes for walls. All tubes connect to the upper drum, *the steam drum*, the most important part of the steam generator. Below the steam drum is a second

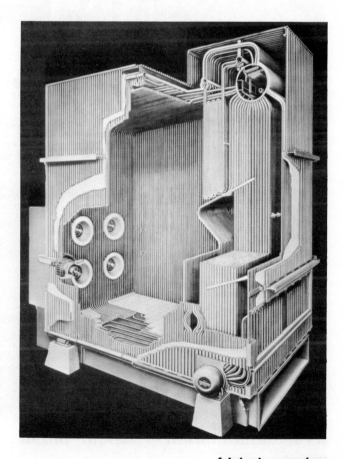

Fig. 198 Steam generator.
(Combustion Engineering VU-60)

(a)

(b)

(c)

Fig. 199 Sequence of erection photographs for a VU-60 steam generator. (a) Automatic welding of sidewall tube panels, (b) front wall showing burner openings, (c) gang bending of tube panels, (d) field erection under way; steam and mud drums in place and tubing being installed. Fig. 199 (e) Sidewall tube panel being lifted into place, (f) two rear-wall tube panels ready for positioning at the back of the steam generator, (g) hoisting the steam drum of a large steam generator. Fig. 199 (h) Steam drum and tube headers of a large steam generator; note the size of the suspension rods and yoke supporting the drum.

(d)

fabrication practices
492

(e)

(f)

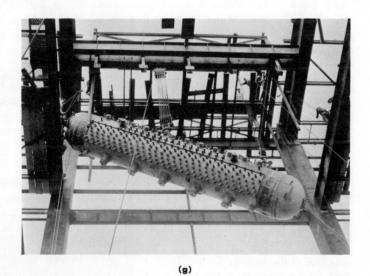

(g)

Fig. 199 (cont.)

fabrication practices
493

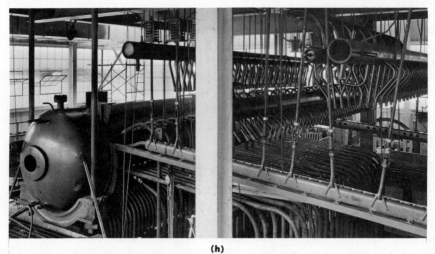

(h)

Fig. 199 (cont.)

drum, *the mud drum*, so named because in former years sludge used to collect here. All tube connections to these drums have a bend in them to take up expansion and thus reduce stresses at the tube-to-drum connection.

Fabrication begins with the two drums. The plate for the drums may be 2 to 6 in. thick, since internal pressures range from 1000 to 3500 psi, with steam temperatures above 1000 F. Such plate is too thick to be rolled. Instead it is repeatedly bent in a large hydraulic press. Bending may have to be interrupted for stress relieving in a furnace. The final shape of the drum must be a perfect circle within 1% error only. The welded joints are made by the submerged arc method and radiographed with cobalt-60 or a linear accelerator.

The tubes in a large generator will be more than 100 ft long. Such tubing will be constructed of shorter lengths flash-welded together. Wherever possible, individual tubes will be assembled in panels and then bent by gang-bending methods. The sequence of photographs shows the shop and field erection procedure for a VU-60 generator. One of the photographs shows a sidewall panel being automatically welded. When this operation is completed, all tubes will be welded into a header at the top and bottom of the tubes. The next photograph in the sequence shows a front panel and the complicated tube bends around the large burner openings. In the next photograph the rear wall tubes are receiving a gang-bend for the connection to the steam drum. This tube bender is a hydraulic bender.

The components of the steam unit are delivered to the jobsite. The first field operation is the raising of the steam drum to its final position. Tube panels are then installed to support the drum. The pressure parts of the steam generator are installed as quickly as possible, and when this work is completed, the unit is filled with water and pressurized for a hydrostatic test at a somewhat higher pressure than the operating pressure. Usually there are a few leaks. If the erection crew is unlucky, they may spend as much as three weeks repairing leaks and retesting. When all leaks are corrected, the refractory, insulation, and boiler casing are closed in. On completion of the unit, an acceptance test is run to put the generator through its paces and to ensure that it meets the guarantees of performance and efficiency imposed upon it.

The VU-60 is a relatively small steam generator. The final two photographs show two stages in the erection of a large unit, the first photograph showing the raising of the steam drum. The last photograph shows a somewhat later stage, and the large 6-in. diameter hanger bolts and yoke supporting the end of the steam drum should be noted. Large units are suspended from the roof and allowed to expand downward. Smaller hangers support the long square header for the sidewall tubes to the right of the drum. The small header drums above the steam drum are superheater headers, part of the tubing system that heats the steam above its boiling point.

22.11 welding contracts

A contract is a binding agreement, binding upon both of the parties to the contract and enforceable by law. A contract in order to be a contract in the eyes of the law must have certain essentials:

1. An *offer* to enter into a contract by one of the parties.
2. An *acceptance* of the offer by the other party.
3. *Consideration* to both parties. This is a legal term meaning that both of the parties must obtain some advantage or benefit, such as money, goods, a copyright, etc., from the contract.
4. A *lawful object*. You cannot contract to break the law, for instance, enter into a contract to steal.
5. A *common understanding* of the terms of the contract.

Consider the following simple contract: Mr. X says to Mr. Y, "I'll sell you this ball-point pen for 25 cents." This is an *offer*. If Mr. Y says "OK," that is his legal acceptance, and by it a contract is established. The contract need not be written: this is a verbal contract. The contract does not require the breaking of any laws. Consideration passes to both parties: Mr. Y gets a ball-point pen, Mr. X gets 25 cents. However, if the pen will not write, presumably Mr. Y may void the contract at his option. If it does not write, the two parties did not share a common understanding of the contract. Mr. X presumably knew that the pen would not write, whereas Mr. Y assumed that it would. Goods are assumed to be merchantable, and the pen was not.

Construction contracts are contracts for the supply and erection of materials, and as such are more complex than simple sales contracts for the supply of goods only. Construction contracts are of one of the following general types:

1. A *general contract* is a contract for a complete project involving the coordination of many subtrades or subcontracts.

    Many construction companies advertise themselves as general contractors. Such companies are equipped to undertake such general construction as excavation, concrete work, and carpentry. They subcontract welding, heating, ventilating, and electrical work. On the other hand, a mechanical subtrade may sometimes become the general contractor, and the construction company the subtrade. This would occur if the bulk of the construction were the stringing of pipe. The piping contractor might then be the general contractor, using the general construction company as a subtrade to pour concrete for machine bases, etc.

2. A *subcontract* is a contract made with a general contractor to complete a specific specialized area of the work, such as the insulation, plumbing, architectural metalwork, installing a sprinkler system, etc.

3. A *fixed-price contract,* or *lump-sum contract*, is a contract to complete the designated work for a fixed sum of money. Most contracts are of this type.

4. A *unit-price contract* designates a price per unit of work. For example, the contract may be for five storage tanks to be built at $25,000 per tank. In a unit-price contract the buyer usually has the option of changing the quantities. He may at any time change the quantity from five tanks to four, or six, each to be supplied at the same price of $25,000. If the contract were a lump-sum contract of $125,000 for five tanks, and later only four tanks were asked for, the contract could be altered only through negotiation with the contractor.

5. A *cost-plus contract* is a contract stating that the contractor will be paid his fair costs plus a percentage markup for profit. These are difficult contracts to write (are items such as entertainment costs legitimate?) but are often advantageous to the owner. On a very large construction job, for which it will take too long to complete the plans and specifications, construction can be started before the plans are finished by means of a cost-plus arrangement with a contractor known for his integrity.

6. A *negotiated contract* is negotiated with a single bidder only—a contractor who has earned a reputation for good and honest work.

7. A *turnkey contract* is a comprehensive contract for design, supply,

construction, and breaking-in ("debugging") of a large project, such as a sulfuric acid plant or a steel mill. The contractor is responsible for all phases of the work, even perhaps the purchase of the real estate and the financing of the work. All the owner has to do is to receive the keys to the property when he takes over from the contractor.

Any construction contract consists of a great many documents, including the following:

1. the invitation to tender
2. a set of plans
3. a set of specifications
4. the tender or proposal of the successful bidder
5. any contract bonds
6. any addenda (later additions) to the specifications
7. any change orders to the contract
8. the contract document itself

The invitation to tender sent out by the owner is legally a request for *offers*—contractors' bids to enter into a contract with the owner. The contract document may be the acceptance, but often the acceptance is a purchase order or a letter of intent advising the contractor that a contract will follow in due course and requesting him to initiate the work, pending completion of contract documents. Contract bonds of several kinds may be called for. These are paid for by the contractor. Frequently a bid bond must accompany the bid. This bond, supplied by an insurance company, ensures that the contractor will enter into a contract if his bid is accepted. A performance bond may also be required. This is a bond posted to ensure that the contractor will complete the work, and upon his failure to do so, the insurance company must pay for completion of the work, up to the limit of the bond. In addition to these bonds, public liability insurance is carried by all contractors to cover accidents.

An *addendum* to the specifications means any change in the specifications after the original set of specifications was distributed for bidding but before the contract is let. A *change order* is any change in the work of the contract, either addition or deletion, issued after the contract is accepted. Change orders require the consent of the contractor and therefore involve some negotiation. They are not considered binding unless given in writing.

A large contract like that for the erection of a large steam generator, will involve perhaps $6 million worth of work and may require eight months or more to execute. No company can afford to wait eight months to collect this amount of money. Therefore it is trade practice for the general contractor on the job to submit a monthly *progress claim* for work executed. At the end of the first month he may claim perhaps 10% of the contract, which would be $600,000 of a $6 million contract. At the same time, all the subcontractors submit to the general contractor their smaller progress claims, which of course are included in the general contractor's more comprehensive progress claim. The owner, or his resident engineer or architect, if the claim is valid, will then pay to the general contractor $600,000 less a *holdback*, which may be 15%, and is of course in the nature of a bond to ensure completion. A progress claim is submitted each month as the contract progresses, and the amount, less holdback, is paid to the general contractor, and by the general contractor to his subtrades. At the termination of the contract, if there are no deficiencies in the work, the owner accepts the work from the contractor (who up until then has owned the work) and the holdback is paid over to the contractor.

22.12 the execution of a contract:
two welded steel storage tanks

In this and the following sections we shall deal with the design, estimating, and job scheduling of a welding contract. The contract requires the erection of two 100,000-gal ground storage tanks for water. The action starts with the invitation to tender.

INVITATION TO TENDER

CAMBRIAN MINING COMPANY, INC.

MACDONALD, SOUTH DAKOTA

TENDERS FOR SUPPLY AND INSTALLATION OF STEEL WELDED TANKS,

WAREHOUSE BUILDING, MACDONALD, SOUTH DAKOTA

SEALED TENDERS, endorsed "Tender for Steel Welded Tanks," will be received until 12:30 P.M., January 18, 1966, by the undersigned. Contractors may obtain plans and specifications upon payment of a certified check in amount of $25. The deposit will be refunded upon return of drawings and specifications in good condition within one month from date of tender closing.

For consideration, tenders must be submitted on the forms provided, and accompanied by a certified check or bid bond for 10% of the tender price.

Plans and specifications will also be displayed at the following locations:
Office of the Purchasing Agent, MacDonald, South Dakota.
Grand Forks Builders' Exchange, Grand Forks, N.D.

The Company reserves the right to reject any or all tenders, and the low tender will not necessarily be accepted.

Cambrian Mining Company, Inc.
R. Twolan
Chief Purchasing Agent

You as a welding contractor send a check for $25 and duly receive a set of plans and specifications. The plans show that the two tanks must be erected indoors in a concrete building, and to fit into the space provided for the tanks, their diameter must not greatly exceed 30 ft. The tanks will require a 10-ft pipe stub with a slip-on flange, located at the bottom of the tank for connection to a water pump, and a 6-in. pipe stub at the top of the tank, complete with slip-on flange, for connection to an overflow pipe. The tank fill line will be installed by another contractor in another contract and is not a part of this contract.

Your tank materials must be shipped by rail. The rail car can be unloaded on to a receiving dock adjacent to the tank room where erection will take place.

You then read the specifications.

SPECIFICATIONS

CAMBRIAN MINING COMPANY, INC.

MACDONALD, S.D.

Contract No. 1224-6. WELDED WATER STORAGE TANKS
WAREHOUSE BUILDING

SPECIFICATION SECTION No. 1. GENERAL CONDITIONS

1.1 GENERAL CONDITIONS. The General Conditions of the Contract are a part of the Specifications and shall govern the work of all trades.

1.2 INTERPRETATION.

(a) Words, phrases, and abbreviations that have a well-known trade meaning shall have that meaning in these specifications.

(b) In case of discrepancy between drawings and specifications, the specifications shall govern.

(c) The drawings and specifications are complementary, and what is called for by either shall be binding as if called for by both. The project shall constitute a finished and operable piece of work which shall be complete in all essentials, notwithstanding that items necessarily involved may not be mentioned in plans or specifications.

1.3 WORK INCLUDED

This contract requires the erection of two 100,000 gallon welded steel water storage tanks in the Warehouse Building of the Company, and connection of these two tanks to the water supply lines and overflow pipes. The Contractor shall provide all labor, materials, equipment, and supervision to complete the work of all trades, including the following:

(a) coordination of the work of all trades

(b) preliminary examination of the site

(c) general protection of the work

(d) shop drawings

(e) control of debris

(f) final clean-up

1.4 SHOP DRAWINGS

The Contractor shall submit four copies of all shop drawings to the Chief Purchasing Agent for approval, and one copy shall be returned approved or with corrections noted.

1.5 GUARANTEE

The Contractor shall guarantee all materials and workmanship for twelve months from the date of acceptance of the work.

1.6 TEMPORARY SERVICES

(a) The building will be heated at the expense of the Company.

(b) Electric energy may be supplied free of charge from existing electrical outlets, but the Contractor shall provide his own temporary lines and equipment.

(c) The Company will accept no responsibility for power interruption, and no compensation will be paid to the Contractor for any power failure.

1.7 HYDRAULIC TEST

The Contractor shall conduct in the presence of the Chief Purchasing Agent or his appointee a hydraulic test of the tanks and piping before painting is begun. Such test shall consist of filling the tank or tanks to operating level, and allowing the water to stand for 24 hours. Any leaks shall be repaired and the test performed again.

1.8 FINAL CLEAN-UP

At the expiration of the work, the Contractor shall leave the premises in broom-clean condition.

1.9 JOB SCHEDULE

Before commencing fabrication and erection, the Contractor shall submit to the Chief Purchasing Agent his complete job schedule for both shop work and field erection. Such schedule shall take account of freight schedules into MacDonald—cars are spotted at the Warehouse Building only on Wednesday and Saturday.

1.10 WELDING PROCEDURES

The Contractor shall submit with his Job Schedule his welding procedure sheets for both butt joints and fillet welds.

SPECIFICATION SECTION No. 2. STEEL WORK

2.1 GENERAL CONDITIONS

The General Conditions are a part of these Specifications and shall govern the work of all trades.

2.2 GENERAL INFORMATION TO THE CONTRACTOR

(a) Because of space limitations, the new tanks shall be approximately thirty feet in diameter.

(b) The tanks shall have no roof.

(c) The tanks shall be welded.

(d) Tank capacity shall be 100,000 gallons for each tank, measured to the bottom of the overflow pipe.

(e) The Contractor may use the rail siding immediately adjacent to the Warehouse Building.

(f) Electric energy is available, 220/60/3 and 110/60/1.

(g) No compressed air is available.

(h) No corrosion allowance shall be added to the tank wall thickness.

(i) The tanks shall be constructed on a levelling slab of concrete twelve inches thick.

(j) The steel shall not be shop-primed.

(k) Shop drawings shall show the following details: dimensions of tanks, thickness of steel plates, layout of bottom plates, edge preparation and welding data for each type of welded joint. Specify type of electrode and diameter for each type of joint.

2.3 STEEL SPECIFICATION

All plate material shall conform to ASTM A283 Grade C or better, and shall not be less than $\frac{1}{4}''$ thick.

2.4 CONSTRUCTION

The tanks shall be constructed in strict accordance with AWWA D 100-65, Specifications for Steel Tanks, etc.

Other specifications pertain to the concrete bases for the tanks and to the painting. You will subcontract these parts of the work however. There are other specifications governing the welding of the tanks: the purchaser's Spec. 2.4 of Section No. 2 refers the contractor to American Water Works Association *Standard D 100-65 for Steel Tanks, Standpipes, Reservoirs, and Elevated Tanks, for Water Storage.* You therefore must consult AWWA D 100-65 for its specifications, from which Standard the following are abstracted:

3.11. Minimum Thickness. The minimum thickness for any part of the structure shall be 3/16 in. for parts not in contact and $\frac{1}{4}$ in. for parts in contact with water contents . . . .

3.12. Joints in Shell Plates. In welded tanks the longitudinal joints in adjacent circumferential courses may be either staggered or in alignment.

3.17. Reinforcement Around Openings. All openings over 4 in. in diameter in the tank shell, suspended bottom, and riser plating, etc., which are subject to hydrostatic pressure from weight or pressure of tank contents, . . . shall be reinforced. This reinforcement may be the flange of a fitting used or an additional ring of metal, or a thicker plate, or any of these items used in combination.

8.7.2. Butt Joint Construction. These joints shall be single welded from the top side, using suitable backing strip or equivalent means to insure at least 90 per cent penetration. Three-plate joints in tank bottoms shall not be closer than 12 in. from each other and also from the tank shell. 8.8. Shell to Bottom Joint (applies to vertical cylindrical shells with flat bottoms). The bottom edge of the lowest course shell plates and the bottom sketch plates shall be joined by continuous fillet welds on both sides of the shell plate. The size of each weld shall be not greater than ½ in., and neither less than the nominal thickness of the bottom plates or shell plates (whichever is smaller) .... The sketch plate shall extend outside the tank shell a distance of at least 1 in. beyond the toe of the weld.

These are perhaps the most critical specifications of AWWA D 100-65. The AWWA Standard itself must be consulted for full details. The tanks must be designed and built on the basis of these specifications, both the purchaser's and D 100-65. The most important specification is the tank capacity: 100,000 gal. This must be the capacity of the tank from the bottom of the tank (or lowest level of the discharge pipe) to the bottom of the overflow pipe at the top of the tank.

To prepare a tender or proposal, the tanks must be designed and estimated. This work will be followed through in the next sections of this chapter.

The tender will be submitted to the chief purchasing agent in duplicate and may read something like this:

Proposal
for: Supply and Erection of Welded Steel Tanks,
     Warehouse Building, Cambrian Mining Company, Inc.
     MacDonald, South Dakota.

Supply and erection of two only 100,000 gallon welded steel tanks, in strict accord with plans and specifications, complete in all respects, to include Public Liability Insurance in amount $300,000, all taxes paid

for the sum of
Fifty Thousand Dollars 00/100 ($50,000.00)
Fluxcore Welding Company

The tanks will not cost $50,000. This is only a casual figure, actually much too high for such a job.

22.13 design of the tanks

In this section we shall design the tanks and compile the information for the shop drawings (Fig. 200). Spec 4.3 of AWWA D 100-65 suggests that tank diameters should be standardized on 2-ft increments. We shall make the tank 30 ft 0 in. in inside diameter.

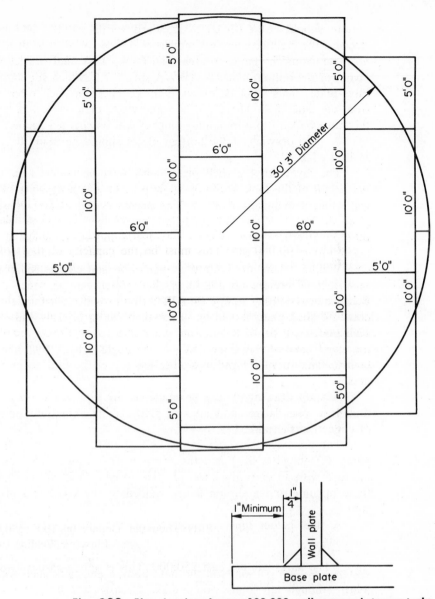

Fig. 200 Plan drawings for two 100,000-gallon ground storage tanks.

The tank plates are specified as $\frac{1}{4}$ in. This gives a tank outside diameter of 30 ft 0½ in. Spec 8.8 of D 100-65 requires a $\frac{1}{4}$-in. fillet weld to join the tank shell to the tank bottom and specifies that the tank bottom shall extend at least 1 in. beyond the toe of the fillet weld. The tank bottom then must be 30 ft 3 in. in diameter.

Designing a circular tank bottom with a diameter of 30 ft 3 in. from rectangular plates is an intriguing problem. The plates for the tank bottom should be restricted to standard widths of 48, 60, and 72 in. Because the erection crew will not have the use of a crane at the jobsite, no plate should be larger in area than 60 sq ft. A final restriction on the layout of the bottom plates is AWWA spec 8.7.2, which stipulates that no three-plate joints shall be closer than 12 in. from each other and also from the tank shell. There will be some waste plate in such a layout, but this must be kept to a minimum, since it will be charged against the job.

A shop drawing of the bottom plates should be made to a scale of ¼ in. to 1 ft.

The layout of the shell plates must next be undertaken. First find the height of the tank to the overflow pipe to give a capacity of 100,000 gal, using a diameter of 30 ft. The necessary calculation constants are given in Sec. 22.9. To this height add 6.625 in., the outside diameter of the 6-in. overflow pipe. A few more inches should be added to the tank height above the top of the overflow pipe. We shall assume that the Flux-core Welding Company is only a small shop and cannot roll plate wider than 5 ft. Therefore no course of shell plates can be wider than 5 ft. Because heavy lifting equipment will not be provided for the field erection crew, no shell plate should be larger than 50 sq ft. This will mean that shell plates will be 10 ft long, one plate sheared to proper length to give the exact circumference required. A top angle 4 by 4 by ¼ in. will be bent to tank curvature and welded to the top of the tank to provide stiffness.

A shop drawing should be made of the tank shell, opened out as though it were flat to show sizes of plates. Plate joints may be staggered or aligned in the tank shell.

The openings flame-cut in the tank shell for the suction line to the pump (10-in. pipe size) and the overflow (6-in. pipe size) must be reinforced with an extra thickness of plate. A pipe stub will be welded into these opening and a slip-on flange welded to the other end of the pipe stub.

A steel ladder must be supplied for the outside and the inside of each tank.

Welding details All joints in the tank bottom and tank shell will be butt joints (though lap joints would make it easier for the erection crew). Since the AWWA specs are concerned about penetration, the welding rods for the butt joints should be either E6010 or 6011, $\frac{5}{32}$-in. diameter. For the two ¼-in. fillet welds joining shell to bottom, select 6024 rods for their high production rate, $\frac{5}{32}$-in. size. To simplify the estimating, no edge preparation will be done, and butt joints will be gapped a small amount to permit good penetration from both sides of the joint. Slag will be trapped at the bottom of double-welded butt joints, but these tanks do not require radiography, since any stresses in the tank wall are trivial. The tank bottom of course will be welded from the top only.

Shop fabrication begins with the unloading of the incoming car of steel. This will be a mill order of ¼-in. plate coming direct from the steel mill. Only a small weight of 4 by 4 by ¼ in. angle will be needed, and this will not be included in the mill order but ordered from a steel warehouse. The Fluxcore Welding Company, being only a small shop, does not have a railroad spur. Instead, the arriving gondola car of plate is spotted on a track a mile away from the shop and must be delivered to the shop by truck.

To unload the car, the Fluxcore Welding Company hires a steel dump truck with driver and parks the truck alongside the gondola car (see Fig. 201). Four helpers will go into the gondola car to unload the plate. They will up-end one side of the plate and lean it against the side of the car, as shown. They will next lift the opposite side of the plate and balance the plate on the side of the car. Then with a heave they will shove the plate toward the dump box. The plate falls into the dump truck and skids into the flat position. The procedure is repeated with the next plate. A full day with four men and a truckdriver will be needed to unload the car.

We assume that the plates will need very little shearing and that most of them can be welded as received from the mill. The plates for the tank bottom are laid out on the shop floor and tacked together. The 30 ft 3-in. circle is then flame-cut at a rate of 1 ft per min. The bottom plates are marked for assembly at the jobsite, the tack welds are snapped, and the bottom plates are ready for shipping.

A shop crew of four men will be needed to roll the side plates. The average time to roll one plate will be about 5 min. The tank ladders will be fabricated in the shop from flat bar and round rungs spaced 12 to 15 in. apart. The slip-on flanges for the pipe connections may be welded to the pipe stubs either in the shop or later in the field erection.

Since this shop does not have an angle bender, shop personnel must show a little ingenuity in bending the 20-ft-long top angles. The best and cheapest way to bend the angle is first to obtain some 9-in. straights

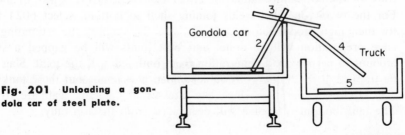

Fig. 201 Unloading a gondola car of steel plate.

(firebrick 9 by 4½ by 2½ in.) and stack these without mortar to make a temporary furnace like the one shown in Fig. 16. A layer of firebrick must be laid on the concrete floor to protect the floor from the spalling caused by furnace heat. A 6-ft-long furnace is sufficient. A length of angle is then inserted into the little furnace and a propane torch introduced in one end for heat. The length of angle iron enclosed in the firebrick furnace will heat to red hot in a very short time. When hot, the angle iron is removed from the furnace and bent by two men around a template cut from scrap half-inch plate. The template can be temporarily welded to a building column. Two men will need two days in which to bend the angle and touch up bad bends with a sledgehammer.

Finally, one day and four men should be required in order to load the outgoing car with the materials and equipment for field erection.

22.15 field erection

The minimum crew needed to erect the two tanks will be two welders and two helpers. This crew will require one day to unload the railroad car at the site. They will then weld the first tank bottom and one course of the tank shell. The partially completed tank will then be filled with a firehose and hydrostatically tested. Scaffolding will be erected and the rest of the courses and the top angle welded. Some of the plates will not have the proper curvature and must be jacked into place by means of a cable and a hydraulic jack, as indicated in Fig. 202. The pipe connections and tank ladders are welded in place and the whole tank given a hydrostatic test. After the hydrostatic test, the tank is drained. The painting subcontractor then cleans and paints the tank inside and out. The area is cleaned up and construction of the second tank commenced.

The total time required to weld one tank can be estimated from the costing tables of Sec. 22.7, using an estimated arc time of 30%, or 18 min in every hour.

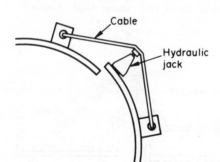

Fig. 202 Jacking tank wall plates to proper curvature.

Tenders closed for this job on January 18, 1966. Let us suppose that the Fluxcore Welding Company receives a letter or intent on January 21 advising it that it is the successful bidder and requesting that work be initiated at once. On January 24 the Fluxcore Welding Company puts its purchase order to the Open Hearth Steel Mills, Inc., in the mail. The student should fill out a purchase order similar to that in Fig. 203 listing all the plates required, in their proper sizes and total weights. The purchase order should specify (see customer's specification 2.3) "All steel to ASTM A283 Grade C."

Let us assume that the steel mill promises to load the steel for ship-

FLUXCORE WELDING COMPANY INC.

Dept. _____   Required _____

P. O. No. _____   Ship Via _____

Date _____   Terms _____

To :

Please supply the following items :

Fluxcore Welding Company Inc.

Purchasing Agent

Fig. 203 **Purchase order for steel plate.**

fabrication practices
507

ment on February 14 and that the steel arrives on February 16. Shopwork can be commenced on February 18.

A contractor who can finish his work in the shortest possible time will have the lowest possible costs and the greatest possible profit, and equally important, he will be able to invoice for the job sooner. A technique in management science concerning how to get things done in a hurry without waste effort is available. This is called critical path method, or CPM, and is not at all difficult to learn. It is becoming common to ask that a critical path analysis of the work be submitted with the contractor's bid: indeed, the critical path method is demanded of contractors bidding for aerospace work. The critical path in any project is the chain or sequence of activities that will take longer than any other and thus controls the time needed to complete the whole project. In this tank contract, obviously, the activity of ordering the steel is on the critical path, since this project occupies the time between January 24, when the purchase order is mailed, and February 16, when the steel arrives, and the contractor can do nothing to shorten this time. While he is waiting for the steel, he can order the angle iron and bend it, or he can fabricate the tank ladders, but none of these lesser activities lie on the critical path.

The technique of critical path planning is not a proper subject for this book, but it is instructive to borrow some of the techniques of the critical path method in laying out the job schedule. Actually this tank contract is not complex enough to require critical path analysis.

The first step in setting up the job schedule is to list the job activities and their minimum times in days. The job schedule will begin with the following activities:

> order steel plate
> order angle iron
> unload incoming car of steel
> roll shell plates
> lay out and cut tank bottoms
> bend angle iron
> etc.

These can then be made up into a job schedule diagram similar to Fig. 204, which is somewhat like a critical path diagram. Activities that can be carried on concurrently are shown as arrows in parallel. Each activity is represented by an arrow, and each arrow begins and ends at a small circle. In the critical path method certain items of information are inserted into the small circles. Here only the date when an activity arrow begins or ends is inserted in the circle.

A job schedule diagram should be made up for the shop work and the field erection. The critical path chain of activities will be reasonably obvious in this project if the erection crew is limited to two welders and two helpers.

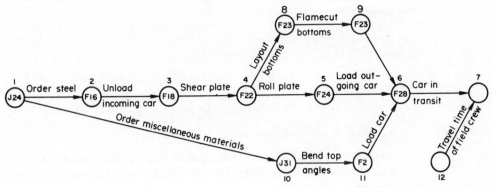

Fig. 204 Job schedule diagram.

22.17 the estimate

Before the tender is submitted to the chief purchasing agent of the Cambrian Mining Company, an estimate must first be prepared. It is often said by estimators that if you estimate high enough to make a profit, you will not get the low bid and will therefore lose the work, but if you estimate low enough to get the work, you will not make a profit. Be that as it may, an estimator is a well paid and very responsible member of any company. He can make great profits, or he can ruin the company. Good estimators have an inherent talent for this occupation and can repeatedly estimate with remarkable accuracy just what the closest competitor will bid.

If the reader has never estimated before, he should find it interesting to prepare an estimate for a tender to build these tanks. It is difficult to give costs in this book, since prices and hourly rates vary from region to region and should be based on local conditions. However, such items as hourly rates, freight rates, steel prices, and electrode prices are easily obtainable.

The first prices to be obtained are subcontractor's prices for concrete work and painting. Let us suppose that the lowest acceptable prices received are those from Wekusko Painting and Brown Construction:

PROPOSAL

Wekusko Painting & Decorating Ltd.
Bemidji, Minnesota

Fluxcore Welding Company

Supply of all labor, supplies, and equipment for painting of two welded storage tanks, MacDonald, South Dakota, in strict accord with plans

fabrication practices
509

and specifications, and in accordance with your job schedule and instructions of letter date January 25, 1966:

For the sum of One Thousand Three Hundred and Twenty Dollars 00/100 ($1320.00), all taxes included.

Brown Construction Company
Webster, South Dakota

Fluxcore Welding Company

Supply of all labor, supplies, and equipment for pouring of two concrete bases for welded steel tanks and placement of reinforcing steel, MacDonald, South Dakota:
$903.00, tax included.

These subcontracts will be marked up 5% by the Fluxcore Welding Company.

The most convenient breakdown of cost estimates is to separate all costs into four lists, as follows:

1. Material
   (a) steel plate, in required sizes
   (b) angle iron
   (c) 2 slip-on flanges, 6 in., 150 lb
   (d) 2 slip-on flanges, 10 in., 150 lb
   (e) 6011 rods, $\frac{5}{32}$ in.
   (f) 6024 rods, $\frac{5}{32}$ in.
   (g) oxygen
   (h) acetylene
   (i) pipe, 6 and 10 in.
2. Shop labor
   (a) unload incoming car
   (b) shear plate
   (c) roll plate
   (d) lay out and cut bottoms
   (e) weld 4 pipe flanges
   (f) bend angle iron
   (g) fabricate 4 ladders
   (h) load outgoing car.
3. Field labor
   (a) unload car at site
   (b) weld tank bottoms
   (c) set up scaffolding
   (d) erect shell plates
   (e) weld top angle
   (f) cut pipe connections, weld pipe
   (g) conduct hydrostatic test
   (h) dismantle scaffolding, load material returns, clean up.

4. Miscellaneous
   (a) fringe benefits—Workmen's Compensation, etc.
   (b) scaffolding, 1000 lb, $200 per month
   (c) rental of two 300-amp welding machines, 1000 lb each
   (d) travel costs
   (e) hotel and meals for field crew
   (f) freight, incoming car
   (g) freight, outgoing car
   (h) freight, returns, LCL
   (i) taxes, if applicable
   (j) overhead, 100 % of payroll
   (k) markup on subcontracts, 5 %
   (l) telephone costs to jobsite
   (m) final markup and bid price

PROBLEMS

1 (a) Is the nominal size of tubing based on the inside or the outside diameter?

(b) Is the nominal size of pipe based on the inside or the outside diameter?

(c) Why can the outside diameter of pipe up to 6-in. nominal size not be varied?

2 What is your explanation of the difference between a pipe and a tube?

3 A 1½-in. Schedule 40 pipe has to be replaced every 100 days because of corrosion. If a Schedule 80 pipe is substituted, how long would you expect it to last under the same conditions?

4 Determine the weight of 1 ft of 3-in. O.D. steel tubing with a wall thickness of 0.250 in.

5 Find the developed length of a double offset expansion bend with a radius of 18 ft, with 8 ft of tangent at each end of the bend.

6 Draw up the layout diagrams to a suitable scale for a 90° T connection to connect two 8-in. pipes.

7 Draw up the layout diagrams to a suitable scale for a 90° T connection between a 14-in. round duct on the run and a 10-in. round duct on the T.

8 Observe a welder for 1 hr and record his total arc time in that period. If possible, make an estimate first and check the actual result against your estimate.

9 For 50 ft of double fillet weld with a 3/16-in. leg, using 6024 rods, estimate the weight of rods needed and the time to do the job. The fillet welds are continuous and in the flat position, tacked and ready. Make your own estimate of arc time per hour.

10 Design a steel smokestack 24 ft high, 22 in. in diameter, 14 gauge, with a rain cap 6 in. high and 4 ft of breeching 22 in. in diameter. Centerline of the breeching is 5 ft above the bottom of the stack.
(b) Select a suitable type of manual rod and diameter for this job.
(c) Estimate the weight of rods needed.
(d) Estimate the welding time required for the smokestack.
(e) Estimate the total time required to build this stack.
(f) Estimate the weight of the stack.
(g) Write up a shear list for the stack.

11 What is the cubic foot capacity of a 10,000-gal tank?
(b) Design a 10,000-gal tank (¼-in. plate), selecting plate sizes for it.
(c) Estimate the weight of welding rods required to weld this tank.

12 Manual shielded arc welding of a butt joint in 2-in.-thick plate is required.
(a) Design the edge preparation.
(b) Select a suitable rod and diameter.
(c) What weight of rods will be required for 1 lineal ft of such a joint?
(d) Estimate the welding time for 1 ft of this joint, including cleaning out slag.

13 Prepare shop drawings for the tank contract discussed in this chapter.

14 Write welding procedures for the butt welds and fillet welds for the above tanks.

15 Estimate the total shop man-hours to fabricate the two tanks.

16 Estimate the weight of 6011 and 6024 rods required to weld the two tanks.

17 Estimate the man-hours required for field erection of the two tanks.

18 Complete the estimate and prepare a proposal for bidding this tank contract.

19 Prepare a complete job schedule diagram for the tank contract, similar to Fig. 204, based on a field crew of 4 men.

20 Prepare a complete job schedule diagram for the tank contract, similar to Fig. 204, based on a field crew of 6 men, 3 welders, and 3 helpers.

21 Prepare a progress claim for the first month's work on site. Deduct 15% holdback.

22 Prepare a progress claim prepared immediately after the car is unloaded at the job site.

23 Make up a purchase order for the steel plate for the tank contract.

This book has attempted to encompass the whole field of welding, from its basic science to some of its practicing crafts. The author hopes for the sake of junior personnel that he may in some degree have captured the stimulating atmosphere of the welding industry. Welding is a young and vigorous technology that began as an undependable method of making repairs to metal parts. It has long reached major status in engineering. It is a ruthless young giant, for it has caused the unemployment of countless boilermakers, riveters, blacksmiths, foundrymen, salesmen, engineers, and businessmen. It seems pertinent then to conclude with some remarks on careers in welding, since by decision or by chance, more and more people will be drawn into the welding field in order to earn their living.

Because of the rapid pace of development in welding, it is not a suitable career for the engineer or craftsman who prefers a static state of affairs or who cannot face the prospect of learning new techniques in the course of his working life. Practitioners of welding must take short courses, attend technical sessions, attend trade fairs, and read sales literature and technical magazines. Those who do not very quickly develop a feeling of inadequacy.

First, the inevitable word about women in welding careers. The author knows of two women who are welding engineers. Both are competent. There are many women welders in the work force, principally in gas welding and microwelding, and during World War II women worked as shipyard and aircraft welders. Women have distinguished themselves

SUMMARY

23

as welding metallurgists, metallographers, radiographers, and factory inspectors. Indeed, there is no welding job at which women cannot excel.

Welding embraces a wide range of job categories, which may be arranged into the following three groups:

1. welding skills used in shop and field production work
2. designing, estimating, and planning operations in the plant offices
3. marketing operations

1. Welding Skills
sheet metal welder
aluminum welder
stainless steel welder
pressure welder
pipeline welder
pipe welder
instrument welder
microwelder
maintenance wdlder
aircraft welder
welding machine operator
layout man
radiographer
inspector

2. Office Positions
tool and fixture designer
welding engineer
welding metallurgist
testing engineer
research engineer
laboratory technician
estimator
purchasing agent
production planner
methods analyst

3. Marketing
technical salesman
service man
technical writer
specification writer
welding instructor

Welding Skills In preparing for a welding career it is probably best to take the longest training course obtainable on the assumption that the longest course must be the best. The course should include such related work as shop mathematics, blueprint reading, layout work, and welding metallurgy. Technological changes suggest that such fringe subjects will be the only permanently useful part of a welder's training. These are the fringe benefits too that lead to better jobs and promotions to foreman and supervisor.

A young man should choose a specific category of welding, such as sheet metal welding (an excellent choice, by the way). There is no such job classification as a general-purpose welder. A sheet metal welder has no hope of obtaining work as a pipeline welder, and the converse is also true.

Most factory production is performed by machine operators in jobs that make only limited demands on manipulative skill, but this does *not* mean that such jobs require limited knowledge or ability: the better machine operators can progress to setup men. Most such machine welding is resistance and MIG-CO_2 welding. If a career with a high degree of variety is desired, perhaps the choice should be maintenance welder, a position requiring welding skill, broad experience, knowledge of metals, and good luck with tricky tasks such as repairing flywheels and cast-iron machine bases. Such jobs as pressure welder and pipeline welder use special techniques and are obtainable only by experienced operators of proven skill and productive speed.

Weld testing and inspection embrace a number of job classes from simple to complex. The work of radiography is perhaps the most interesting and is not especially difficult. Perhaps the most difficult techniques to learn are certain ultrasonic methods, but such training is an asset in the labor market.

Office Positions Welding is one of the major branches of production technology. It is not generally understood that the most important operation in any production process is "tooling-up." Tool designers, toolmakers, tool engineers, and setup men therefore are well paid. The word "tool" as used in the sense of tooling has no reference to hand tools or production machines but pertains to the special fixtures and holders that position the part being produced. Such tooling includes punches, dies, welding jigs, positioners, stock feeders, clamping devices, coil handlers, automatic welding heads, and automatic work stations. These are invariably specially designed to suit the particular characteristics of the part being produced and therefore make considerable demands on the experience, technical skills, knowledge, and imagination of the designer. The broad field of tooling must be recommended above many others for a career, especially because industry has generally abandoned hope of ever finding a sufficient supply of skilled personnel for such work. Since tooling is such a critically important step in production technology, it is unfortunate that it is so little known and understood, and so rarely "sold" by career counselors.

Estimators, in welding and elsewhere, are the personnel who read the blueprints, take off quantities, estimate costs and times, and finally put the price on the job. In a competitive economy it is the estimator who determines whether the company will thrive or fail. Estimators quickly develop a "sixth sense" which tells them exactly how much can be bid for a job. They can sometimes aim to be a hundred dollars below a competitor—and succeed. An estimator, however, must be cool under stress, for he constantly works against deadlines amid the repeated ringing of telephones; interruptions; sales calls; and the manipulation of masses of paper, such as subquotations, bid forms, large blueprints, and bound volumes of specifications. Though he may be harassed at times, if he gets the job he is king of the company until the excitement wears off.

The methods analyst has the job of improving on production methods, either to upgrade quality or to reduce costs. It is not possible to provide a brief description of the work of a methods analyst. Instead, the following example from one analyst's career is offered.

A company produced an agricultural implement that required much fillet welding. This was done by manual methods. After extensive study, the analyst recommended to management that MIG welding be substituted for manual welding to reduce costs. This was done, and costs were considerably reduced. However, the narrow bead and deep penetration of the MIG method produced unfortunate results in marketing. Farmers distrusted the small fillet welds. The analyst was told that the product would not sell without large fillet welds. He could not produce large fillets cheaply by the solid-wire MIG method. In the end he solved the problem by the use of flux-cored wire, a method combining the requirements of minimum cost and market acceptance.

The laboratory technician may have a variety of duties. The standard tests described in this book, such as the tension test, the Charpy test, and the guided bend test, are among his routine tasks. He may section welds for microscopic examination or analyze the elements in a batch of welding rods by X-ray diffraction, a laboratory method not discussed in this book.

Research and development (R & D) activities are no doubt glamor activities in the public eye. They are hardly so in practice. Looking first at the unfavorable side of research, it might be said that the career researcher must combine the abilities of drudgery, intellect, politics, and convincing report writing. Politics is needed when you have spent three years of a company's or government's time and money in a research project that just did not have God's blessing on it. Politics is also needed by research men of lesser gifts to ensure that they are not assigned to projects beyond their capabilities. Again, there is much drudgery in developing the necessary data. The research man may have to analyze two or three hundred weld samples before he can come to any useful conclusions. But men and women of superior ability will always be attracted to this field and have as their continuing reward the constant gift of new

Fig. 205 An artist's impression of the welding trade; part of the mural at the entrance to the Manitoba Institute of Technology.

discoveries, the companionship of stimulating minds, the admiration of their fellow men, and constant job offers. Researchers, however, do not work a 40-hour week. This is not a field in which the average worker sets the pace. The *best* man sets the pace in this hotly competitive field, and to keep abreast you must come back to work after supper. The constant progress in welding technology implies that there is a constant demand for research work in this field and a constant demand for R & D personnel.

Marketing Positions The importance of marketing is summed up in the often-quoted statement "Nothing happens until somebody writes up an order." There is no production, there is no research, without the efforts of the marketing department of industrial firms. Unfortunately the nature of the work of an industrial salesman is little understood by young men who must select a career. This type of salesman does little selling. The bulk of his work is education.

Suppose that a certain R & D department has perfected a laser welder that is an improvement on other types of welder. The research work is all in vain if this equipment is not installed on production lines. It will never be so installed unless a salesman explains it to buyers, discusses its cost savings, solves the manifold problems of integrating it with other production equipment, expedites the delivery of the equipment, sets it up on the factory floor, trains the operator, and nurses the equipment and its operating personnel over the initial troubles. This is industrial marketing, demanding a broad range of intellectual gifts from the salesman. Without him, there is no justification for new developments.

He is nowadays such an important person that plant managers cannot keep their job unless they talk to salesmen, for they are the men who keep the plant manager up-to-date on current practices. Selling, however, requires a high degree of self-discipline, because salesmen are given little supervision. The man who cannot budget his time, who talks too much, who is not strongly motivated, or who lacks pride in himself, will not succeed in industrial marketing.

Industrial marketing is recommended for anyone as the fastest method of learning an engineering field. The salesman visits every plant in his area, knows them all intimately, and quickly acquires a broad knowledge of the whole field that his product embraces.

Welding instructors are in great demand for both industrial plants and government training institutes. There is little basic difference between the work of an industrial salesman and an instructor, for both have the function of effective communication of information. An instructor will not be successful if he cannot "sell" his training to students, for students must first be motivated. Instructors who cannot motivate discover inadvertently that the human race has a latent streak of stupidity. Everyone remembers unhappy experiences with incompetent school teachers, and such experiences ought to be avoided in order not to repel a person from a career as an instructor. Remember too that training practices are rapidly becoming more efficient and more stimulating. However, it is probably not possible to enjoy a life of instruction unless you work hard at it. But if you are attracted to instruction as a means of avoiding the competitive hurly-burly of the world at large, you must assume that you are not really equipped for instruction as a career—it is not possible to avoid joining the human race. If you find some government institutes too hidebound for your taste, remember that industry and the armed forces employ instructional staff also; or you may try the other instructional career, selling.

INDEX

34039

DATE DUE

AUG 4 '69			
MAR 22 '71			
NOV 29 '71			
MAY 9 '72			
MAY 7 '73			
JAN 31 '78			
GAYLORD			PRINTED IN U.S.A.